The Open University

Block C

Random processes and simulations

About this course

MS325 Computer algebra, chaos and simulations uses the software package *Maple*™ (copyright Maplesoft™, a division of Waterloo Maple Inc., 2007) which is provided as part of the course. Maple is a computer-assisted algebra package and its usage is the main subject of *Block A Computer algebra*. Advice on such matters as the installation of Maple, the loading and saving of Maple worksheets and other basic 'getting-started' issues is given in the *Computing Guide*.

Maplesoft™ and Maple™ are trademarks of Waterloo Maple Inc. All other trademarks are the property of their respective owners.

The cover image is composed of a photograph of the Saturnian moon Hyperion (courtesy of NASA) overlaid with a time-T map (in yellow). The view of Hyperion was taken during the close flyby of the spacecraft Cassini on 26 September 2005. Time-T maps are covered in *Block B Chaos and modern dynamics*. This one shows Hyperion's spin rate plotted against its orientation and was generated using Maple from a mathematical model. Regions containing an apparently random scatter of dots indicate chaotic motion in Hyperion's spin angle, the so-called chaotic tumbling.

This publication forms part of an Open University course. Details of this and other Open University courses can be obtained from the Student Registration and Enquiry Service, The Open University, PO Box 197, Milton Keynes MK7 6BJ, United Kingdom (tel. +44 (0)845 300 6090, email general-enquiries@open.ac.uk).

Alternatively, you may visit the Open University website at www.open.ac.uk where you can learn more about the wide range of courses and packs offered at all levels by The Open University.

To purchase a selection of Open University course materials visit www.ouw.co.uk, or contact Open University Worldwide, Walton Hall, Milton Keynes MK7 6AA, United Kingdom, for a brochure (tel. +44 (0)1908 858793, fax +44 (0)1908 858787, email ouw-customer-services@open.ac.uk).

The Open University, Walton Hall, Milton Keynes, MK7 6AA.

First published 2010.

Edited, designed and typeset by The Open University, using the Open University TeX System.

Printed and bound in the United Kingdom by Hobbs the Printers Limited, Brunel Road, Totton, Hampshire SO40 3WX.

ISBN 978 1 8487 3233 9

1.1

Contents

UNIT 1 Random variables

Study guide

This unit relies on the working knowledge of Maple developed in Block A. The sections should be studied in numerical order, and you will require access to a computer to study most of them. Apart from reading the text and understanding the examples, it is crucial that you work through the exercises, as these are essential to learning the material. For solutions to exercises that depend on generated random numbers, you may obtain numerical results that are slightly different to those given in the text.

Introduction

In this unit we introduce the basic ideas of probability and random numbers required for applications considered later in this block. No assumptions about previous knowledge of probability are made. In addition to elementary mathematical ideas we also introduce useful Maple commands and use Maple to illustrate various important ideas. The exercises set throughout the text are an important part of the learning process and most should be attempted, *without* consulting the supplied solutions. In this unit the Maple components of all exercise solutions are not printed, but can be found on the course CD and website, which also contains most of the procedures defined in this text.

There are three basic ideas introduced in Sections 1.1–1.3. In order to provide an overview of these sections, these ideas are listed and briefly described next. In Sections 1.1–1.3 we illustrate these ideas with examples in order to help you develop an intuitive understanding; there is no need for concern if you find the following descriptions too brief.

Outcomes An outcome is the result of an experiment or measurement; for instance, the toss of a coin results in a head or a tail, which are the two possible outcomes for this experiment; the measurement of the number of spots on a giraffe results in an integer with unknown upper and lower bounds.

The set of all possible outcomes of an experiment or measurement is the fundamental object of probability theory; a particular experiment or measurement is equivalent to choosing a member from this set. By definition, any outcome is distinct from all others.

Probabilities There is a probability associated with each and every outcome. Intuitively, the probability of an outcome is understood to be the relative frequency that this outcome occurs in a large number, N, of experiments. Mathematically, we let $N \to \infty$, and therein lies a fundamental problem not addressed here.

Random variables The notion of a random variable is best introduced through particular examples. A formal definition exists, but this is practically useless until some intuition has been developed, and it is not given in this course.

It is important to observe that randomness is a result of the underlying measurement, and is often the result of not having control over all significant variables.

The unit ends with a simulation of the growth of a simple population in Section 1.4, where we introduce the ideas of deterministic and stochastic approximations, and show when they are equivalent.

1.1 Discrete probabilities

In this section we introduce the idea of probability through simple, common examples with a finite number of outcomes. The simplest example is a coin toss, with only two, equally likely outcomes which are mutually exclusive, meaning that both cannot occur simultaneously. In N tosses, if there are respectively n_h heads and n_t tails, so $n_h + n_t = N$, then for an unbiased coin we expect

$$P_h = \lim_{N \to \infty} \frac{n_h}{N} = \frac{1}{2} \quad \text{and} \quad P_t = \lim_{N \to \infty} \frac{n_t}{N} = \frac{1}{2}. \tag{1.1}$$

The limit P_h is named the **probability** of the coin falling with the head side up; and P_t is named the probability of the other outcome. Clearly, since $n_h + n_t = N$, it follows that $P_h + P_t = 1$. It is immediately apparent that neither of these probabilities can be measured directly because the definition requires an infinite number of tosses. Instead, we do one of the following.

- Compute the probabilities from first principles, in this case by assuming that the coin is unbiased, that the toss is sufficiently insensitive to the initial impulse, and that the result of one toss affects no subsequent toss, to see that both outcomes are equally likely.

- Estimate the probabilities from measurements involving a finite number of tosses. Each set of tosses is named a **trial** or a **realisation**.

Another common example is a die, a roll of which will result in one of the six outcomes $\{1, 2, 3, 4, 5, 6\}$, all equally likely if the die is fair. So the probability of each outcome is $1/6$, that is, $P_k = 1/6$, $k = 1, 2, \dots, 6$; this is an obvious result, derived shortly.

These two examples have the following important properties which are shared by many other examples.

(a) Coin tosses or die rolls are unaffected by previous events.

(b) In any toss or roll, one and only one outcome can occur, so all possible outcomes are mutually exclusive.

(c) The sum of the probabilities of all outcomes is unity.

(d) If the probability of a particular outcome o is $P(o)$, then from (c) the probability of this outcome not occurring is $1 - P(o)$.

The following definition of dice is attributed to Ambrose G. Bierce (1842–probably 1914), an American writer: dice are small polka-dotted cubes of ivory constructed like a lawyer to lie upon any side, commonly the wrong one.

In general, if an experiment has m possible outcomes $\{x_1, x_2, \ldots, x_m\}$ and it is performed N times with x_k occurring n_k times, then the probability P_k of outcome x_k is defined to be

$$P_k = \lim_{N \to \infty} \frac{n_k}{N}. \tag{1.2}$$

The sum of all these probabilities is unity because $n_1 + n_2 + \cdots + n_m = N$ and hence

$$P_1 + P_2 + \cdots + P_m = \sum_{k=1}^{m} \lim_{N \to \infty} \frac{n_k}{N} = \lim_{N \to \infty} \frac{1}{N} \sum_{k=1}^{m} n_k = 1.$$

If we know that all possible outcomes are equally likely, as for the throw of a die or a coin toss, that is, $P_1 = P_2 = \cdots = P_m$, then the above equation gives $P_k = 1/m$. For a die $m = 6$, so $P_k = 1/6$ for all relevant k.

Exercise 1.1

(a) What is the probability that a roll of a die gives an even number?

(b) What is the probability that a roll of a die gives either a 3 or a 5?

(c) What is the probability of drawing the ace of hearts from a deck of 52 cards?

Probabilities of successive independent events

If two independent events e_1 and e_2 have probabilities P_1 and P_2 of occurring separately, then the probability of both events occurring is the product of the individual probabilities, $P_1 P_2$; successive coin tosses are examples of independent events. If the two events are connected, the rule for the probability that both occur is more involved; in this course only independent events are considered.

As an example, the probability of obtaining two fours from two successive die throws is $(1/6)^2$.

Exercise 1.2

(a) How many outcomes exist when a die is thrown twice if the order is (i) important, or (ii) immaterial?

(b) What is the probability of throwing first a 4 and then a 3?

(c) What is the probability of throwing a 4 and a 3 in either order?

(d) What is the probability that in two throws the sum of the results is 7?

(e) What is the probability of obtaining exactly two sixes in three throws?

Simulation of throwing a die

In most circumstances, *a priori* calculation of probabilities is not possible and we usually resort to estimating probabilities from finite samples, which is the subject of much of this unit. Such calculations inevitably have errors and these must be understood. In order to introduce the method, we use it to estimate the probability of obtaining a particular number in a single throw of a die.

If we throw a die N times, and n_k, $k = 1, 2, \ldots, 6$, is the number of times k occurs, then the associated probability, P_k, is formally defined by the limit in Equation (1.2). For a fair die, all six outcomes are equally probable and $P_k = 1/6$ for $k = 1, 2, \ldots, 6$.

An experiment or a simulation that measures P_k directly can use only finite values of N, and then P_k is estimated by the formula

$$P_k = \frac{n_k}{N}, \tag{1.3}$$

which is just the relative frequency of occurrence of the number k in N throws. Note that we use the same symbol for the random number n_k/N as for its limiting value, which is just a number. If we perform two or more experiments, each with N throws, we are likely to obtain different values for n_k and hence estimates of P_k. Each experiment leading to a particular value of n_k is often named a *realisation* of n_k, because the value of n_k is a particular number drawn from a set of random numbers.

An experiment that involves actually throwing a die N times is, for large N, too time-consuming, and a computer simulation is preferable. For this we use a **random number generator**, and in Maple an appropriate procedure for some applications is generated by `rand(n..m)`, where m and n are two integers with $m > n$, which produces integers j in the interval $n \le j \le m$ with equal probability: since there are $m - n + 1$ outcomes, the probability of obtaining any integer in this interval is $1/(m - n + 1)$. Setting $n = 1$ and $m = 6$ therefore simulates a die throw.

This random number generator is produced by the command

```
>   r := rand(1..6):
```

The subsequent command

```
>   j := r();
```

$$j := 2$$

generates an integer in the interval $[1, 6]$, each possible outcome being equally likely, and assigns it to j. Every subsequent value of `r()` is independent of previous uses, just as each throw of a die is independent of previous throws: **this means that in all examples given here, you may obtain results that differ from those shown**.

There is, however, one very important difference between a real die and a pseudo-die simulated by Maple. If we `restart` the worksheet, the same sequence of 'random' numbers is reproduced, whereas with a die we cannot go back in time to restart an identical set of throws. This allows programs to be checked more easily, but is also why the experiment of actually throwing a die is not the same as a computer simulation, although we expect the measurable outcomes to be the same. In addition, if a computer is used to generate a huge set of random numbers, then subtle problems may arise; but these difficulties do not occur in this course.

The following short procedure `P(N)` uses `rand(1..6)` to calculate the relative frequency of occurrence of the number 1 in N die throws, that is, P_1 as defined in Equation (1.3). In `P(N)` the local variable n is used to count the number of times `r()=1`, so n is set to zero in line #1, and the required relative frequency, Equation (1.3), is just n/N.

```
>  restart:
>  r := rand(1..6):
>  P := proc(N)
>    local k,n;
>    n := 0:                                              #1
>    for k from 1 to N do;                    # Start loop
>      if r()=1 then n:=n+1 end if;    # Count occurrences of 1
>    od;
>    evalf(n/N);                # Compute relative frequency  #2
>  end proc:
```

Applying this procedure 12 times, that is, carrying out 12 realisations or trials, each with $N = 10$ throws, gives the following relative frequencies of the occurrence of the number 1:

```
>  z := [seq(evalf[2](P(10)),k=1..12)];
```
$$z := [0.20, 0.40, 0., 0.20, 0.40, 0.10, 0., 0.10, 0.10, 0.20, 0.10, 0.]$$

You will notice that these estimates of P_1 fluctuate significantly, the smallest being 0 and the largest 0.4. This is fairly typical of trials involving relatively small sample sizes, 10 in this case; it is one problem that bedevils opinion polls and affects simulations where small sample sizes are imposed by physical or economic constraints.

Such fluctuations are reduced by increasing the sample size N. For instance, with $N = 1000$ we obtain in 12 realisations

```
>  z := [seq(evalf[2](P(1000)),k=1..12)];
```
$$z := [0.16, 0.17, 0.17, 0.13, 0.17, 0.15, 0.16, 0.17, 0.19, 0.18, 0.18, 0.19]$$

and now the smallest and largest estimates are 0.13 and 0.19.

Exercise 1.3

(a) Repeat the above calculation with $N = 10^4$ and $N = 10^5$, each with 15 realisations. In each case find the minimum and maximum values in the list z. Notice that as N increases, the spread in the values of $P_1(N)$ decreases.

(b) Now consider the effect of increasing the number of realisations. For $N = 10$ and 100, use $M = 10$, 100 and 1000 realisations to examine the spread in $P_1(N)$. You should observe that the spread increases slightly as the number of realisations increases, as might be expected.

One way of understanding these fluctuations is to fix N, the number of throws, and repeatedly compute $n_1 = NP_1$, the number of times 1 occurs, using different random numbers: here we use n_1 rather than n_1/N because integers are easier to deal with. It is important to remember that n_1 is a random number, which may take any value in $[0, N]$: we shall eventually estimate the probability that n_1 takes any value in this interval and understand how this changes with N.

Consider 20 realisations of n_1, computed using the procedure P(N), but with the expression in line #2 replaced by n, so that n_1 is output rather than n_1/N. With $N = 120$, representative outputs are

$$[17, 30, 18, 27, 20, 21, 22, 26, 16, 14, 17, 18, 23, 23, 19, 17, 29, 15, 22, 23].$$

$$(1.4)$$

In this list, various values of n_1 occur with the frequencies listed in the following table.

Value of n_1	14	15	16	17	18	19	20	21	22	23	26	27	29	30
Frequency	1	1	1	3	2	1	1	1	2	3	1	1	1	1

In this set of 20 realisations, the number 1 occurs 17 times in 3 trials, and 22 times in 2 trials. Thus estimates of $P(17)$ and $P(22)$ are $P(17) \simeq 3/20$ and $P(22) \simeq 2/20$.

Such a small set of trials gives neither a clear idea of the spread of n_1 nor the frequency with which each value is produced. Indeed, in this case, the expected value, $120/6 = 20$, occurs only once; other numbers occur more frequently. For this problem, however, a relatively simple Maple procedure – spread, listed below – runs a variant of procedure P(N) sufficiently many times to give a clearer picture of the variation of values of n_1 and of the probabilities $P(n_1)$.

In Figure 1.1, two such sets of data are shown, each using $M = 50\,000$ trials. On the left $N = 120$, and on the right $N = 600$. The solid line is the graph of the function

$$P(n_1) = \frac{1}{\sqrt{2\pi Np(1-p)}} \exp\left(-\frac{(n_1 - Np)^2}{2Np(1-p)}\right) \quad \text{with } p = \tfrac{1}{6}, \tag{1.5}$$

which is an approximation to the probability $P(n_1)$ valid for $N \gg 1$; the origin of this approximation is discussed in Sections 1.1–1.3, in particular Equation (1.16) (page 20). The abscissae are the possible values of n_1; the ordinate is the relative frequency with which a particular value of n_1 occurs. For instance, with $N = 120$, $n_1 = 20$ occurs 4802 times in $50\,000$ realisations, giving a relative frequency of $4802/50\,000 = 0.096\,04$; Equation (1.5) gives 0.098.

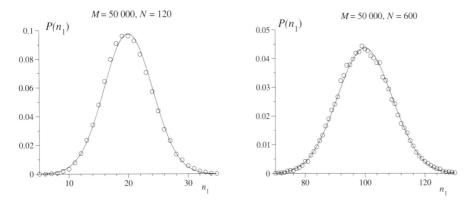

Figure 1.1   Graphs showing the relative frequency of occurrence of given values of n_1, in $50\,000$ trials of N throws of a die. On the left $N = 120$, and on the right $N = 600$. The solid line is the graph of the function $P(n_1)$, defined in Equation (1.5).

We expect that as $N \to \infty$, $n_1/N \to 1/6$, but for finite values of N we observe significant spread about this limiting value.

In the left-hand figure, where $N = 120$, we see that $n_1 = 15$ and 25 occur with about half the frequency of $n_1 = 20$. An analysis of the raw data shows that about $3/4$ of the $50\,000$ trials lead to n_1 in the interval 20 ± 4. This means that in a single trial there is a 75% chance of the estimated probability n_1/N being in the range $\tfrac{1}{6} \pm \tfrac{1}{30}$, that is, in the interval $[0.13, 0.20]$.

In the right-hand figure, $N = 600$ and now $n_1 = 90$ and 110 occur with about half the frequency of $n_1 = 100$. In a single trial there is a 75% chance of the estimated probability being in the range $\frac{1}{6} \pm \frac{1}{60}$, that is, in the interval $[0.15, 0.18]$.

Later we shall see that if $N \gg 1$, there is a 75% chance of the estimated probability being in the range $1/6 \pm 0.43/\sqrt{N}$: that is, to halve the uncertainty requires a fourfold increase in N.

This set of data shows that a single estimate of P_1, that is with $M = 1$, can be misleading if the number of throws N is small.

The data for this graph were computed using the procedure spread(M,N,R) listed and described below. In essence this procedure just counts the number of times that n_1 has a given value, but there are some necessary details that make it appear more complicated. We expect the value of n_1, denoted by n in the procedure, to be close to $N/6$, and there to be few occurrences of n_1 where $|N/6 - n_1|$ is large. Therefore we collect data only if n_1 is inside the interval $[N/6 - R, N/6 + R]$, where R is a number provided in the argument list; data outside this range are ignored. Appropriate values of R for each N are chosen by trial and error using a relatively small number of trial runs, that is, when M is small.

The inputs for this procedure are:

M the number of realisations or trials, that is, the number of times n_1 is computed, for the same N, with different sets of random numbers – in Figure 1.1 this is 50 000;

N the number of die throws in each trial – in Figure 1.1 this is 120 and 600 on the left and right, respectively;

R a measure of the range of values of n_1 counted.

```
>   restart:
>   spread := proc(M,N,R)
>      local k,nmin,nmax,P,n,i,r;
>      r := rand(1..6):
>      nmin := floor(N/6-R):  nmax := floor(N/6+R):            #1
>      if nmin<0 then nmin:=0 fi;                              #2
>      P := Array(nmin..nmax);   # Initialise probability list #3
>      for k from 1 to M do;               # Loop round trials #4
>        n := 0:                                               #5
>        for i from 1 to N do;         # Loop round N throws #6
>          if r()=1 then n:=n+1 fi;   # Count occurrences of 1 #7
>        od:
>        if n<=nmax and n>=nmin then
>          P[n] := P[n]+1;                 # Update list element #8
>        fi;
>      od;                                                     #9
>      [seq([k,evalf[4](P[k]/M)],k=nmin..nmax)]:               #10
>   end proc:
```

We now give some notes about this procedure.

#1 Define the minimum and maximum values of n to be considered.

#2 If $R > N/6$, nmin will be negative, and thus smaller than the minimum possible value of n_1, which is 0.

#3 Here we initialise a one-dimensional `Array`, which is a Maple data structure, and in this context we use it as a list, but the index starts not at 1, but at `nmin`. When initialised in this way, all elements are 0. Usually a computation with an `Array` is faster than the equivalent computation with a list.

In the present case, the element `P[k]` is used to count the number of times that $n_1 = k$.

#4 This is the beginning of the loop round the Mth trial: it ends at line #9.

#5 The counter $\mathtt{n} = n_1$ is set to 0 for each trial.

#6 This is the beginning of the loop round the N throws of the die.

#7 In this line `n` is incremented by 1 if the number 1 is thrown.

#8 If `n` is in a suitable range, the relevant `Array` element is incremented by 1.

#10 This defines the output as a list of the lists `[k,P[k]]`, with `k=nmin..nmax`.

A typical output of this procedure, given with the command `spread(100,60,3);`, where $M = 100$, $N = 60$ and $R = 3$, is

$$[[7., 0.0900], [8., 0.110], [9., 0.110], [10., 0.130],$$
$$[11., 0.100], [12., 0.120], [13., 0.120]].$$

The fourth element of this list, $[10., 0.130]$, shows that the probability of n_1 being 10 for $N = 60$ is estimated from 100 realisations to be $P(10) \simeq 0.130$; Equation (1.5) gives $P(10) = 0.138$. Note that other runs with the same parameters may give different estimates because different random numbers may be used.

In the next exercise we compare the output of `spread(M,N,R)` with the function defined in Equation (1.5), which is a good approximation to $P(n_1)$ for large N; this function is derived at the end of Subsection 1.1.2. An important lesson of this exercise is to see how good this approximation can be.

Exercise 1.4

Use the procedure `spread` to plot graphs like those in Figure 1.1 for $N = 36$ and 60, with M as large as feasible on your computer. On the same graph, plot the function defined in Equation (1.5) (page 10).

As a guide to the size of M, the solution uses $M = 50\,000$, but you should first find the time taken with a smaller value in order to estimate the computational time for larger values of M.

Exercise 1.5

A coin is tossed N times, with the kth toss defining the random number x_k according to the rule $x_k = 1$ if a head occurs and $x_k = -1$ otherwise. We define the random variable s by the sum

$$s = x_1 + x_2 + \cdots + x_N.$$

The possible values of s are $\{-N, -N+2, \ldots, N-2, N\}$. Write a procedure similar to `spread(M,N,R)`, and plot the frequency of occurrence of values of s for $(N, R) = (10, 10)$, $(100, 35)$ and $(1000, 100)$ and a suitable value of M. The solution uses $M = 50\,000$, but this takes a long time, so you should experiment, as suggested in Exercise 1.4.

Exercise 1.6

There are three political parties, P_1, P_2 and P_3, in a country with, respectively, 20%, 39% and 41% of the vote. A polling company takes a survey of 1000 voters to estimate the result of the vote on polling day. Use Maple to estimate the probability that it will predict a win for P_2.

[*Hint*: One method is to use `rand(1..100)` and give votes appropriately when random numbers fall in the intervals $[1, 20]$, $[21, 59]$ and $[60, 100]$.]

1.1.1 Random variables

The outcome of a particular die roll is not predictable, although it is known to be an integer in the interval $[1, 6]$, each with equal likelihood. The lifetime of an electric light bulb, the height of a randomly chosen child from a classroom or the time taken for a regularly occurring journey also cannot be predicted, and neither can the upper or lower limits of their values. Such variables are named **random variables**.

The set of all possible values a random variable can take is named its **range**. The range may contain a finite or countably infinite number of values, in which case the random variable is said to be **discrete**: the outcome of rolling a die is a discrete random variable. Or the range may be continuous, as in the lifetime of a light bulb or the height of a child, and then the random variable is said to be **continuous**. In practice, however, there is often little difference between discrete and continuous variables because all measurements have finite resolution; for instance, the height of a child cannot easily be measured to within the nearest millimetre. In general, any number representing a measurement will be an integer multiple of the smallest number the measuring instrument can detect. It is, however, usually convenient to make a mathematical distinction between discrete and continuous variables, so we discuss them separately, the latter being deferred until Section 1.2.

Discrete random variables

Consider, as an illustration, the die with k denoting the score in any throw, so the range of k is $\{1, 2, 3, 4, 5, 6\}$. The function that specifies the probability that k takes each value of the range is denoted by $P(k)$ or P_k, which is named the **probability function** (or **probability distribution**) of k. For a die,

$$P(k) = p_k = \tfrac{1}{6}, \quad k = 1, 2, \ldots, 6. \tag{1.6}$$

Another example is the choice of a card from a standard pack: the probability P_{p} of choosing a picture card is $3 \times 4/52 = 3/13$, and the probability P_{n} of choosing a number card is $P_{\mathrm{n}} = 10 \times 4/52 = 10/13 = 1 - P_{\mathrm{p}}$, when an ace is counted as a number card. These probability functions can be calculated precisely, but most are not so simple; for instance, the number of eggs in a bird's nest varies from zero to an unknown maximum, with a probability function that can only be approximately determined by experiment.

In general, if there are N distinct possible outcomes, $\{x_1, x_2, \ldots, x_N\}$, of a process, the probability function will be a rule

$$P_k = P(x_k) = p_k \quad \text{with} \quad 0 \leq p_k \leq 1, \ k = 1, 2, \ldots, N, \tag{1.7}$$

associating the probability p_k with each outcome x_k. The range $\{x_1, x_2, \ldots, x_N\}$ is a list of non-repeating, distinct items, with a defined

Here we use the notation $\{x_1, x_2, \ldots, x_N\}$ to denote the range, which is a list, rather than $[x_1, x_2, \ldots, x_N]$, because with just two outcomes, 0 and 1 for instance, the notation $[0, 1]$ could be confused with the interval $0 \leq x \leq 1$. Maple uses curly brackets to denote sets, but there should be no confusion.

order. If the x_k are numbers, then normally $x_k < x_{k+1}$; but the range could be $\{h, t\}$ when representing the toss of a coin. By defining an order there is a one-to-one correspondence between x_k, the list element, and k, the index, which need not start at 1. This is why either notation, $P(x_k)$ or P_k, can be used to denote the probability function.

Since probabilities sum to unity, we must have

$$\sum_{k=1}^{N} P_k = 1. \tag{1.8}$$

An example of a random number with $N + 1$ outcomes, where N is any integer, is the integers n_k of Equation (1.3) (page 8), which vary between 0 and N, representing the number of times the face 1 appears in N throws of a die.

Another important random number is the ratio n_k/N, used in Equation (1.3) to estimate the probability P_k. Thus we see that the limit, defined in Equation (1.2) (page 7), is a real number but the ratio (1.3), used to define this limit, is a random variable. This distinction is important.

Exercise 1.7

A roulette wheel is divided into 37 sectors numbered 0–36, not in numerical order. The segments are alternately red and black, except the sector containing zero. What are the probabilities of the following events?

(a) The ball falls on a red segment.

(b) The ball falls on an odd number.

In the examples of a card pack, a coin or a die, the probabilities can be determined from elementary considerations. Usually this is not possible and it is necessary to estimate probabilities by experiment or computer simulations. We show below how a simulation is performed for simple examples.

The numerical estimation of probabilities

The numerical estimation of probabilities is essentially an exercise in counting, and we illustrate the method with a simple example.

A die is rolled four times with outcomes d_1, d_2, d_3 and d_4. The random number s is defined by the relation

$$s = \left\lfloor d_1 + d_2^{1/2} + d_3^{1/3} + d_4^{1/4} \right\rfloor, \tag{1.9}$$

where $\lfloor x \rfloor$ denotes the integer part of x, e.g. $\lfloor 4.6 \rfloor = 4$. This random number has the smallest value $s = 4$ and largest value $s = 11$, when all d_k are respectively 1 and 6, although these values of s are also given by other combinations. We wish to estimate the probabilities $P(s)$.

This can be achieved by computing s, $M \gg 1$ times, each time using four independent random numbers in the range 1–6. If s takes the value k, m_k times with $k = 4, 5, \ldots, 11$, then $P(k) \simeq m_k/M$.

With $M = 10^4$, the following estimates of the probability distribution $P(s)$ are obtained.

s	4	5	6	7	8	9	10	11
$P(s)$	0.0273	0.1200	0.1650	0.1632	0.1702	0.1702	0.1378	0.046 30

This table shows that in $M = 10^4$ trials we expect the outcome to be $s = 4$ about 273 times. In this example it is possible to compute $P(s)$ exactly: in Exercise 1.10 we see that $P(4) = 1/36 \simeq 0.0278$.

The Maple procedure count(M) used to compute these values is listed next; it has only one argument, M, the number of trials.

```
>   restart:
>   count := proc(M)
>      local P,s,k,r,i;
>      r := rand(1..6):          # Set up random number generator
>      P := Array(4..11):              # Initialise the Array P
>      for i from 1 to M do:          # Start loop round M trials
```

Form the sum defined in Equation (1.9):

```
>         s := floor(add(r()^(1/k),k=1..4));
>         P[s] := P[s]+1;                # Update Array elements
>         # Now P[s] is the number of occurrences of number s
>      od:
```

Finally, compute the probabilities and put them in a list:

```
>      [seq([j,evalf[4](P[j]/M)],j=4..11)];
>   end proc:
```

Exercise 1.8

A die is rolled 5 times in succession to give 5 random numbers d_k, $k = 1, 2, \ldots, 5$, each in the range $\{1, 2, 3, 4, 5, 6\}$. The sum of these numbers,

$$s = d_1 + d_2 + d_3 + d_4 + d_5,$$

is another random variable, with the range $\{5, 6, \ldots, 30\}$. Use Maple to estimate the probability function $P(s)$ and plot its graph.

Exercise 1.9

A pair of n-sided dice with outcomes $\{1, 2, 3, \ldots, n\}$ are thrown to produce a pair of random integers (x_1, y_1) that defines a point in the Cartesian plane. Two more points, (x_2, y_2) and (x_3, y_3), are found similarly. These points can be joined to form a triangle, the area of which is

$$A = \tfrac{1}{2} \left| x_1(y_2 - y_3) + x_2(y_3 - y_1) + x_3(y_1 - y_2) \right|.$$

This is a random number with the range $\left\{ 0, \frac{1}{2}, 1, \ldots, \frac{(n-1)^2}{2} \right\}$.

(a) If $n = 2$, show that $P(0) = \frac{5}{8}$ and $P(\frac{1}{2}) = \frac{3}{8}$, exactly.

(b) Write a Maple procedure to estimate P_k, with $x_k = (k-1)^2/2$, for any n, and check that for $n = 2$ your procedure gives results consistent with the exact result derived above. Use your procedure to find approximations to the probabilities when $n = 6$ and $n = 10$.

Exercise 1.10

For the random number s defined in Equation (1.9), the number of possibilities is $6^4 = 1296$, so the probabilities $P(k)$, $k = 4, 5, \ldots, 11$, can be computed exactly. Use Maple to perform this calculation, and show that $P(4) = 1/36$ and $P(6) = P(7) = P(8) = P(9)$.

1.1.2   Special distributions

Here we describe a few useful and common distributions of discrete random variables. In practical simulations we require sets of random numbers drawn from given distributions, and Maple has many built-in procedures to supply these; the simplest is `rand(n..m)`, introduced on page 8 and used in all previous applications.

There are many other distributions available in Maple, and we shall make use of several throughout the remainder of this course. All are accessed using the `Statistics` package, which also contains tools to manipulate random numbers; you may obtain an overview by typing `?Stats`, if you wish, but it is not necessary at this stage. We introduce each distribution and the various tools as necessary.

Uniform distributions

The discrete random variable x with n possible outcomes and range $\{x_1, x_2, \ldots, x_n\}$ is said to be uniformly distributed if the probability distribution satisfies

$$P(x) = \frac{1}{n}, \quad x = x_k, \; k = 1, 2, \ldots, n, \tag{1.10}$$

that is, all outcomes are equally likely. The toss of a coin and score of a die throw give uniform distributions with $n = 2$ and 6, respectively. Random integers uniformly distributed in the interval $[n, m]$ are produced by the procedure returned with the command `rand(n..m)`, as described on page 8. But they can also be generated using the relevant commands from the `Statistics` package

```
>   restart:   with(Statistics):
```

Once the `Statistics` package has been invoked, the `RandomVariable` command can be used to create a random variable with a specified distribution. For instance, a discrete uniform distribution in the interval $[1, 10]$ is created by

```
>   X := RandomVariable(DiscreteUniform(1,10)):
```

This is equivalent to the command `rand(1..10)` and associates X with an integer random variable uniform in the range $\{1, 2, \ldots, 10\}$. The variable X can be used in a variety of ways. For example, the probability function of this distribution is given with the command

In this procedure the limits of the range, 1 and 10 in this example, must be integers otherwise, in Maple 11, numerical errors may occur.

```
>   p := ProbabilityFunction(X,u);
```

$$p := \begin{cases} 0 & u < 1 \\ \dfrac{1}{10} & u \leq 10 \\ 0 & 10 < u \end{cases}$$

so that the value at $u = 1$ is given by

```
>   eval(p,u=1);
```

$$\frac{1}{10}$$

Alternatively, we can create a Maple function

```
>   p := u->ProbabilityFunction(X,u);
```

$$p := u \rightarrow \textit{Statistics:-ProbabilityFunction}(X, u)$$

and now the value at $u = 2$ is given by

The argument of this function can be a real number, not only an integer as suggested by the definition, although this function should be defined only on the integers.

```
>  p(2);
```
$$\frac{1}{10}$$

We often require a sample of random numbers from such a distribution; a sample of 10 numbers, for instance, is given with the command

```
>  z := Sample(X,10);
```
$$z := [9., 10., 7., 8., 8., 4., 7., 2., 8., 1.]$$

and another execution of the command gives a different result, for instance

```
>  z := Sample(X,10);
```
$$z := [3., 1., 1., 9., 7., 4., 10., 1., 5., 4.]$$

As with `rand(n..m)`, restarting the worksheet reproduces previous results.

The variable `z` is a `Vector` data type, not a `list`, and can usefully be used in various functions, some of which are introduced in Subsection 1.3.1.

Bernoulli trials

Any statistical problem can be reduced to just two outcomes by grouping all possible outcomes into two mutually exclusive sets. For instance, in a throw of a die, one set could be the outcome 6, with probability $p = 1/6$, and the other set the outcomes $\{1, 2, 3, 4, 5\}$, with probability $1 - p = 5/6$. In a horse race, for some the only significant outcomes are whether a particular horse wins or loses.

An experiment with precisely two outcomes is named a **Bernoulli trial**. These outcomes are often described as a **success** or a **failure** with probabilities p and $1 - p$, respectively.

A random variable k with range $\{0, 1\}$ and with $P(0) = 1 - p$ and $P(1) = p$ is said to have a **Bernoulli distribution** with parameter p; this probability distribution can be written succinctly in the form

$$P(k) = p^k(1 - p)^{1-k}, \quad k = 0 \text{ or } 1. \tag{1.11}$$

The result of a single coin toss is a Bernoulli distribution with $p = \frac{1}{2}$.

Exercise 1.11

Give the probability of a success in the following Bernoulli trials.

(a) Drawing a single card from a pack of 52, a success being an ace of spades.

(b) Drawing a single card from a pack of 52, a success being either a king or a queen.

(c) Throwing two dice, a success being when the sum of the two outcomes is 11.

Binomial distributions

Consider a set of n random variables x_j, $j = 1, 2, \ldots, n$, each with outcome 0 or 1, and with a Bernoulli distribution with parameter p. The sum

$$s = x_1 + x_2 + \cdots + x_n \tag{1.12}$$

is another discrete random variable, with range $\{0, 1, 2, \ldots, n\}$. The distribution of s can be shown to be

$$P(s) = \frac{n!}{s!\,(n-s)!}\, p^s(1-p)^{n-s}, \quad s = 0, 1, \ldots, n. \tag{1.13}$$

It is named the **binomial distribution** and it has three factors with the following meanings.

- The factor $n!/(s!\,(n-s)!)$ is named the **binomial coefficient**. It is the number of ways of choosing s things from a set of n things. For instance, from a list of three items $[a,b,c]$, there are $3!/(2!\,1!) = 3$ ways of choosing any pair, $[a,b]$, $[a,c]$ or $[b,c]$, when the order is immaterial.
- The component p^s is the probability that there are s ones.
- The component $(1-p)^{n-s}$ is the probability that there are $n-s$ zeros.

Note that the binomial coefficient in Equation (1.13) is so useful that it is often denoted by one of three special symbols:

$$\frac{n!}{s!\,(n-s)!} = \binom{n}{s} = {}^nC_s = {}_nC_s.$$

We use the first of these.

The probability $P(s)$ equals the sth term of the binomial expansion

$$(a+b)^n = \sum_{s=0}^{n} \frac{n!}{s!\,(n-s)!} a^s b^{n-s}, \quad \text{with } a=p \text{ and } b=1-p. \quad (1.14)$$

Putting $a=p$ and $b=1-p$ shows directly that $\sum_{s=0}^{n} P(s) = 1$.

The Maple command to generate random numbers with the binomial distribution $P(s)$, Equation (1.13), is similar to the command for the discrete uniform variable. There are two parameters, n and p, and a variable s:

```
>  with(Statistics):
>  X := RandomVariable(Binomial(n,p)):
>  P := ProbabilityFunction(X,s);
```

$$P := \begin{cases} 0 & s < 0 \\ \text{binomial}(n,\,s)\,p^s\,(1-p)^{(n-s)} & otherwise \end{cases}$$

where 'binomial$(n,\,s)$' is the Maple terminology for the binomial coefficient $\binom{n}{s}$.

A collection of 9 random numbers drawn from a distribution with $n=10$ and $p=\frac{1}{2}$ is obtained as follows:

```
>  Y := RandomVariable(Binomial(10,0.5)):
>  R := Sample(Y,9);
```

$$R := [7., 6., 3., 4., 5., 8., 8., 3., 8.]$$

A similar set of random numbers can be produced by tossing a coin 10 times, scoring 1 for a head and 0 for a tail, and adding these 10 scores. Since either 10 consecutive heads or 10 consecutive tails is unlikely, $P(10)$ and $P(0)$ are very small. For very many tosses, $n \gg 1$, we expect the score to be close to $n/2$.

Exercise 1.12

A coin is tossed n times. By associating each of the tosses with a random variable k, with $k=1$ for a head and $k=0$ for a tail, use Equations (1.12) and (1.13) to show that the probability of obtaining h heads, in any order, is

$$P(h) = \frac{1}{2^n} \frac{n!}{h!\,(n-h)!}.$$

Also show that $P(h) = P(n-h)$.

Exercise 1.13

A die is rolled four times, with a result 1–5 scoring zero and a 6 scoring one, with the total score being the sum of these four subsidiary scores. Show that the outcomes are $\{0, 1, 2, 3, 4\}$, and find their associated probabilities.

Exercise 1.14

Use the Maple function defined for the binomial distribution to plot the graphs of $P(xn)$, $0 < x < 1$, for:

(a) $n = 10$, with $p = 0.1$ and 0.5;

(b) $n = 100$, with $p = 0.1$ and 0.5.

Exercise 1.15

Use the Maple command **sum** to show that

$$\sum_{s=0}^{n} sP(s) = np \quad \text{and} \quad \sum_{s=0}^{n} s^2 P(s) = np + n(n-1)p^2,$$

where $P(s)$ is defined in Equation (1.13).

Exercise 1.16

Use a suitable Maple procedure to obtain $M \gg 1$ random numbers x_k, $k = 1, 2, \ldots, M$, from a binomial distribution with $n = 20$ and parameter $p = 0.4$, and demonstrate that for large M,

$$\frac{1}{M} \sum_{k=1}^{M} x_k \simeq np.$$

Exercise 1.17

(a) By differentiating both sides of Equation (1.14) with respect to a, show that

$$an(a + b)^{n-1} = \sum_{s=0}^{n} \frac{sn!}{s! \, (n-s)!} a^s b^{n-s}.$$

By putting $a = p$ and $b = 1 - p$, deduce that, as in Exercise 1.15,

$$\sum_{s=0}^{n} sP(s) = np$$

where $P(s)$ is given in Equation (1.13).

(b) Show, with a further differentiation, that

$$an(a + b)^{n-1} + n(n-1)a^2(a + b)^{n-2} = \sum_{s=0}^{n} \frac{s^2 n!}{s! \, (n-s)!} a^s b^{n-s}, \quad n \geq 1,$$

and deduce that

$$\sum_{s=0}^{n} s^2 P(s) = np + n(n-1)p^2.$$

For small values of n, the binomial distribution is simple to compute, but for large n it is more difficult; more to the point, it is difficult to understand how it behaves with n, s and p. However, for large n, s and $n - s$, Stirling's approximation to the factorial function, namely $k! \simeq \sqrt{2\pi k}\,(k/e)^k$, accurate for large k, can be used to show that Equation (1.13) can be approximated by

$$P(s) = \frac{n!}{s!\,(n-s)!}p^s(1-p)^{n-s}$$

$$\simeq \frac{1}{\sqrt{2\pi np(1-p)}}\exp\left(-\frac{(s-np)^2}{2np(1-p)}\right). \qquad (1.15)$$

This result is derived on the course CD.

Exercise 1.18

For $n = 100$, make a graphical comparison of the binomial distribution $P(s)$ defined by Equation (1.13), for $p = 0.1$, 0.2 and 0.5, with the approximation given in Equation (1.15).

___

The binomial distribution is important and will be used in Section 1.4 to understand some aspects of population growth. Here we use it to understand Figure 1.1 (page 10), which shows the distribution of n_1, the number of times that a particular side of a die falls face up in N throws. For the kth throw, set $x_k = 1$ for a successful throw and $x_k = 0$ otherwise. Then

$$x_1 + x_2 + \cdots + x_N = n_1.$$

Since each x_k has a Bernoulli distribution with $p = \frac{1}{6}$, it follows that the distribution of n_1 is given by Equation (1.13) with $p = \frac{1}{6}$ and $n = N$, and that for large N this is approximated by Equation (1.15) to give

$$P(n_1) \simeq \frac{6}{\sqrt{10\pi N}}\exp\left(-\frac{18(n_1 - N/6)^2}{5N}\right). \qquad (1.16)$$

The graph of this function is shown by the solid lines in Figure 1.1 (page 10).

1.2   Continuous random variables

Many random variables occurring in nature are continuous; three examples were given at the beginning of Subsection 1.1.1. Continuous random variables pose practical problems in both the measurement of the distribution functions and their estimation using a computer simulation. Consider, for instance, the times of a frequently taken journey, such as to work each day: time is, for all practical purposes, a continuous variable, but measurement of a particular journey time will be accurate to, say, 1 minute, so all times in the interval $(30, 31]$ minutes are considered equivalent. Thus for practical purposes a continuous random variable is treated exactly like a discrete variable, although there are important mathematical niceties associated with continuous random variables.

In general, a continuous random variable x has a range $a \leq x \leq b$; that is, there are infinitely many outcomes and the probability of x having a particular value is zero. Thus we need to consider the probability that x lies in an interval $x_1 < x \leq x_2$, which we denote by $P(x_1, x_2)$, with $x_2 > x_1$.

The probability $P(x_1, x_2)$ depends upon the two variables x_1 and x_2, but if $x_2 - x_1$ is sufficiently small, we expect $P(x_1, x_2)$ to be proportional to $\delta x = x_2 - x_1$. Consider, for instance, a large barrel of assorted apples: typically apples weigh between 100 g and 300 g, so if we choose all those weighing between 190 g and 210 g, we should expect about half to weigh between 190 g and 200 g, because for small intervals we expect the distribution to be uniform.

Thus for small positive δx we expect

$$P(x, x + \delta x) \simeq \rho(x)\, \delta x, \tag{1.17}$$

where $\rho(x)$ depends only upon x and is a non-negative function. Further, the smaller δx, the better this approximation is expected to be. The function $\rho(x)$ is simpler than $P(x, x + \delta x)$ because it depends upon only one variable, x, rather than two. It is named the **probability density** or **density function**. Notice that while the probability $P(x_1, x_2)$ is dimensionless, the density has dimensions which are the inverse of those of x. The density is *not* a probability and, in particular, can exceed unity.

The interval $[a, b]$ can be divided into M equal-length subintervals $I_1 = [x_0, x_1]$ and $I_k = (x_{k-1}, x_k]$, $k = 2, 3, \ldots, M$, with $x_k - x_{k-1} = (b - a)/M$, $x_0 = a$ and $x_M = b$. The probability of x being in the interval $[a, x_n]$, $n \leq M$, is, by definition, $P(a, x_n)$, and this must equal the sum of the probabilities that x is in one of the subintervals I_k, $k = 1, 2, \ldots, n$, that is,

$$P(a, x_n) = \sum_{k=1}^{n} P(x_{k-1}, x_k) \simeq \sum_{k=1}^{n} \rho(x_{k-1})\, \delta x, \quad \delta x = \frac{b - a}{M}. \tag{1.18}$$

In the limit as $M \to \infty$, that is, $\delta x \to 0$, the second sum becomes an integral and we obtain

$$P(a, x) = \int_a^x du\, \rho(u), \quad a \leq x \leq b. \tag{1.19}$$

If a is the left-hand limit of the range of x, it is normal and more convenient to write $P(a, x) = P(x)$, and henceforth we adopt this convention. See Figure 1.2 for an illustration.

The probability $P(x)$ is named the **cumulative distribution function** and is the probability that the random variable u is in the interval $[a, x]$. Since the variable must lie in $[a, b]$, we have

$$P(b) = 1 \quad \text{and} \quad \int_a^b du\, \rho(u) = 1. \tag{1.20}$$

This integral is named the **normalisation condition** for the probability density $\rho(x)$.

The interval $[a, b]$ need not be finite: it could be half the real line, $[a, \infty)$, or the whole real line, $(-\infty, \infty)$, for instance.

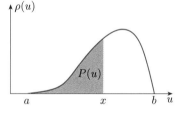

Figure 1.2   An illustration of Equation (1.19) using the convention $P(x) = P(a, x)$

Exercise 1.19

For the density $\rho(x)$, defined on the whole real line, express the probability that x lies in the interval $[x_1, x_2]$ in terms of the cumulative probability.

An example of a continuous distribution is that of the wind speed, v, at a particular location and height, which is important in the positioning of wind farms. It transpires that, to a good approximation, most measurements can be fitted to the two-parameter **Weibull distribution**, the density of which is defined by the formula,

$$\rho_w(v) = \frac{\beta}{\eta}\left(\frac{v}{\eta}\right)^{\beta-1} \exp\left(-\left(\frac{v}{\eta}\right)^{\beta}\right), \tag{1.21}$$

where η is known as the scale parameter and β the shape parameter, which is usually about 2 in these applications. Some values of these parameters and the mean wind speed at various locations are given in the following table.

	Bala, Wales	Brest, France	Carcassonne, France	Stornoway, Scotland	Cork, Eire
Average wind speed $(\mathrm{m\,s^{-1}})$	7.04	6.87	7.62	7.68	6.96
Scale parameter η $(\mathrm{m\,s^{-1}})$	7.85	7.75	8.60	8.65	7.85
Shape parameter β	1.58	2.02	2.06	1.86	1.95

Exercise 1.20

(a) Show that the cumulative distribution of the Weibull density is

$$P(v) = 1 - \exp\left(-\left(\frac{v}{\eta}\right)^{\beta}\right),$$

and deduce that this distribution is normalised.

(b) Wind turbines work only in a restricted speed range; typically this is between 5 and $25\,\mathrm{m\,s^{-1}}$, that is, 11 to 56 mph. Find the probability that the wind speed is in this interval for the sites listed in the table.

Note that in practice it is necessary to allow for the direction of the wind, and variations in this will also decrease the availability (and energy output).

1.2.1   Special continuous distributions

The uniform distribution

A continuous random variable x with a uniform distribution on $a \leq x \leq b$ has the density

$$\rho(x) = \begin{cases} \dfrac{1}{b-a}, & \text{if } a \leq x \leq b, \\ 0, & \text{otherwise.} \end{cases} \tag{1.22}$$

Random numbers from this distribution are generated with the Maple command `X := RandomVariable(Uniform(a,b))`, and a `Vector` of M such random numbers is produced with the command `Sample(X,M)`, provided that a (with $b > a$) and M evaluate to real numbers.

The exponential distribution

A non-negative random variable x with the density

$$\rho(x) = \lambda e^{-\lambda x}, \quad x \geq 0, \tag{1.23}$$

where λ is any positive number, is said to have an **exponential distribution**. A Vector of M random numbers from this distribution is generated with the Maple commands

```
>   with(Statistics):
>   X := RandomVariable(Exponential(L)):
>   R := Sample(X,M);
```

where $L = 1/\lambda$ must be a positive real number.

Exercise 1.21

Show that the cumulative distribution for the uniform and the exponential distributions are, respectively,

$$P(x) = \frac{x - a}{b - a}, \quad a \leq x \leq b, \qquad \text{and} \qquad P(x) = 1 - e^{-\lambda x}, \quad x \geq 0.$$

The Gaussian or normal distribution

A random variable x with the density

$$\rho(x) = \frac{1}{\sigma\sqrt{2\pi}} \exp\left(-\frac{(x - \mu)^2}{2\sigma^2}\right), \tag{1.24}$$

where σ is a positive number, is said to be normally distributed with a **normal distribution**; this is also named a **Gaussian distribution**. It is an important distribution and will be discussed in a little more detail in Subsection 1.3.2; meanwhile, note that Equation (1.15) (page 20) shows that if $n \gg 1$, the binomial distribution is approximated by a normal distribution with $\mu = np$ and $\sigma^2 = np(1 - p)$. It occurs frequently in *Unit 2*.

A Vector of M random numbers with this distribution is generated with the Maple commands

```
>   with(Statistics):
>   X := RandomVariable(Normal(mu,sigma)):
>   R := Sample(X,M):
```

Exercise 1.22

(a) Use Maple to plot the graph of the Gaussian distribution for $\mu = 0$ and various values of σ, for instance $\sigma = 0.5$, 1, 2 and 5.

(b) Use the fact that

$$\int_0^\infty dx\, e^{-x^2} = \tfrac{1}{2}\sqrt{\pi} \quad \text{to show that} \quad \frac{1}{\sigma\sqrt{2\pi}} \int_{-\infty}^\infty dx\, \exp\left(-\frac{(x - \mu)^2}{2\sigma^2}\right) = 1.$$

[*Hint*: Define a suitable new integration variable.]

1.2.2 Changing variables

It is often necessary to find the density of one variable z when it is related to another variable x with a known density $\rho(x)$. For instance, if x is uniformly distributed on $(0,1)$, what would be the density of z if $z = x^2$? We show here that there is a very simple relation between the density functions of x and z.

Suppose that $z = f(x)$ and that $f(x)$ is strictly monotonic increasing for $a \le x \le b$, as shown in Figure 1.3, and that in this interval the density for x is $\rho(x)$. Because $f(x)$ is increasing, the equation $z = f(x)$ can be inverted to give x in terms of z, $x = g(z)$; for example, if $z = x^2$, for $x > 0$, then $x = \sqrt{z}$.

Consider a small interval, of length δx, along the x-axis. The probability of x being in this interval is, by definition, $\rho(x)\,\delta x$. From the construction shown with the dotted lines, this interval is projected onto an interval of length δz along the z-axis, and the probability that z lies in this interval is $r(z)\,\delta z$, where $r(z)$ is the density of z that we need to find. These two probabilities must be equal, hence

$$\rho(x)\,\delta x = r(z)\,\delta z.$$

Also, if the interval on the x-axis is $(x, x + \delta x)$, the z-axis interval is $(f(x), f(x + \delta x))$, and since, for small δx, $f(x + \delta x) \simeq f(x) + f'(x)\,\delta x$, we have $\delta z = f'(x)\,\delta x$. Thus the required density is

$$r(z) = \frac{1}{f'(x)}\rho(x), \quad \text{where } x = g(z). \tag{1.25}$$

For instance, if $f(x) = x^2$ and x is uniform on $[0,1]$, with

$$\rho(x) = \begin{cases} 1, & \text{if } 0 \le x \le 1, \\ 0, & \text{otherwise,} \end{cases}$$

then since $f'(x) = 2x$ and $g(z) = \sqrt{z}$, Equation (1.25) gives

$$r(z) = \begin{cases} \dfrac{1}{2\sqrt{z}}, & \text{if } 0 < z \le 1, \\ 0, & \text{if } z < 0 \text{ or } z > 1. \end{cases} \tag{1.26}$$

Notice that in this case the density $r(z)$ is unbounded as $z \to 0$, although the probability that z lies in any finite-length subinterval of $[0,1]$ is less than 1.

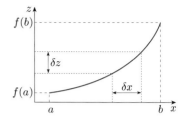

Figure 1.3 Sketch showing how the interval of width δx is mapped onto an interval δz by the monotonic increasing function $z = f(x)$

Recall that $f(x)$ is monotonic increasing on $[a,b]$ if $f(x_1) \le f(x_2)$ whenever $a \le x_1 < x_2 \le b$, whereas $f(x)$ is *strictly* monotonic increasing on $[a,b]$ if $f(x_1) < f(x_2)$ whenever $a \le x_1 < x_2 \le b$. Similar definitions hold for monotonic decreasing functions.

Exercise 1.23

(a) Confirm that $r(z)$ in Equation (1.26) is normalised.

(b) Confirm that $r(z)$ as given in Equation (1.25) is normalised provided that $\rho(x)$ is.

Exercise 1.24

Show that if $z = f(x)$ where $f(x)$ is a positive, strictly monotonic *decreasing* function on $[a,b]$, that is, $f'(x) < 0$ (with possible exceptions at isolated points where $f'(x) = 0$) for $a \le x \le b$, with inverse $x = g(z)$, then

$$r(z) = \frac{1}{|f'(x)|}\rho(x), \quad x = g(z). \tag{1.27}$$

This relation is the general result, valid when $f(x)$ is strictly monotonic increasing or decreasing.

A common transformation is that of scaling a variable, so $z = cx$, where c is a positive constant; then Equation (1.25) becomes $r(z) = \rho(z/c)/c$. For instance, Figure 1.1 (page 10) shows the distribution function of n_1, the number of times the number 1 occurs in N die throws, and in Equation (1.16) we give an approximate formula for this distribution. Since n_1 is roughly proportional to N, a more convenient variable is $z = n_1/N$, for we expect the distribution of z to have its maximum at $z = 1/6$ independent of the value of N. Applying Equation (1.25) to Equation (1.16) (page 20) with $c = 1/N$ gives

$$\rho(z) = NP(zN) = 6\sqrt{\frac{N}{10\pi}} \exp\left(-\frac{18N(z - 1/6)^2}{5}\right), \quad z = \frac{n_1}{N}. \quad (1.28)$$

Exercise 1.25

A projectile is fired with moderate speed v at an angle θ to the horizontal. Neglecting air resistance, the horizontal range is $R = (v^2/g)\sin 2\theta$. If the speed has a distribution uniform in $v_1 \leq v \leq v_2$, show that the distribution of the range is

$$\rho(R) = \frac{1}{2\sqrt{R}(\sqrt{R_2} - \sqrt{R_1})}, \quad R_k = \frac{v_k^2}{g}\sin 2\theta, \ k = 1, 2.$$

1.2.3   The simulation of a continuous distribution

The numerical calculation of the density $\rho(x)$ of a continuous random variable x is similar to that for a discrete random variable, but there is one important difference that requires some thought. It is not usually possible to compute $\rho(x)$ at every point, and it is therefore necessary to divide the range of x into suitably small intervals, which in this course are taken to have equal length δx; we then compute the number of events falling into each interval, which provides an approximation to $\rho(x)\,\delta x$. In any application the length of the interval δx needs to be chosen carefully, for reasons we discuss at the end of this section.

More precisely, if $a \leq x \leq b$, we define N small intervals (x_{k-1}, x_k), $k = 1, 2, \ldots, N$, with $x_k = a + k\,\delta x$ and $N\,\delta x = b - a$, so $x_0 = a$ and $x_N = b$, as shown in Figure 1.4 for $N = 5$.

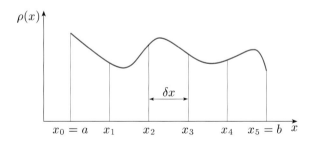

Figure 1.4   Scheme for estimating $\rho(x)$ in $N = 5$ equally spaced intervals

The probability of x being in (x_{k-1}, x_k) is approximately

$$P_k = \rho\left(x_k - \tfrac{1}{2}\delta x\right)\delta x, \quad k = 1, 2, \ldots, N, \quad (1.29)$$

where ρ is evaluated at the mid-point of the interval; this is a good approximation if the interval is sufficiently small that $\rho(x)$ varies little across it. An estimate of P_k, $k = 1, 2, \ldots, N$, then provides an estimate for $\rho(x)$ at the discrete set of N points $x_k - \delta x/2$, $k = 1, 2, \ldots, N$.

The method is most easily described by applying it to a simple problem, which we take to be a variation of the problem given in Exercise 1.9. Take three pairs of random numbers (x_i, y_i), $i = 1, 2, 3$, with all six random numbers uniformly distributed in $[0, 1]$. Each pair defines a point in the xy-plane, and hence the three pairs define a triangle. The area A of the triangle is

$$A = \tfrac{1}{2} \left| x_1(y_2 - y_3) + x_2(y_3 - y_1) + x_3(y_1 - y_2) \right|,$$

and this is another random variable in the interval $[0, \tfrac{1}{2}]$; we require $\rho(A)$, the density of A.

In order to clarify this process, we split the calculation into simple stages. First, we define a procedure to compute the area using six suitable random numbers, as follows.

```
>   restart:  with(Statistics):
```

Define the random variable

```
>   X := RandomVariable(Uniform(0,1)):
```

and then a procedure using X to generate 6 random numbers such that $x_i = $ R[i] and $y_i = $ R[i+3], and then compute the area of the triangle:

```
>   A := proc()
>      local R;
>      R := Sample(X,6);                # Define 6 random numbers
>      abs(R[1]*(R[5]-R[6])+R[2]*(R[6]-R[4])
             +R[3]*(R[4]-R[5]))/2;
>   end proc:
```

Note that this procedure has no input arguments.

A typical output from this procedure is

```
>   A();
```
$$0.01407195570$$

The value of A is in $[0, \tfrac{1}{2}]$, and for the purposes of this preliminary calculation we divide this interval into $N = 10$ equal-length intervals

```
>   N := 10:
```

and define $A_j = j/(2N)$, $j = 0, 1, \ldots, N = 10$. Next define an **Array** such that the element P[j] will be the probability that the value of A lies in the jth interval (A_{j-1}, A_j); the **Array** P is initialised with the command

```
>   P := Array(1..N):
```

Recall that this command assigns the value 0 to all the elements of P.

Now all that is necessary is to compute the area sufficiently many times and count the number of times that A falls into each interval. In this case $0 \le A \le \tfrac{1}{2}$, and $0 \le 2NA \le N$, so we compute the value of $2NA$ and if this has a value in $[j, j+1)$, for some integer $0 \le j \le N - 1$, we increment P[j+1] by 1; the Nth interval must also include the limit $2NA = N$. The required value of $j + 1$ is given with the command 1+floor(2*A*N). This calculation is performed in the next set of commands, in which the number of trials, M, is set to 100.

```
>   M := 100:                          # Set number of trials
>   for k from 1 to M do:                   # Loop round trials
>      j := 1+floor(2*A()*N);         # Compute the interval label
>      if j>N then j:=N fi;                             #1
>      P[j] := P[j]+1;         # Increment relevant Array element
>   od:
```

Line #1 deals with the case $A = \frac{1}{2}$, for which the previous term gives $j = N + 1$, which would lead to an error when trying to access the `Array` element `P[N+1]`. Also, numerical errors could lead to values of A slightly larger than $\frac{1}{2}$.

The probabilities of A being in each interval are obtained by dividing each element of `P` by `M`, the number of trials:

```
>   [seq(evalf[3](P[k]/M),k=1..N)];
```
$$[0.540, 0.240, 0.130, 0.0500, 0.0100, 0.0200, 0., 0.0100, 0., 0.]$$

Thus the probability that $0 \le A < 1/20$ is about 0.54, as given by the first element of this list. These probabilities are related to the density $\rho(A)$ by the formula $\rho(A)\,\delta A = P$, and since $\delta A = 1/(2N)$ this gives

$$\rho\left(A_j - \frac{\delta A}{2}\right) = \frac{2N}{M}P_j, \quad A_j - \frac{\delta A}{2} = \left(j - \frac{1}{2}\right)\frac{1}{2N}. \tag{1.30}$$

In the following command we create a list of the lists $[A_j - \delta A/2, \rho(A_j - \delta A/2)]$, suitable for plotting a graph of $\rho(A)$:

```
>   rho := [seq([(j-1/2)/(2*N),evalf[3](2*N*P[j]/M)],j=1..N)];
```

$$\rho := \left[\left[\frac{1}{40}, 10.8\right], \left[\frac{3}{40}, 4.80\right], \left[\frac{1}{8}, 2.60\right], \left[\frac{7}{40}, 1.\right], \left[\frac{9}{40}, 0.200\right],\right.$$
$$\left.\left[\frac{11}{40}, 0.400\right], \left[\frac{13}{40}, 0.\right], \left[\frac{3}{8}, 0.200\right], \left[\frac{17}{40}, 0.\right], \left[\frac{19}{40}, 0.\right]\right]$$

The following command will plot the graph of this function, as a solid line and the set of points where it is actually calculated.

```
>   with(plots):
>   plot([rho,rho],style=[point,line],colour=[black,red],
        symbol=cross);
```

This gives the curve shown in Figure 1.5 with the crosses. The other curve, passing through the circles, is obtained with $N = 100$ intervals and $M = 50\,000$ trials, which provides a more accurate estimate of $\rho(A)$.

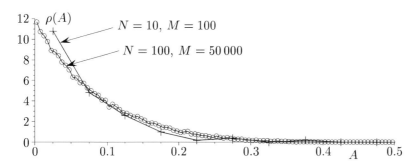

Figure 1.5   Graphs of the estimated values of the density $\rho(A)$ computed using $N = 10$ intervals and $M = 100$ samples (crosses), and 100 intervals with $50\,000$ samples (circles)

The calculation of $\rho(A)$ involves choosing values for two independent parameters: N, the number of intervals, and M, the number of trials.

The interval size is proportional to $1/N$, and since $\rho(A)$ is a continuous function, large values of N provide a smoother approximation to ρ, particularly if it changes rapidly. This suggests that we make N as large as possible.

The number of trials m that lead to A falling into a given interval is proportional to M and inversely proportional to N, i.e. $m \propto M/N$. We need m to be large otherwise there will be significant fluctuations between adjacent intervals, as seen in the data reproduced in Equation (1.4) (page 9) showing the fluctuations in the die simulation using a small sample. Thus for a smooth representation of $\rho(A)$ we need $m \gg 1$, that is, $M \gg N$.

However, in complicated applications the evaluation of each trial is often computationally time-consuming, with each taking days or more of computing time. So practical considerations often impose upper limits on the number of trials M, and thus impose a lower limit on the interval size. The consequences of changing M, with N fixed, are shown in Figure 1.6.

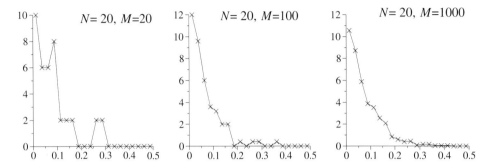

Figure 1.6   Graphs showing how the estimates of $\rho(A)$ change with the number of trials M, for a fixed number of intervals $N = 20$. On the left, $M = 20$ and the estimates in adjacent intervals fluctuate significantly. As M increases, these fluctuations decrease in magnitude to produce a smoother line.

In the three examples shown in Figure 1.6 we fix $N = 20$ and increase M from left to right: so in each case $\rho(A)$ is estimated at $A_j = (j - 1/2)/40$, $j = 1, 2, \ldots, 20$. In the left-hand panel the number of trials equals the number of intervals, $M = N = 20$, and we see significant fluctuations in the estimates of $\rho(A)$. In the central panel $M = 100$ and we see that the fluctuations are present, but less significant. In the right-hand panel, where $M = 1000$, we see this smoothing continuing and also that the smaller values of $\rho(A)$, near $A = 0.2$, are estimated more accurately. This last approximation should be compared with the case $N = 100$ and $M = 50\,000$ shown in Figure 1.5.

In practice, the choice of the number of intervals N, and the sample size M, is a compromise which involves judgements about the accuracy required and the computational resources and time available.

Exercise 1.26

The logistic map $x_{n+1} = ax_n(1 - x_n)$, $0 < a \le 4$, $0 < x_0 < 1$, was considered in Block B, where it was shown to display chaotic behaviour if $a > 3.6$.

For a given value of x_0, say $x_0 = 0.2$, the iterates $\{x_1, x_2, \ldots\}$ all lie in $(0, 1)$, and the density $\rho(x)$ is defined in terms of the relative frequency with which these points lie in given intervals.

Write a Maple procedure to estimate this density and plot its graph for $a = 3.5$, 3.6 and 3.9. For $a = 4$ the density can be shown to have the simple form $\rho(x) = 1/(\pi\sqrt{x(1 - x)})$, which can be used to check your procedure.

1.3 The statistics of a random variable

The density gives the fullest description of a random variable, but its accurate measurement requires very many observations so it is sometimes convenient to describe a random variable by single numbers, or **statistics**, that encapsulate important information and are easier to understand, though great care is usually needed when drawing conclusions from a single statistic.

For instance, in 2002 the average weekly earnings in the UK was £465 per week; this measure is one accepted number describing the wealth of the nation, and for some purposes is quite useful. However, the distribution of wages is such that half the working population earned less than £383 per week; this is named the **median**. The most common wage was £241 per week; this is named the **mode**. The reason why the average, the median and the mode are different is shown in Figure 1.7, which depicts an approximation to the distribution of earnings $\rho(E)$; from this we observe that the average is heavily distorted by the relatively few high earners.

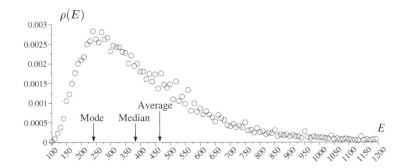

Figure 1.7 Graph showing an approximation to the distribution function of weekly earnings in 2002 in the UK. Here $\rho(E)$ is approximated at £10 intervals.

After this cautionary tale we now describe some basic statistics.

The simplest statistic is the average; for a set of N random numbers x_i, $i = 1, 2, \ldots, N$, the **sample average** is defined to be

$$\overline{x} = \frac{1}{N} \sum_{i=1}^{N} x_i. \tag{1.31}$$

We shall also call this the **average**. The average is also a random number, but as $N \to \infty$ we expect it to approach a definite limit. In practice, $\overline{x}$ is computed using a finite sample of N values, and different samples will give different estimates, as shown in the next exercise.

Exercise 1.27

Use Maple to find 100 different estimates of $\overline{x}$ with $N = 10$, where the x_i are drawn from a sample of integers uniformly distributed in $[1, 100]$. Represent your results graphically; also find the minimum and maximum of your estimates.

If the random variables in the sum (1.31) are from a set with $m \leq N$ distinct outcomes $\{x_1, x_2, \ldots, x_m\}$, in a representative sample there are n_k occurrences of x_k, with $n_1 + n_2 + \cdots + n_m = N$, so the sum may be rearranged to the form

$$\bar{x} = \frac{1}{N} \sum_{k=1}^{m} n_k x_k = \sum_{k=1}^{m} \frac{n_k}{N} x_k. \tag{1.32}$$

As $N \to \infty$, the ratio $n_k/N \to P(x_k)$, the probability of event x_k, and this sum becomes

$$\langle x \rangle = \lim_{N \to \infty} \sum_{k=1}^{m} \frac{n_k}{N} x_k = \sum_{k=1}^{m} x_k \, P(x_k). \tag{1.33}$$

This sum is a number named the **mean**, the **distribution mean** or the **expectation value** of the distribution with the range $\{x_1, x_2, \ldots, x_m\}$, each x_k being associated with the probability $P(x_k)$. It is important to distinguish between the average and the mean.

- The *average* or *sample average* is a random number obtained from an incomplete sample: it is defined in Equation (1.31) and is denoted by $\bar{x}$.
- The *mean* is a number and is a statistic depending on the probability function, Equation (1.33), and is denoted by $\langle x \rangle$.

Some texts do not distinguish between the average and the mean.

Sometimes the term expectation value is used for the mean, but this is a misnomer; for instance, if $x_k = \pm 1$ with equal probability, then the mean is zero, a value that cannot be expected to occur.

Exercise 1.28

(a) Show that for a die, $\langle x \rangle = 7/2$.

(b) What is $\langle x \rangle$ for a Bernoulli distribution with parameter p?

The expression (1.33) for $\langle x \rangle$ generalises directly to continuous random variables. For a density $\rho(x)$, $a \leq x \leq b$, divide the interval into N intervals of equal length δx, so $x_j = a + j \, \delta x$ and $N \, \delta x = b - a$, as shown in Figure 1.8 for $N = 5$.

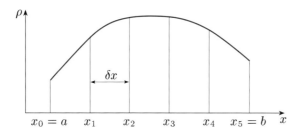

Figure 1.8

The probability P_k that an event occurs in the kth interval is, by definition, approximately $\rho(x_k) \, \delta x$, so Equation (1.33) becomes

$$\langle x \rangle \simeq \sum_{k=1}^{N} x_k \, \rho(x_k) \, \delta x. \tag{1.34}$$

On taking the limit $N \to \infty$, the expression on the right-hand side of this approximation becomes an integral, thus the mean of a continuous distribution is

$$\langle x \rangle = \int_a^b dx \, x \, \rho(x). \tag{1.35}$$

Exercise 1.29

Find the means of the uniform distribution, Equation (1.22), the exponential distribution, Equation (1.23), and the normal distribution, Equation (1.24).

The mean is not the only statistic. The kth **moment**, M_k, of a random variable x is defined to be the mean value of x^k and is given by the formulae

$$M_k = \langle x^k \rangle = \begin{cases} \displaystyle\sum_{j=1}^m x_j^k P_j, & \text{for a discrete variable,} \\[2ex] \displaystyle\int_a^b dx \, x^k \rho(x), & \text{for a continuous variable in } (a,b). \end{cases} \tag{1.36}$$

By putting $k = 1$ we see that the first moment is the mean; the next most important moment is M_2, which we discuss soon.

These formulae for the moments may be generalised to any function of x, not just powers: thus the mean of $f(x)$ over a random variable x is

$$\langle f(x) \rangle = \begin{cases} \displaystyle\sum_{j=1}^m f(x_j) \, P_j, & \text{for a discrete variable,} \\[2ex] \displaystyle\int_a^b dx \, f(x) \, \rho(x), & \text{for a continuous variable in } (a,b). \end{cases} \tag{1.37}$$

For a sample of random variables x_k, $k = 1, 2, \ldots, M$, the sample average of a given function $f(x)$ is defined to be the random number

$$\overline{f(x)} = \frac{1}{M} \sum_{k=1}^M f(x_k). \tag{1.38}$$

The sample nth moment M_n is obtained by setting $f(x) = x^n$.

The example of earnings discussed at the beginning of this section shows that the mean or average can be a misleading statistic. The standard example of the man with feet in the oven and head in the fridge being, on average, at the correct temperature illustrates the danger of ascribing too much significance to an average.

An important additional piece of information about a distribution of a random variable x is its **standard deviation**, denoted by σ, and the related number the **variance** of x, $\mathrm{Var}(x) = \sigma^2$. The standard deviation is defined in terms of the mean of $(x - \langle x \rangle)^2$, so is a measure of the spread of the distribution about its mean value. The square of σ and the variance are defined by the equation

$$\sigma^2 = \mathrm{Var}(x) = \left\langle (x - \langle x \rangle)^2 \right\rangle. \tag{1.39}$$

For a continuous distribution this expression can be expressed as an integral:

$$\sigma^2 = \int_a^b dx \left(x^2 - 2x \langle x \rangle + \langle x \rangle^2 \right) \rho(x)$$

$$= \int_a^b dx \, x^2 \rho(x) - 2 \int_a^b dx \, x \langle x \rangle \, \rho(x) + \int_a^b dx \, \langle x \rangle^2 \rho(x).$$

Because $\langle x \rangle$ is a number,

$$\int_a^b dx \, x \langle x \rangle \, \rho(x) = \langle x \rangle \int_a^b dx \, x \, \rho(x) = \langle x \rangle^2 \quad \text{and} \quad \int_a^b dx \, \langle x \rangle^2 \rho(x) = \langle x \rangle^2,$$

hence

$$\sigma^2 = \text{Var}(x) = \langle x^2 \rangle - \langle x \rangle^2 = M_2 - M_1^2. \tag{1.40}$$

The value of σ is a measure of the spread of a random variable: for small σ the variable is more often close to its mean value.

This last expression for σ^2 in terms of the first two moments is also valid for discrete probabilities, as proved in the next exercise.

Exercise 1.30

Show that Equation (1.40) is true for the discrete random variable with range $\{x_1, x_2, \ldots, x_n\}$ and associated probabilities $P(x_k)$, $k = 1, 2, \ldots, n$.

Exercise 1.31

If $y = f(x)$, where x is a random variable on $[a, b]$ with density $\rho(x)$, show that the mean of any function $g(y)$ of y is given by

$$\langle g(y) \rangle = \int_a^b dx \, \rho(x) \, g(f(x)).$$

Exercise 1.32

Show that the standard deviation of the binomial distribution, Equation (1.13) (page 17) with parameters n and p, is given by $\sigma^2 = np(1 - p)$.

[*Hint*: Use the results of Exercise 1.17.]

Exercise 1.33

(a) Show that the sum of the means of $f(x)$ and $g(x)$ is the mean of $f(x) + g(x)$.

(b) If x is a random variable, show that the mean of the average equals the mean, that is,

$$\langle \overline{x} \rangle = \langle x \rangle \quad \text{where} \quad \overline{x} = \frac{1}{N} \sum_{i=1}^N x_i.$$

Note that this result is not true for arbitrary functions of x: for instance, $\langle \overline{x}^2 \rangle \neq \langle x^2 \rangle$ (see Exercise 1.56).

Exercise 1.34

(a) Find the first four moments and the standard deviation of the continuous distribution, uniform on $[0, 1]$.

(b) Find the first four moments and the standard deviation of the random numbers produced by a six-sided die.

(c) Sketch a graph of the density function

$$\rho(x) = \begin{cases} \frac{1}{2}, & -2 \leq x \leq -1 \ \text{ or } \ 1 \leq x \leq 2, \\ 0, & \text{otherwise}, \end{cases}$$

and find the kth moment, its mean and standard deviation.

Exercise 1.35

The energy that can be extracted from wind by a wind turbine is proportional to

This exercise is optional.

$$E(v) = \begin{cases} v^3, & v_1 \leq v \leq v_2, \\ 0, & \text{otherwise}, \end{cases}$$

where v is the wind speed. Find the mean and standard deviation of $E(v)$ for $(v_1, v_2) = (5, 25)\,\text{m}\,\text{s}^{-1}$, assuming that the wind speed satisfies the Weibull distribution, Equation (1.21) (page 22), for the five cases listed in the table after Equation (1.21).

1.3.1   Maple functions for mean and variance

The `Statistics` package has built-in functions to compute the average, mean and variance of random variables, which are best described using a specific example; for this we choose the **geometric distribution**, the probability function of which is

$$P(s) = p(1-p)^s, \quad 0 < p < 1, \ s = 0, 1, 2, \dots, \tag{1.41}$$

where p is a parameter and the range of s, $\{0, 1, 2, \dots\}$, is infinite. A physical interpretation of this distribution is that if p is the probability of success in a Bernoulli trial, then $P(s)$ is the probability that in $s + 1$ trials, the first s all fail and trial $s + 1$ is a success.

Before dealing with the Maple implementation of this, you should do the following exercise.

Exercise 1.36

For the geometric probability defined by Equation (1.41), show that

$$\sum_{s=0}^{\infty} P(s) = 1, \quad M_1 = \frac{1-p}{p} \quad \text{and} \quad M_2 = \frac{1}{p^2}(1-p)(2-p),$$

and hence find the standard deviation.

[*Hint*: The sum of $P(s)$ is a geometric series; other useful sums can be obtained from this by differentiating with respect to p.]

The geometric distribution is invoked with the commands

```
>  restart:  with(Statistics):
>  X := RandomVariable(Geometric(p)):
```

The Maple function `Mean` will find the mean of the distribution

```
>  Mean(X);
```
$$\frac{1-p}{p}$$

and will also find the average of a sample. For instance, if $p = 0.1$, a sample of 10 random numbers from this distribution is given by

```
>  Y := RandomVariable(Geometric(0.1)):  R := Sample(Y,10);
```
$$R := [4., 12., 7., 4., 1., 2., 0., 15., 17., 4.]$$

and the average of these is given by

```
>  M1 := Mean(R);
```
$$M1 := 6.600000000$$

This Maple procedure takes the argument `R`, which must be an **Array** or a **Vector**; but it also allows the computation of averages of functions of the sample. For instance, the averages of R_k^2, the second moment, and $\sin(R_k)$ are given by

```
>  M2 := Mean(map(x->x^2,R));
```
$$M2 := 76.$$

and

```
>  Mean(map(x->sin(x),R));
```
$$-0.07103350453$$

There is another procedure, `Moment(R,m)` or `Moment(X,m)`, which computes the mth moment M_m of the random numbers `R` or the distribution `X`. The Maple procedure `Mean` yields a mean or an average according to the nature of its argument. There is a similar procedure that computes the distribution variance, for example,

```
>  Variance(X);
```
$$\frac{1-p}{p^2}$$

But for a sample of N random numbers, the same function computes the **sample variance** V, defined by the equation

$$V = \frac{1}{N-1}\sum_{i=1}^{N}(R_i - M_1)^2 = \frac{N}{N-1}\left(M_2 - M_1^2\right) = \frac{N}{N-1}\sigma^2. \quad (1.42)$$

The sample variance V is a random number, and this definition, rather than that given in Equation (1.40), is often used to ensure that its mean, $\langle V \rangle$, is equal to the distribution variance, i.e. $\langle V \rangle = \sigma^2$: the proof of this is provided on the course CD. Thus the sample `R` has the sample variance given by

```
>  V := Variance(R);
```
$$V := 36.04444444$$

whereas the first and second moments give

```
>   sig2 := M2-M1^2;
```
$$sig2 := 32.44000000$$

and we see that $V = 10\sigma^2/9$. For large samples the difference between σ^2 and V is insignificant, but in the next unit we shall encounter an application where the difference cannot be ignored as it is in this unit.

1.3.2 *Mean and standard deviation of the normal distribution*

In many of the applications described later, the normal distribution is important, so it is helpful to know some of its statistics. Its mean, or first moment, is given by

$$M_1 = \langle x \rangle = \frac{1}{\sigma\sqrt{2\pi}} \int_{-\infty}^{\infty} dx \, x \exp\left(-\frac{(x-\mu)^2}{2\sigma^2}\right). \qquad (1.43)$$

This integral is most easily evaluated by writing $x = (x - \mu) + \mu$ and setting $z = x - \mu$, as in the solution to Exercise 1.29, to give

$$\langle x \rangle = \mu \int_{-\infty}^{\infty} dx \, \rho(x) = \mu. \qquad (1.44)$$

The second moment is

$$M_2 = \sigma^2 + \mu^2. \qquad (1.45)$$

From this relation it follows that σ is the standard deviation of the normal distribution.

Exercise 1.37

Derive Equation (1.45).

The geometric significance of μ and σ is illustrated in Figure 1.9, showing the graph of the normal distribution for $\mu = \sigma = 1$, the solid line, and $\mu = 1$ and $\sigma = 2$, the dashed line. This shows that at $x = \mu$ the distribution has a local maximum. The figure also shows when the width of the distribution is 2σ, between $x = \mu \pm \sigma$, for $\sigma = 1$; the width decreases as σ decreases.

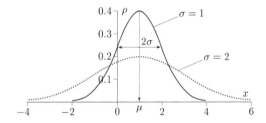

Figure 1.9 Graph showing the meaning of the parameters μ and σ of the normal distribution, defined in Equation (1.24) on page 23

The standard deviation is a measure of the width of the distribution. The probability that a value of x lies in the interval $(\mu - \sigma, \mu + \sigma)$ is

$$P_1 = \frac{1}{\sigma\sqrt{2\pi}} \int_{\mu-\sigma}^{\mu+\sigma} dx \exp\left(-\frac{(x-\mu)^2}{2\sigma^2}\right)$$

$$= \frac{1}{\sqrt{\pi}} \int_{-1/\sqrt{2}}^{1/\sqrt{2}} dw \, e^{-w^2}, \quad \text{where } x = \mu + \sigma w \sqrt{2}.$$

This integral is most easily evaluated numerically, and Maple gives $P_1 = 0.683$, that is, there is about a 68% chance of x falling within one standard deviation of the mean. In the next exercise we show that there is about a 95% chance of x falling within two standard deviations of the mean.

Exercise 1.38

Show that the probability of x falling in the interval $(\mu - k\sigma, \mu + k\sigma)$ can be expressed as the integral

$$P_k = \frac{2}{\sqrt{\pi}} \int_0^{k/\sqrt{2}} dw\, e^{-w^2},$$

and find numerical values of P_1, P_2 and P_3.

One application of this type of analysis is to Figure 1.1 (page 10), describing the relative frequency of one side of a die falling face up in $N \gg 1$ throws. The binomial distribution, Equation (1.13) (page 17), describes this phenomenon exactly, and this is approximated by a Gaussian distribution in Equation (1.16) (page 20) with mean $N/6$ and standard deviation $\sigma = \sqrt{5N}/6$, so that

$$\frac{1}{6}\left(1 - \sqrt{\frac{5}{N}}\right) \le \frac{n_1}{N} \le \frac{1}{6}\left(1 + \sqrt{\frac{5}{N}}\right) \qquad \text{with probability } 0.68.$$

This shows that to halve the width about the mean into which about $\frac{2}{3}$ of the throws fall requires four times as many throws: to decrease the width by a factor of 10 requires a hundredfold increase in N.

1.4   Population growth

In this section we introduce two types of approximation commonly used to understand population dynamics. These types of problem arise in many guises, for instance, the genetic change in a population, the spread of diseases, chemical and nuclear reactions; but here we concentrate on a simple one-species population in order to isolate essential ideas.

First, we introduce a *deterministic approximation* to the population of a single species, in which the population $N(t)$ is a function of the time t and can be determined precisely if the initial population is known.

Second, we introduce a *stochastic approximation* in which it is assumed that the number of births in a given time interval is a random number chosen from a given distribution; now the population at any given time is a random number.

The two types of approximation appear to be fundamentally different; but one aim is to show that under some, but not all, conditions they yield the same results.

1.4.1   A deterministic approximation

In this type of approximation the population at time t is assumed to be a function $N(t)$ of t which can be determined precisely if the initial population $N(0) = N_0$ is known, which is why it is named a **deterministic approximation**.

For a single-species population with no deaths, the only parameter describing the population dynamics is the *birth rate*. If $N(t)$ is the population at time t, it is assumed that the increase δN, during any small time interval δt, is proportional to the population and the time interval,

$$\delta N = b\,N(t)\,\delta t, \tag{1.46}$$

where the parameter b is named the **birth rate**: it has units of $(\text{Time})^{-1}$ and may be a function of time, or the population, or both, but here we assume it to be constant.

With this assumption, the population at $t + \delta t$ is, by definition,

$$N(t + \delta t) = N(t) + N(t)\,b\,\delta t, \quad \text{that is,} \quad \frac{N(t + \delta t) - N(t)}{\delta t} = b\,N(t). \tag{1.47}$$

On taking the limit as $\delta t \to 0$, using the definition of a derivative, we obtain the first-order differential equation

$$\frac{dN}{dt} = bN, \quad N(0) = N_0. \tag{1.48}$$

If b is a constant, this equation has the solution

$$N(t) = N_0 e^{bt}, \tag{1.49}$$

which is the equation for a continuous, exponential population growth. This is a deterministic approximation because if N_0 and b are known, the value of $N(t)$ is known exactly for $t \geq 0$.

Exercise 1.39

If b is not a constant but depends upon time, how do Equations (1.48) and (1.49) change?

In the approximation leading to Equation (1.49) it was assumed that births can occur at all times. But many species, for instance birds, breed only during particular seasons, so the limit used to derive Equation (1.48) is not valid. In such instances we normally measure the population at times nT, $n = 0, 1, 2, \ldots$, that straddle the breeding season. Thus on setting $\delta t = T$ and $t = (n-1)T$, Equation (1.47) becomes

$$N(nT) = (1 + bT)\,N((n-1)T), \quad n = 1, 2, \ldots, \quad \text{with } N(0) = N_0, \tag{1.50}$$

so that the population at time nT is a multiple of the population at time $(n-1)T$: because this multiple is larger than unity, the population increases geometrically.

Exercise 1.40

Use Equation (1.50) to show that

$$N(nT) = (1 + bT)^n N_0. \tag{1.51}$$

Equation (1.51) describes the population growth when time needs to be treated as a discrete variable.

1.4.2   A stochastic description of population growth

The derivations of both Equations (1.48) and (1.50) assume that in given intervals, δt for Equation (1.47) and T for Equation (1.50), the population increase is a *known* proportion of the population at the beginning of the interval. However, a real population comprises individuals making independent decisions; hence the number of births in a given time interval cannot be a fixed, known proportion of the population, but must include some random variation.

The easiest way to understand the effects of this random variation is to consider the discrete time model, the deterministic approximation being given by Equation (1.50). Now we assume that during the breeding season each member of the population has a probability bT of a single birth, and a probability $1 - bT$ of not giving birth: no other events are allowed. We use the same symbol, b, as for the birth rate in the previous section because, as will be seen, they represent the same quantity.

If N_0 is the (known) initial population and N_1 the population at time T, then N_1 could have any value between between N_0 (no births) and $2N_0$ (N_0 births). That is,

$$N_1 = N_0 + r_0, \tag{1.52}$$

where r_0 is a random number with range $\{0, 1, \ldots, N_0\}$. Notice that now N_1 is a random number and not a function of time, as in the previous approximations, which is why we use the notation N_1 and not $N(T)$.

In general, by the same arguments, if N_k is the population at time kT, the relation between N_k and N_{k-1} is

$$N_k = N_{k-1} + r_{k-1}, \tag{1.53}$$

where r_{k-1} is a random number with range $\{0, 1, \ldots, N_{k-1}\}$. Thus starting with a given value of N_0, a realisation of the population growth is obtained by successively adding appropriate random numbers. This is known as a **stochastic approximation**.

Our aim is to understand the connection between the random numbers N_k, $k = 1, 2, \ldots$, and the function $N(kT)$. First, we consider a numerical simulation in order to make a numerical connection between these entities. Then we formally justify the numerical results.

In order to simulate this process we need the distribution function for r_{k-1}; this is obtained by assuming that each member of the population is independent, and that there are two outcomes for each member, a birth with probability bT or no birth with probability $1 - bT$. This is an example of a Bernoulli trial (see page 17). For a population of N it follows that the random number r has the binomial distribution

$$P(r) = \frac{N!}{r!\,(N-r)!}(bT)^r(1-bT)^{N-r}. \tag{1.54}$$

Hence the mean increase in the population during the breeding season is (see Exercise 1.28, page 30)

$$\sum_{r=0}^{N} r\,P(r) = bTN,$$

which is the number assumed when deriving the deterministic approximation, Equation (1.50).

With this information we can use Maple to simulate the population growth. Here we set $T = 1$ and $bT = 0.1$ and use various values of N. If N is large, the probability $P(r)$ has a maximum at $r = bN$, as is shown in

Figure 1.10, where $P(r)$ is shown when $N = 100$ and $b = 0.1$, 0.2 and 0.3.

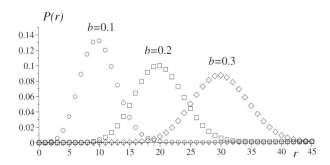

Figure 1.10   Graph showing values of $P(r)$, defined in Equation (1.54), with $N = 100$ and $T = 1$. The circles are for $b = 0.1$, the squares for $b = 0.2$ and the diamonds for $b = 0.3$. Note that the maximum in $P(r)$ is near Nb.

In order to simulate this population dynamics using Maple we first need a random number generator that gives a binomial distribution: this is given by the command X := RandomVariable(Binomial(N,b)), where N and b are the parameters defined above. Then a Vector of M random numbers from this distribution is given with the command Sample(X,M); for example, with $N = 100$ and $b = 0.1$, a sample of 10 such random numbers is given by the following commands.

```
>   restart:  with(Statistics):
>   X := RandomVariable(Binomial(100,0.1)):
>   R := Sample(X,10);
```
$$R := [13., 14., 7., 14., 11., 6., 8., 10., 15., 16.]$$

It is seen that these are bunched in the neighbourhood of $Nb = 10$, as expected from the data shown in Figure 1.10.

We simulate the population growth with two procedures. The first, evol1(N,b), uses Equation (1.53) to evolve the population though one breeding cycle. Here N is the population at the beginning of the cycle, and b is the birth rate, taken to be 0.1 in all the following; the output is the population immediately after the breeding period. If $N = 0$ there can be no change.

```
>   evol1 := proc(N,b)
>      local X;
>      if N=0 then return 0 fi;           # No change if N=0
>      X := RandomVariable(Binomial(N,b)):   # Define generator
>      N+Sample(X,1)[1];               # Add the number of births
>   end:
```

Running evol1(N,0.1) 20 times with $N = 1$ gives

```
>   N := 1:  P := [seq(evol1(N,0.1),k=1..20)];
```
$$P := [1., 2., 2., 1., 1., 1., 1., 2., 1., 2., 1., 1., 1., 2., 1., 1., 1., 1., 1.]$$

In these 20 trials the population changes in 5 cases, rather more than expected; other trials will yield different results. Starting with $N = 1000$, we obtain

```
>   N := 1000:  P := [seq(evol1(N,0.1),k=1..10)];
```
$$P := [1089., 1095., 1100., 1105., 1109., 1095., 1101., 1103., 1103., 1099.]$$

which shows that the population increases by about 100 every time.

The growth of a particular population over K breeding cycles is given by repeatedly using evol1. This calculation is performed in the next procedure, evol2(K,N0,b), where N0 is the initial population N_0. The output of this procedure is a list of the lists $[k, N_k]$, $k = 1, 2, \ldots, K$, where N_k is the population at time k.

```
>   evol2 := proc(K,N0,b)
>     local M,pop,k;
>     M := N0:  pop := [0,M];      # Define first element of list
>     for k from 1 to K do;
>       M := evol1(M,b);           # Compute population at time k
>       pop := pop,[k,M];                    # Increment list
>     od:
>     [pop];                       # Create a list of lists
>   end:
```

You need to execute evol1 before using this procedure.

An example of the population growing from $N_0 = 1$ over 10 cycles is

```
>   evol2(10,1,0.1);
```

$$[[0, 1], [1, 1.], [2, 1.], [3, 1.], [4, 2.], [5, 2.],$$
$$[6, 2.], [7, 2.], [8, 2.], [9, 2.], [10, 2.]]$$

This particular realisation shows a slow initial growth; others would be different.

A clearer picture of the possible types of population growth is obtained by setting $K = 50$, $N_0 = 1$, and displaying the results graphically. The deterministic approximation, $N(kT) = N_0(1 + bT)^k$, grows exponentially, so it is more convenient to consider

$$\ln N(kT) = \ln N_0 + k \ln(1 + bT), \tag{1.55}$$

which increases linearly with k (recall that $T = 1$ in the simulations). Thus it is better to plot $\ln N_k$, rather than N_k, which we expect to increase exponentially for large k.

The following two lines of code compute the data in the relevant form. The first line simply computes a list of $[k, N_k]$; the second uses this to create a list of the coordinates $[k, \ln N_k]$ needed to plot a graph.

```
>   z := evol2(50,1,0.1):
>   zz := [seq([z[k][1],evalf(log(z[k][2]))],k=1..nops(z))]:
```

A graph of this realisation can be plotted with the command plot(zz).

Figure 1.11 shows five carefully chosen realisations of the population, with the jagged lines; the straight, red line through the origin is the graph of $\ln N(k)$, Equation (1.55). In the time shown it is seen that most of the populations eventually increase exponentially, and in Exercise 1.43 you will show that the rate of increase is close to that of the deterministic model if N_0 is large enough.

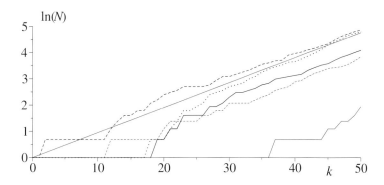

Figure 1.11   Graph showing five realisations, the black lines; the straight red line represents the deterministic approximation, Equation (1.55). Here $N_0 = 1$, $b = 0.1$ and $T = 1$.

The next three exercises explore some of the relations between the deterministic approximation, Equation (1.50), and the stochastic approximation, with increasing N_0.

In Exercise 1.41 we see that as N_0 increases, most realisations of the stochastic population become closer to the deterministic value, that is, $N(kT) \simeq N_k$.

In Exercise 1.42 we consider the time taken for the population to grow from N_0 to $N_0 + 1000$ and show that as N_0 increases, its average tends to that of the deterministic approximation and its variation decreases, as would be expected from Exercise 1.41.

In Exercise 1.43 you will see that the average growth rate of the stochastic population from N_0 to $N_0 + 1000$ tends to that of the deterministic approximation as N_0 increases, and that the variation decreases.

Exercise 1.41

Produce graphs such as those shown in Figure 1.11, but for $N_0 = 2, 5, 10, 100$ and 500, with $b = 0.1$ and $T = 1$.

Exercise 1.42

Write a procedure to compute the time for a population to grow from an initial value N_0 to first exceed $N_0 + 1000$. For $b = 0.1$ find the average and standard deviation of this random number for a representative sample of N_0 lying in the range $1 \leq N_0 \leq 800$, and compare these values with those given by the deterministic approximation.

[*Hint*: Use a relatively small number of realisations, say $M = 20$.]

Exercise 1.43

Write a procedure to evolve a population starting with an initial value N_0,   This exercise is optional.
with a given growth rate $b = 0.1$ and $T = 1$, until the population first exceeds $N_0 + 1000$, at time KT. The procedure should compute the rate of growth, g, of a particular population, as defined by the deterministic equation $N_0 + 1000 = (1 + gT)^K N_0$.

Find the mean and standard deviation of g for a representative sample of N_0 lying in the range $1 \leq N_0 \leq 800$; deduce that $g \simeq b$.

[*Hint*: Use a relatively small number of realisations, say $M = 20$.]

The average over many realisations

Here we consider in a little more detail how the stochastic and deterministic approximations are related, by computing the average of many realisations. First we shall show, numerically, that

$$\overline{N_k} \simeq N(kT), \quad N_0 \geq 1,$$

and later we shall outline a proof showing that $\langle N_k \rangle = N(kT)$ for all N_0. But we shall also demonstrate, numerically, that the standard deviation about the mean is large if N_0 is small, so we cannot assume that any realisation will be close to the deterministic approximation, even after the population has become large. But when N_0 is large enough, the standard deviation is sufficiently small for the deterministic theory to be a good approximation to most realisations of the stochastic growth.

Now consider the average of M realisations of the population, each for KT units of time; it is convenient to represent the data as an $M \times (K+1)$ matrix R, where each row is one realisation and the kth column is the population of each realisation at time $(k-1)T$; the first column contains the initial population N_0.

The matrix R is computed in a double loop; as an example, to compute $M = 3$ realisations for $5T$, we set $K = 5$, $M = 3$, $T = 1$ and each population has the same initial size N_0, here chosen to be 1. In this code we assume that the procedures evol1(N,b) and evol2(K,N0,b) are already defined; with(plots) is needed because later the display command is used.

```
>  with(Statistics):  with(plots):
>  M := 3:  K := 5:  N0 := 1:
```

Define the birth rate b and initialise the matrix R:

```
>  b := 0.1:  R := Matrix(M,K+1):
```

Now compute M realisations of the system:

```
>  for j from 1 to M do:          # Loop round realisations
>    R[j,1] := N0;                # The initial population
>    z := evol2(K,N0,b);          # Compute a realisation
>    for k from 2 to K+1 do:
>      R[j,k] := z[k][2]:                     # Store result
>    od:
>  od:
```

In this example, three possible realisations are

```
>  R;
```

$$\begin{bmatrix} 1 & 1. & 1. & 1. & 2. & 2. \\ 1 & 1. & 1. & 1. & 1. & 1. \\ 1 & 2. & 3. & 3. & 4. & 4. \end{bmatrix}$$

In this set of realisations the populations at $t = 5$, the sixth column, are 2, 1 and 4.

The logarithm of the average of these realisations is obtained from the average of each column, which involves the sum of R[j,k] for j=1..M and each k:

```
>  Av := NULL:              # Null sequence for list of averages
>  for k from 1 to K+1 do:
>    s := add(R[j,k],j=1..M)/M;   # Avg. of populations at (k-1)T
```

```
>    Av := Av,[k-1,evalf(log(s))];                    # Update list
> od:
```

which gives, in this example,

```
> evalf[3]([Av]);
     [[0., 0.], [1., 0.288], [2., 0.511], [3., 0.511], [4., 0.847], [5., 0.847]]
```

In this calculation the logarithm of the average at $t = 3$ is 0.511. The logarithm of the deterministic population is, since here $T = 1$,

```
> pd := k->log(N0)+k*log(1+b);
```
$$pd := k \to \log(N0) + k \log(1 + b)$$

In Figure 1.12 this deterministic approximation is compared with the average over 500 realisations of the stochastic approximation, both with $b = 0.1$ and $N_0 = 1$. The stochastic approximation is depicted by the red line, but the difference between the two lines is barely distinguishable.

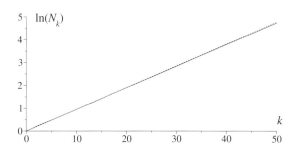

Figure 1.12   A graph comparing the deterministic approximation (dashed, black line) with an average over 500 realisations of the stochastic approximation for $N_0 = 1$ and $b = 0.1$ (red line). The two lines are barely distinguishable.

The graphs in Figure 1.12 show that $\overline{N_k} \simeq N(kT) = N_0(1 + bT)^k$, for $N_0 = 1$. In the light of the few realisations shown in Figure 1.11, this is perhaps surprising. However, if we look more carefully at the data in R we see that the spread in N_k increases with k. This is seen by computing the maximum value and the standard deviation of N_k for each k, a computation performed in Exercise 1.45. The natural logarithms of these data are shown in Figure 1.13. At $k = 50$ the deterministic approximation, Equation (1.55), and the average of the 500 realisations have the values 117.4 and 113.1, respectively; but the maximum value of N_{50} in the sample is 611, and the standard deviation is 102. Thus for this example we deduce that, in spite of the result shown in Figure 1.12, the deterministic theory will give a poor approximation to most realisations.

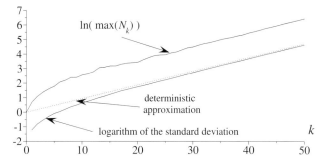

Figure 1.13   A graph of the maximum value of $\ln(N_k)$ (red curve) in the 500 realisations of the stochastic approximation, the logarithms of the standard deviation (solid black curve) and the deterministic approximation (dotted black straight line), Equation (1.55). Here $N_0 = 1$ and $b = 0.1$.

If the initial population is large, the results are quite different. Figure 1.14 shows results for $N_0 = 1000$ and $b = 0.1$. The two red higher curves are the minimum and maximum values of the logarithm of the population in a sample size $M = 500$; the dashed black curve in between is the deterministic approximation. The lower solid black curve is the logarithm of the standard deviation: at $k = 20$, $\sigma = 164 \ll \overline{N_{20}} = 6700$.

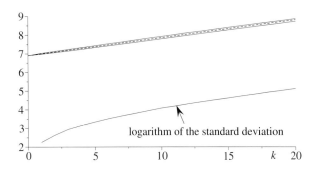

Figure 1.14   A graph of the maximum and minimum values of $\ln(N_k)$ (red curves) in the 500 realisations of the stochastic approximation; in between these is a dashed black curve representing the deterministic approximation, Equation (1.55). The logarithm of the standard deviation is depicted by the solid black curve. Here $N_0 = 1000$ and $b = 0.1$.

We infer that $\overline{N_k} \simeq N(kT)$ for all N_0, but that if N_0 is small, the standard deviation of the stochastic simulations is large, and the deterministic approximation is unlikely to give results representative of any particular realisation. This means that when N_0 is small, it is impossible to predict the population of a particular realisation: only statistics can be estimated. But if N_0 is large, the deterministic theory gives a good approximation to almost all realisations. The analysis presented in Subsection 1.4.3 supports this inference.

Exercise 1.44

Write a Maple procedure to plot graphs similar to those in Figure 1.12 for any N_0 and b.

Exercise 1.45

Write a Maple procedure to compute the average, the standard deviation and the maximum value of N_k, in M realisations for a given N_0 and b with $T = 1$. Use this procedure to investigate the effect of increasing N_0 from 1 to 1000, and demonstrate that

$$\frac{\sigma}{\overline{N_k}} \simeq \sqrt{\frac{1-b}{1+b}} \frac{1}{\sqrt{N_0}}.$$

1.4.3   Formal connection between the stochastic and deterministic approximations

In this subsection we provide a non-rigorous explanation for the behaviour seen in Figure 1.12, which shows that the average over many realisations of the stochastic growth is the same as the deterministic growth. The basic idea used here is quite simple, but the notation needed to express it is rather clumsy; for this reason this section is not assessed.

If $N_k^{(j)}$ is the population of the jth realisation at time kT, then this realisation is defined by the relation

$$N_k^{(j)} = N_{k-1}^{(j)} + r_{k-1}^{(j)}, \quad k = 1, 2, \ldots. \tag{1.56}$$

Suppose that there are M realisations, $j = 1, 2, \ldots, M$. Then the average shown in Figure 1.12 is

$$\overline{N_k} = \frac{1}{M} \sum_{j=1}^{M} N_k^{(j)}, \tag{1.57}$$

which satisfies the relation

$$\overline{N_k} = \overline{N_{k-1}} + \frac{1}{M} \sum_{j=1}^{M} r_{k-1}^{(j)}. \tag{1.58}$$

This is similar to the recurrence relation for each realisation because the equations are linear. The problem is to find a simple expression for the averages

$$\overline{r_k} = \frac{1}{M} \sum_{j=1}^{M} r_k^{(j)},$$

where each $r_k^{(j)}$ is a random number with a binomial distribution with parameters p and $N_k^{(j)}$. If all the $N_k^{(j)}$ were the same, $\overline{N_k}$, then this sum would simply be the average of random numbers which, for large M, could be approximated by the mean, $bT\overline{N_k}$. Then Equation (1.58) becomes the same as Equation (1.50). This result is, in fact, correct but we need a little more care to prove it because for most j, $N_k^{(j)} \neq \overline{N_k}$.

Divide the set of $N_k^{(j)}$ into m disjoint subsets in which $N_k^{(j)}$ has the values $N_k^{(j_1)}, N_k^{(j_2)}, \ldots, N_k^{(j_m)}$, with M_{j_s} members in the subset j_s, so $M = M_{j_1} + M_{j_2} + \cdots + M_{j_m}$. In the subset for $N_k^{(j_s)}$ we label the random numbers $r_k^{(j_s)}$ belonging to these realisations by $R_k^{(i_s)}$, $i_s = 1, 2, \ldots, M_{j_s}$, and hence

$$\sum_{j=1}^{M} r_k^{(j)} = \sum_{i_1=1}^{M_{j_1}} R_k^{(i_1)} + \sum_{i_2=1}^{M_{j_2}} R_k^{(i_2)} + \cdots + \sum_{i_m=1}^{M_{j_m}} R_k^{(i_m)}.$$

Each of these sums is an average of random numbers over the same binomial distribution, with parameters $(N_k^{(j_s)}, bT)$, so that as shown in Exercises 1.16 and 1.17 (page 19),

$$\sum_{i_s=1}^{M_{j_s}} R_k^{(i_s)} \simeq M_{j_s} bT N_k^{(j_s)}, \quad \text{provided that } M_{j_s} \gg 1.$$

Hence

$$\sum_{j=1}^{M} r_k^{(j)} \simeq bT \left(M_{j_1} N_k^{(j_1)} + M_{j_2} N_k^{(j_2)} + \cdots + M_{j_m} N_k^{(j_m)} \right)$$

$$= bT \sum_{j=1}^{M} N_k^{(j)} = bTM\overline{N_k},$$

and it follows that Equation (1.58) becomes

$$\overline{N_k} = (1 + bT)\overline{N_{k-1}}, \quad \overline{N_0} = N_0. \tag{1.59}$$

This is exactly the same as Equation (1.50) with $N(kT)$ replaced by $\overline{N_k}$, which is the result demonstrated in Figure 1.12.

Using the same method it can be shown that the standard deviation is given by

$$\sigma_k^2 = N_0(1 - bT)(1 + bT)^{k-1}\left((1 + bT)^k - 1\right), \tag{1.60}$$

so that, for large k,

$$\frac{\sigma_k}{N_k} = \frac{1}{\sqrt{N_0}}\sqrt{\frac{1 - bT}{1 + bT}}. \tag{1.61}$$

These results are derived on the course CD.

1.4.4 Populations with births and deaths

This subsection is optional and is not assessed.

If the population has a non-zero death rate it should be clear that when the initial population is small, the stochastic and deterministic approximations can yield quite different predictions: some realisations will die out even if the birth rate is larger than the death rate.

In order to illustrate this effect, we consider an idealised population with a short breeding season at time kT, but now we include a death rate and assume that deaths can occur at any time. As before we first consider the deterministic approximation.

If the birth rate is b, the increase in the population during the breeding season kT is $bTN(kT)$, $k = 1, 2, \ldots$. But between these times some members of the population will die, and if the death rate is d, the equation describing the population change is

$$\frac{dN}{dt} = -dN, \tag{1.62}$$

so just before the kth breeding season the population is $N(kT - \delta) = N((k-1)T)e^{-dT}$. After this season the population will be

$$N(kT) = (1 + bT)e^{-dT}N((k-1)T),$$

where we assume that a negligible number of deaths occur during the breeding season. This gives the equivalent of the recurrence relation (1.50) (page 37) and, as in Exercise 1.40, leads to

$$N(nT) = (1 + bT)^n e^{-ndT} N_0. \tag{1.63}$$

If $1 + b > e^d$, that is, $b > d$ for small d, the deterministic approximation of the population increases without bound.

For the stochastic approximation we assume that a death can occur at any time between breeding seasons, so immediately prior to the kth breeding season the population is

$$N_k' = N_{k-1} - d_{k-1}, \tag{1.64}$$

where d_{k-1} is a random number from a binomial distribution with parameters (N_{k-1}, d). Then immediately after the breeding season the population will be

$$N_k = \begin{cases} N_k' + b_k, & N_k' \neq 0, \\ 0, & N_k' = 0, \end{cases} \tag{1.65}$$

where b_k is a random number from a binomial distribution with parameters (N_k', b).

Exercise 1.46

(a) Modify the procedures evol1(N,b) and evol2(K,N0,b) to include a death rate d, and compare the average of $M = 200$, or more, realisations with $N_0 = 1$, $T = 1$, $b = 0.1$ and $b = 0.2$ with $d = 0.25b$, $0.5b$ and $0.75b$, with the deterministic approximation for $0 \le k \le 50$. In each case determine the proportion of the realisations that lead to extinction.

(b) Repeat the calculations described in part (a) for $N_0 = 2$, 4 and 8.

The extinction ratios for the cases suggested in Exercise 1.46, computed with $0 \le k \le 50$ and 1000 realisations, are listed in Table 1.1.

Table 1.1   Extinction probabilities for $b = 0.1$, $M = 1000$ realisations and various values of the death rate d and initial population N_0

d	$N_0 = 1$	2	4	8	10	15
0.01	0.093	0.009	0	0	0	0
0.025	0.258	0.066	0.006	0	0	0
0.05	0.492	0.239	0.068	0.003	0	0
0.075	0.719	0.509	0.291	0.082	0.043	0.01

From the data in this table we see that if $N_0 = 1$, even the smallest death rate considered, $d = 0.1b$, gives a 10% probability of extinction, and this increases to over 70% when $d = 0.75b$. But as N_0 increases, the extinction probability decreases dramatically.

A zero extinction probability does not, however, ensure that the deterministic approximation, Equation (1.63), provides accurate predictions; for this the standard deviation of the sample needs to be small. Figure 1.15 shows how the standard deviation decreases in relation to $\overline{N_k}$ as N_0 increases. In this figure we show $\ln(\overline{N_k})$ (solid black line), $\ln(\min(N_k))$ and $\ln(\max(N_k))$ (dashed black lines), where the minimum and maximum values are taken from the 500 realisations used.

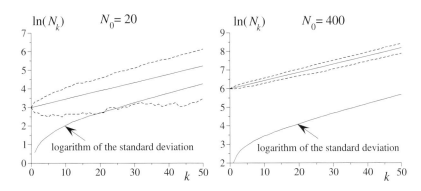

Figure 1.15   Graphs relating to the population growth for $b = 0.1$, $d = 0.05$ for $N_0 = 20$ and 400, each using 500 realisations. The black lines are logarithms of the average population (solid) and minimum and maximum values (dashed) in the set considered. The red line is the logarithm of the standard deviation.

In the left-hand panel $N_0 = 20$ and here $\max(N_{50}) = 404$ and $\min(N_{50}) = 29$, compared with $\overline{N_{50}} = 178$; also, $\sqrt{N_0}\,\sigma_{50}/\overline{N_{50}} = 1.65$. In this example the spread of the population across the 500 realisations is large, so the deterministic approximation is invalid.

In the right-hand panel $N_0 = 400$ and here $\max(N_{50}) = 4567$ and

$\min(N_{50}) = 2664$, compared with $\overline{N_{50}} = 3605$; also, $\sqrt{N_0}\,\sigma_{50}/\overline{N_{50}} = 1.62$. In this example the deterministic approximation provides a reasonable estimate of all realisations. These sets of data are consistent with the suggestion that $\sqrt{N_0}\,\sigma_k/\overline{N_k}$ is practically independent of the initial populations, as when $d = 0$.

1.5 End of unit exercises

These exercises can be used for revision.

Exercise 1.47

Find the standard deviation of the exponential distribution.

Exercise 1.48

If $y = \sin x$ and x is uniformly distributed in $[0, \pi/2]$, what is the distribution of y?

Exercise 1.49

If x is uniformly distributed in $[0, 1]$ and $y = -\ln x$, show that y has the exponential distribution $\rho(y) = \exp(-y)$, $y \geq 0$.

Exercise 1.50

(a) Show that if x is uniformly distributed in $[0, 1]$ and $y = x^a$, $a > 0$, then $\rho(y) = 1/(ay^{1-1/a})$, $0 \leq y \leq 1$.

(b) Use this result to write a Maple procedure that gives N random numbers from the distribution with density $\rho(y) = 1/(2\sqrt{y})$, $0 \leq y \leq 1$, and check your procedure by finding and comparing the mean and average and by comparing the estimates of various moments with their exact values.

Exercise 1.51

Find the nth moment and the standard deviation of the triangular distribution

$$\rho(x) = \begin{cases} \dfrac{1}{a^2}(a - |x|), & \text{if } |x| \leq a, \\ 0, & \text{if } |x| > a, \end{cases}$$

where a is a positive constant.

Exercise 1.52

The real symmetric matrix

$$M = \begin{pmatrix} \cos^2\theta & 1 \\ 1 & \sin^2\theta \end{pmatrix}$$

has eigenvalues $\lambda_1(\theta)$ and $\lambda_2(\theta)$. If $s = |\lambda_1(\theta) - \lambda_2(\theta)|$ and θ is a random variable uniformly distributed on $[0, \pi/4]$, show that the density of s is

$$\rho(s) = \frac{2}{\pi} \frac{s}{\sqrt{(5 - s^2)(s^2 - 4)}}, \quad 2 \le s \le \sqrt{5}.$$

Exercise 1.53

The function $x = x(t)$ is defined to be the solution of the equation

$$\frac{dx}{dt} = (k + \varepsilon r)x, \quad x(0) = 1,$$

where r is a random variable uniform on $[-1, 1]$, and k and ε are constants.

Find the solution, x, and hence show that its density is given by

$$\rho(x) = \frac{1}{2\varepsilon x t}, \quad e^{(k-\varepsilon)t} \le x \le e^{(k+\varepsilon)t}.$$

Show that the mean and standard deviation of x are given by

$$\langle x \rangle = \frac{1}{\varepsilon t} e^{kt} \sinh \varepsilon t \quad \text{and} \quad \sigma^2 = \frac{1}{2} \left(\frac{e^{kt}}{\varepsilon t} \right)^2 (\varepsilon t - \tanh \varepsilon t) \sinh 2\varepsilon t,$$

and that $\sigma \simeq \langle x \rangle \sqrt{\varepsilon t}$ as $t \to \infty$.

Exercise 1.54

In a game a die is rolled. If it shows 6, then a player moves three spaces forward; if it shows 4 or 5, he moves two spaces forward; and if it shows 1, 2 or 3, he moves one space backwards.

A player starts at the origin and stops playing when he has moved a positive distance greater than or equal to 15 spaces. Use Maple to simulate this game and estimate the distribution function $P(n)$ for the number of rolls, n, to end the game. Plot the graph of $P(n)$.

Exercise 1.55

The exponential growth of a population, as in Equation (1.49), is physically unrealistic because eventually resources will be insufficient to sustain the population and the birth rate must decline (or the death rate increase).

A method of introducing this effect into a deterministic approximation is to allow a variable birth rate that tends to zero as the population reaches a finite size M. Then Equation (1.48) (page 37) becomes

$$\frac{dN}{dt} = bN f(N, M), \quad N(0) = N_0 < M,$$

$$\text{where} \quad f(N, M) \begin{cases} > 0, & 0 \le N < M, \\ = 0, & N = M. \end{cases}$$

One simple example is $f = 1 - N/M$, so that if $N \ll M$, the equation is approximately the same as Equation (1.47), and if $N \simeq M$, $\dot{N} \simeq 0$ and there is little growth.

(a) Show that the solution of the deterministic equation

$$\frac{dN}{dt} = bN \left(1 - \frac{N}{M} \right), \quad N(0) = N_0 < N,$$

is

$$N(t) = \frac{M}{1 + B \exp(-bt)}, \quad B = \frac{M}{N_0} - 1.$$

(b) In the stochastic approximation the populations at times $k - 1$ and k are related by

$$N_k = N_{k-1} + r_{k-1}$$

where r_k is a random variable with the range $\{0, 1, 2, \ldots, N_k\}$. Assuming that r_k has a binomial distribution with mean $bN_k(1 - N_k/M)$, write a Maple procedure that simulates this process, and compare the average over many realisations with the deterministic approximation for various values of M and N_0, with $b = 0.1$.

Exercise 1.56

If x is a random variable, show that

$$\langle \overline{x}^2 \rangle = \langle x \rangle^2 + \frac{\sigma^2}{N}$$

where $\overline{x}$ is the sample average over N values.

This result is the reason why Equation (1.42) (page 34) is sometimes used to compute the sample variance for small samples.

Learning outcomes

After studying this unit you should be able to:

- compute probabilities for simple situations, as exemplified by the examples and exercises in the text;
- use in simple situations, common terms such as sample, trial, realisation and probability distribution when applied to random variables;
- recognise some common probability distributions, such as the uniform, Bernoulli, binomial, exponential and Gaussian (or normal) distributions;
- calculate the probability distribution of a transformed variable $z = f(x)$ (for $f(x)$ monotonic) from the probability distribution $\rho(x)$, for simple situations;
- calculate statistical quantities such as the standard deviation and the moments of discrete and continuous probability distributions and of samples, in simple cases;
- use Maple to calculate samples of random variables from common probability distributions, and to calculate the standard deviations and the moments of the samples;
- demonstrate an understanding of the deterministic model of population growth described in Subsection 1.4.1, by solving exercises such as those in the text;
- use Maple to simulate the stochastic model of population growth described in the text, averaged over many realisations, and interpret the results.

Solutions to Exercises

Solution 1.1

(a) There are three even numbers, so $P = 1/2$.

(b) Rolling either a 3 or a 5 are two possible outcomes from a total of six, so $P = 2/6 = 1/3$.

(c) There is just one ace of hearts, so $P = 1/52$.

Solution 1.2

(a) If the order is important, there are 6^2 outcomes; if not, there are 21, because there are 6 outcomes with both numbers the same and $6 \times 5/2$ in which they are different.

(b) and (c) The two events are independent, and since the probability of rolling a 4 or a 3 is $1/6$, the probability of rolling the ordered pairs $(4, 3)$, $(3, 4)$ is $1/36$, so the probability of any order occurring is $1/18$.

(d) The successful outcomes are $(n, 7 - n)$ for $n = 1, 2, \ldots, 6$; each outcome has probability $1/36$, so the required probability is $1/6$.

(e) There are 6^3 possible outcomes: for the outcome $(6, 6, n)$ where $1 \le n \le 5$, the probability is $1/6 \times 1/6 \times 5/6$, and since there are three such suitable outcomes, the probability of obtaining exactly two sixes is $15/6^3 \simeq 0.0694$.

Solution 1.3

See the Maple worksheet.

Solution 1.4

See the Maple worksheet.

Solution 1.5

See the Maple worksheet.

Solution 1.6

See the Maple worksheet.

Solution 1.7

(a) There are 37 possible outcomes, of which 18 are red, so $P = 18/37 \simeq 0.4865$.

(b) There are 18 odd numbers, so $P = 18/37 \simeq 0.4865$.

Solution 1.8

See the Maple worksheet.

Solution 1.9

(a) If $n = 2$, there are four outcomes when two dice are thrown: the points $(0, 0)$, $(1, 0)$, $(1, 1)$ and $(0, 1)$, at the corners of a unit square. Hence when two dice are thrown three times, there are 4^3 possible outcomes.

Some of these will include coincident points, and the areas of these triangles are zero.

The alternative is three distinct points, and the areas of all these triangles are $A = \frac{1}{2}$. There are 24 possible ways to form these triangles: in the first throw there are 4 possibilities, in the second there are 3, and in the third just 2, and $4 \times 3 \times 2 = 24$. Hence

$$P(\tfrac{1}{2}) = \tfrac{24}{64} = \tfrac{3}{8} \quad \text{and} \quad P(0) = 1 - P(\tfrac{1}{2}) = \tfrac{5}{8},$$

because the area is either 0 or $\frac{1}{2}$.

(b) See the Maple worksheet.

Solution 1.10

See the Maple worksheet.

Solution 1.11

(a) $1/52$

(b) $p = 8/52 = 2/13$

(c) There are two successful outcomes, $(5, 6)$ in any order, from a total of 36, so $p = 1/18$.

Solution 1.12

Since $s = x_1 + x_2 + \cdots + x_n$, with $x_k = 1$ or 0 representing a head or a tail, the value $s = h$ represents obtaining h heads in any order. Each x_k is a Bernoulli trial with $p = \frac{1}{2}$, so, from Equation (1.13),

$$P(h) = \frac{n!}{h!\,(n - h)!} \left(\tfrac{1}{2}\right)^h \left(\tfrac{1}{2}\right)^{n-h} = \frac{1}{2^n} \frac{n!}{h!\,(n - h)!}.$$

Replacing h by $n - h$ in this equation shows that $P(n - h) = P(h)$.

Solution 1.13

Each roll is a Bernoulli trial with parameter $p = \frac{1}{6}$ for a score of 1: the sum $s = x_1 + x_2 + x_3 + x_4$ can take any integer value from 0 to 4, and these outcomes have a binomial distribution, so

$$P(s) = \frac{4!}{s!\,(4 - s)!} \left(\tfrac{1}{6}\right)^s \left(\tfrac{5}{6}\right)^{4-s},$$

which gives the following.

s	0	1	2	3	4
$P(s)$	$\left(\tfrac{5}{6}\right)^4$	$\tfrac{125}{324}$	$\tfrac{25}{216}$	$\tfrac{5}{324}$	$\left(\tfrac{1}{6}\right)^4$
	0.482	0.386	0.116	0.0154	0.00077

Solution 1.14

See the Maple worksheet.

Solution 1.15

See the Maple worksheet.

Solution 1.16

See the Maple worksheet.

Solution 1.17

(a) Differentiate Equation (1.14) with respect to a and multiply by a to give

$$an(a+b)^{n-1} = \sum_{s=1}^{n} \frac{sn!}{s!\,(n-s)!} a^s b^{n-s}.$$

Putting $a = p$ and $b = 1 - p$ gives

$$np = \sum_{s=1}^{n} sP(s) = \sum_{s=0}^{n} sP(s).$$

(b) Repeating the differentiation and multiplication by a gives, for $n \geq 1$,

$$an(a+b)^{n-1} + a^2 n(n-1)(a+b)^{n-2}$$
$$= \sum_{s=1}^{n} \frac{s^2 n!}{s!\,(n-s)!} a^s b^{n-s}.$$

Putting $a = p$ and $b = 1 - p$ gives

$$np + n(n-1)p^2 = \sum_{s=1}^{n} s^2 P(s) = \sum_{s=0}^{n} s^2 P(s).$$

Solution 1.18

See the Maple worksheet.

Solution 1.19

If $P(x)$ is the cumulative distribution, the required probability is

$$P = \int_{x_1}^{x_2} dx\, \rho(x)$$
$$= \int_{-\infty}^{x_2} dx\, \rho(x) - \int_{-\infty}^{x_1} dx\, \rho(x)$$
$$= P(x_2) - P(x_1).$$

Solution 1.20

(a) The integral required for the cumulative distribution is

$$P(v) = \frac{\beta}{\eta} \int_0^v dv \left(\frac{v}{\eta}\right)^{\beta-1} \exp\left(-\left(\frac{v}{\eta}\right)^{\beta}\right)$$
$$= \int_0^x dx\, e^{-x},$$

where $x = (v/\eta)^\beta$. Thus $P(v) = 1 - \exp\left(-(v/\eta)^\beta\right)$.

Putting $v = \infty$ gives $P(\infty) = 1$, so the distribution is normalised.

(b) By definition, $P(v_1, v_2) = P(v_2) - P(v_1)$, hence

$$P(v_1, v_2) = \exp\left(-\left(\frac{v_1}{\eta}\right)^\beta\right) - \exp\left(-\left(\frac{v_2}{\eta}\right)^\beta\right).$$

Typically $\beta \simeq 2$, $\eta \simeq 8$ and the last term is about 5×10^{-5} and can be neglected, so

$$P(v_1, v_2) \simeq P(v_1, \infty) = \exp\left(-\left(\frac{v_1}{\eta}\right)^\beta\right).$$

The probabilities are given in the following table, where $P(5, \infty)$ and $P(5, 25)$ are both computed using Maple.

	Bala	Brest	Carcas.	Storn.	Cork
$\bar{v}\ (\mathrm{m\,s^{-1}})$	7.04	6.87	7.62	7.68	6.96
η	7.85	7.75	8.60	8.65	7.85
β	1.58	2.02	2.06	1.86	1.95
$P(5, \infty)$	0.6124	0.6619	0.7209	0.6971	0.6604
$P(5, 25)$	0.6105	0.6619	0.7208	0.6964	0.6603

Here, $\bar{v}$ denotes the average wind speed.

Solution 1.21

For the uniform distribution, with $a \leq x \leq b$,

$$P(x) = \frac{1}{b-a} \int_a^x dx = \frac{x-a}{b-a}.$$

For the exponential distribution, for $x \geq 0$,

$$P(x) = \lambda \int_0^x dx\, e^{-\lambda x} = 1 - e^{-\lambda x}.$$

Solution 1.22

(a) See the Maple worksheet.

(b) In the integral, set $x = \mu + w\sigma\sqrt{2}$ to give

$$\frac{1}{\sigma\sqrt{2\pi}} \int_{-\infty}^{\infty} dx \exp\left(-\frac{(x-\mu)^2}{2\sigma^2}\right)$$
$$= \frac{1}{\sqrt{\pi}} \int_{-\infty}^{\infty} dw\, e^{-w^2} = \frac{2}{\sqrt{\pi}} \int_0^{\infty} dw\, e^{-w^2} = 1.$$

Solution 1.23

(a) The normalisation integral is

$$\int_0^1 dz\, r(z) = \frac{1}{2} \int_0^1 \frac{dz}{\sqrt{z}} = \left[z^{1/2}\right]_0^1 = 1.$$

(b) Suppose that the limits are (a, b), with $f(x)$ monotonic increasing on this interval. If $a' = f(a)$ and $b' = f(b)$, the normalisation integral for $r(z)$ can be written as

$$\int_{a'}^{b'} dz\, r(z) = \int_a^b dx\, \frac{dz}{dx} \frac{\rho(x)}{f'(x)},$$

but since $z = f(x)$, differentiating with respect to x gives $dz/dx = f'(x)$, and hence

$$\int_{a'}^{b'} dz\, r(z) = \int_a^b dx\, \rho(x),$$

and $r(z)$ is normalised if $\rho(x)$ is.

Solution 1.24

The interval δz is given by $\delta z = f(x) - f(x + \delta x)$, because $f(x)$ is decreasing. Thus $\delta z = -f'(x)\,\delta x > 0$ (since $f'(x) < 0$) and

$$r(z)\,\delta z = \rho(x)\,\delta x \quad \text{gives} \quad r(z) = \frac{1}{-f'(x)}\rho(x),$$

which can be written in the form

$$r(z) = \frac{1}{|f'(x)|}\rho(x), \quad x = g(z).$$

Notice that this equation is also valid when $f'(x) > 0$.

Solution 1.25

The distribution of R is given by $\rho(R) = \rho(v)\,dv/dR$, and since

$$v = \sqrt{\frac{Rg}{\sin 2\theta}}, \quad \frac{dv}{dR} = \frac{1}{2}\sqrt{\frac{g}{R\sin 2\theta}}$$

and

$$\rho(v) = \frac{1}{v_2 - v_1} = \sqrt{\frac{\sin 2\theta}{g}} \frac{1}{\sqrt{R_2} - \sqrt{R_1}},$$

the distribution function for R is

$$\rho(R) = 1/\left[2\sqrt{R}(\sqrt{R_2} - \sqrt{R_1})\right].$$

Solution 1.26

See the Maple worksheet.

Solution 1.27

See the Maple worksheet.

Solution 1.28

(a) Since $x_k = k$, $k = 1, 2, \ldots, 6$, and $P_k = \frac{1}{6}$,

$$\langle x \rangle = \frac{1}{6}\sum_{k=1}^{6} k = \frac{21}{6} = \frac{7}{2}.$$

(b) The mean is

$$\langle x \rangle = \sum_{k=0}^{1} x_k\, P(x_k) = p$$

since $P(0) = 1 - p$ and $P(1) = p$.

Solution 1.29

The uniform distribution gives

$$\langle x \rangle = \frac{1}{b-a}\int_a^b dx\, x = \frac{1}{2}(a+b).$$

The exponential distribution gives

$$\langle x \rangle = \lambda \int_0^\infty dx\, x e^{-\lambda x}$$

$$= \lambda\left[-\frac{x}{\lambda}e^{-\lambda x}\right]_0^\infty + \int_0^\infty dx\, e^{-\lambda x} = \frac{1}{\lambda},$$

where we have used integration by parts.
The normal distribution gives

$$\langle x \rangle = \frac{1}{\sigma\sqrt{2\pi}}\int_{-\infty}^{\infty} dx\, x \exp\left(-\frac{(x-\mu)^2}{2\sigma^2}\right)$$

$$= \frac{1}{\sigma\sqrt{2\pi}}\int_{-\infty}^{\infty} dx\, (x-\mu)\exp\left(-\frac{(x-\mu)^2}{2\sigma^2}\right)$$

$$+ \frac{\mu}{\sigma\sqrt{2\pi}}\int_{-\infty}^{\infty} dx\, \exp\left(-\frac{(x-\mu)^2}{2\sigma^2}\right).$$

The first integral is zero because the integrand is an odd function about $x = \mu$, and the second integral is just the normalisation integral, so $\langle x \rangle = \mu$.

Solution 1.30

Since, by definition, $\langle f(x) \rangle = \sum_{k=1}^{n} f(x_k)\,P_k$, we have

$$\sigma^2 = \sum_{k=1}^{n} (x_k - \langle x \rangle)^2\, P_k$$

$$= \sum_{k=1}^{n} x_k^2 P_k - 2\langle x \rangle \sum_{k=1}^{n} x_k P_k + \langle x \rangle^2 \sum_{k=1}^{n} P_k$$

$$= M_2 - M_1^2.$$

Alternatively, and more simply,

$$\sigma^2 = \langle x^2 - 2\langle x \rangle x + \langle x \rangle^2 \rangle$$

$$= \langle x^2 \rangle - 2\langle x \langle x \rangle \rangle + \langle \langle x \rangle^2 \rangle$$

$$= \langle x^2 \rangle - \langle x \rangle^2.$$

Solution 1.31

We need the mean of $g(y) = g(f(x))$, which is given by the quoted integral.

Solution 1.32

The results of Exercise 1.17 show that $M_1 = \langle s \rangle = np$ and $M_2 = \langle s^2 \rangle = np + n(n-1)p^2$, and hence the result.

Solution 1.33

(a) For a continuous distribution, the sum of the means is

$$\int_a^b dx\, f(x)\,\rho(x) + \int_a^b dx\, g(x)\,\rho(x)$$

$$= \int_a^b dx\,(f(x) + g(x))\,\rho(x) = \langle f(x) + g(x)\rangle.$$

(b) We have

$$\overline{x} = \frac{1}{N}\sum_{i=1}^{N} x_i \quad \text{and hence} \quad \langle \overline{x} \rangle = \frac{1}{N}\sum_{i=1}^{N}\langle x_i \rangle = \langle x \rangle$$

since $\langle x_i \rangle = \langle x \rangle$.

Solution 1.34

(a) Since $\rho(x) = 1$ for $0 \leq x \leq 1$ and $\rho(x) = 0$ otherwise,

$$M_k = \int_0^1 dx\, x^k = \frac{1}{k+1}$$

and

$$\sigma^2 = M_2 - M_1^2 = \frac{1}{12}.$$

(b) In this case $P(n) = \frac{1}{6}$, $n = 1, 2, \ldots, 6$, so

$$M_k = \frac{1}{6}\sum_{n=1}^{6} n^k = \begin{cases} 7/2, & k = 1, \\ 91/6, & k = 2, \\ 147/2, & k = 3, \\ 2275/6, & k = 4, \end{cases}$$

and $\sigma^2 = 91/6 - 49/4 = 35/12$.

(c) A sketch of the graph of the density $\rho(x)$ is shown in Figure 1.16.

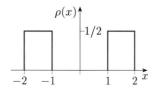

Figure 1.16

The moments are given by

$$M_k = \tfrac{1}{2} \int_{-2}^{-1} dx\, x^k + \tfrac{1}{2} \int_{1}^{2} dx\, x^k$$

$$= \left(1 + (-1)^k\right) \tfrac{1}{2} \int_{1}^{2} dx\, x^k.$$

In the first integral set $y = -x$ to derive the result. Hence the odd moments, and therefore the mean, are zero, and

$$M_{2n} = \int_{1}^{2} dx\, x^{2n} = \frac{1}{2n+1}\left(2^{2n+1} - 1\right),$$

giving

$$\sigma^2 = M_2 = \tfrac{7}{3}.$$

Note that the odd moments are zero because the distribution function is an even function of x.

Solution 1.35

Consider the function $f_n(v) = v^n$ for $v_1 \leq v \leq v_2$ and zero elsewhere. Its mean is

$$\langle f_n \rangle = \frac{\beta}{\eta} \int_{v_1}^{v_2} dv\, v^n \left(\frac{v}{\eta}\right)^{\beta-1} \exp\left(-\left(\frac{v}{\eta}\right)^{\beta}\right).$$

Put $x = (v/\eta)^{\beta}$ to cast this in the form

$$\langle f_n \rangle = \eta^n \int_{x_1}^{x_2} dx\, x^{n/\beta} e^{-x}, \quad x_k = \left(\frac{v_k}{\eta}\right), \quad k = 1, 2.$$

The mean and standard deviation of the energy are therefore given by

$$\langle E \rangle = \langle f_3 \rangle \quad \text{and} \quad \sigma_E^2 = \langle f_6 \rangle - \langle f_3 \rangle^2.$$

The values of these integrals are computed in the Maple worksheet associated with this solution and give the following.

	η	β	$\langle E \rangle$	σ_E
Bala	7.85	1.58	826.96	1590.93
Brest	7.75	2.02	596.44	942.33
Carcassonne	8.60	2.06	804.88	1219.37
Stornoway	8.65	1.86	906.49	1498.30
Cork	7.85	1.95	644.41	1052.39

Solution 1.36

The first sum is

$$\sum_{s=0}^{\infty} P(s) = p \sum_{s=0}^{\infty} (1-p)^s,$$

but if $|r| < 1$,

$$\sum_{s=0}^{\infty} r^s = \frac{1}{1-r},$$

hence

$$\sum_{s=0}^{\infty} P(s) = \frac{p}{1-(1-p)} = 1.$$

The first moment is

$$M_1 = p \sum_{s=0}^{\infty} s(1-p)^s.$$

Consider the function

$$f(p) = \sum_{s=0}^{\infty} (1-p)^s = \frac{1}{p},$$

so

$$f'(p) = -\sum_{s=0}^{\infty} s(1-p)^{s-1} = -\frac{1}{p^2},$$

which gives $(1-p)f'(p) = -M_1/p$, that is, $M_1 = (1-p)/p$.

The second moment is

$$M_2 = p \sum_{s=0}^{\infty} s^2 (1-p)^s.$$

But as above,

$$(1-p)\left((1-p)f'(p)\right)' = \sum_{s=0}^{\infty} s^2 (1-p)^s$$

$$= \frac{1}{p^3}(1-p)(2-p),$$

and hence $M_2 = (1-p)(2-p)/p^2$.

The standard deviation is given by

$$\sigma^2 = M_2 - M_1^2 = (1-p)/p^2.$$

Solution 1.37

By setting $x = (x - \mu) + \mu$, where $\mu = \langle x \rangle$, the second moment can be written in the form

$$M_2 = \int_{-\infty}^{\infty} dx\, (x-\mu)^2 \rho(x) + 2\mu \int_{-\infty}^{\infty} dx\, (x-\mu)\rho(x)$$

$$+ \mu^2 \int_{-\infty}^{\infty} dx\, \rho(x).$$

But

$$\int_{-\infty}^{\infty} dx\, (x-\mu)^2 \rho(x)$$

$$= \frac{1}{\sigma\sqrt{2\pi}} \int_{-\infty}^{\infty} dx\, (x-\mu)^2 \exp\left(-\frac{(x-\mu)^2}{2\sigma^2}\right)$$

$$= \frac{2\sigma^2}{\sqrt{\pi}} \int_{-\infty}^{\infty} du\, u^2 e^{-u^2} = \sigma^2,$$

where the second equality follows from the change of variable $u = (x-\mu)/\sqrt{2}\sigma$, and the final equality comes from

$$\int_{-\infty}^{\infty} du\, u^2 e^{-u^2} = \frac{\sqrt{\pi}}{2}.$$

Also, from Equation (1.44),

$$\int_{-\infty}^{\infty} dx\, (x-\mu)\rho(x) = \langle x \rangle - \mu = 0,$$

hence $M_2 = \sigma^2 + \mu^2$.

Solution 1.38

The probability is (see Exercise 1.19)

$$P_k = \frac{1}{\sigma\sqrt{2\pi}} \int_{\mu-k\sigma}^{\mu+k\sigma} dx\, \exp\left(-\frac{(x-\mu)^2}{2\sigma^2}\right),$$

so putting $x = \mu + w\sigma\sqrt{2}$ gives

$$P_k = \frac{1}{\sqrt{\pi}} \int_{-k/\sqrt{2}}^{k/\sqrt{2}} dw\, e^{-w^2} = \frac{2}{\sqrt{\pi}} \int_0^{k/\sqrt{2}} dw\, e^{-w^2}.$$

These integrals can be evaluated using Maple to give $P_1 = 0.6827$, $P_2 = 0.9545$ and $P_3 = 0.9973$. (See the Maple worksheet.)

Solution 1.39

If b depends upon t, Equations (1.47) and (1.48) remain valid; but separation of variables gives

$$\int_{N_0}^{N} \frac{dN}{N} = \int_0^t dt\, b(t)$$

and hence

$$N(t) = N_0 \exp\left(\int_0^t dt\, b(t)\right).$$

If b is constant, this formula reduces to Equation (1.49).

Solution 1.40

Write $N(nT) = N_n$, so $N_n = (1+bT)N_{n-1}$ $= (1+bT)^2 N_{n-2} = \cdots = (1+bT)^k N_{n-k}$. Putting $k = n$, we obtain the required result.

Solution 1.41 – 1.46

See the Maple worksheet.

Solution 1.47

For the exponential distribution the first and second moments are

$$M_1 = \lambda \int_0^\infty dx\, x e^{-\lambda x} = \frac{1}{\lambda},$$

$$M_2 = \lambda \int_0^\infty dx\, x^2 e^{-\lambda x} = \frac{2}{\lambda^2},$$

and since $\sigma^2 = M_2 - M_1^2$, $\sigma = 1/\lambda$.

Solution 1.48

Applying Equation (1.25) (page 24) with $f(x) = \sin x$ gives, since $\rho(x) = 2/\pi$, $0 \le x \le \pi/2$,

$$z(y) = \frac{2}{\pi \cos x} = \frac{2}{\pi\sqrt{1-y^2}}, \quad 0 \le y \le 1.$$

Solution 1.49

In this example $y(x)$ is a monotonic decreasing function of x, so by Equation (1.27) on page 24, $\rho(y) = \rho(x)/|y'(x)|$.
But $y'(x) = -1/x = -\exp(y)$, and $\rho(x) = 1$, so $\rho(y) = \exp(-y)$, $y \ge 0$.

Solution 1.50

(a) The general formula is $\rho(y) = 1/|dy/dx|$, since $\rho(x) = 1$. But $y' = ax^{a-1} = ay^{1-1/a}$, hence the required result.

(b) Here we need the moments,

$$M_k = \frac{1}{a} \int_0^1 dy\, \frac{y^k}{y^{1-1/a}} = \frac{1}{ka+1}, \quad k \ge 0.$$

See the Maple worksheet for the remainder of the solution.

Solution 1.51

The density is even, so all odd moments are zero; see the solution to Exercise 1.34. The even moments are

$$M_{2n} = \frac{2}{a^2} \int_0^a dx\, x^{2n}(a-x) = \frac{a^{2n}}{(n+1)(2n+1)},$$

and

$$\sigma^2 = M_2 = \frac{a^2}{6}.$$

Solution 1.52

The trace and determinant of M are 1 and $\cos^2\theta \sin^2\theta - 1$, so the eigenvalues are given by the solutions of the equation

$$\lambda^2 - \lambda - (1 - \cos^2\theta \sin^2\theta) = 0,$$

that is,

$$2\lambda = 1 \pm \sqrt{5 - \sin^2 2\theta}.$$

Hence $s = \sqrt{5 - \sin^2 2\theta}$. The density is

$$\rho(s) = \frac{4}{\pi} \frac{1}{|ds/d\theta|}$$

where

$$s\frac{ds}{d\theta} = -2\sin 2\theta \cos 2\theta = -\sqrt{(5-s^2)(s^2-4)}.$$

Hence

$$\rho(s) = \frac{2}{\pi} \frac{s}{\sqrt{(5-s^2)(s^2-4)}}, \quad 2 \le s \le \sqrt{5}.$$

Solution 1.53

The solution of the equation is $x = x(t) = \exp(k+\varepsilon r)t$. Since r is a random variable uniform on $[-1,1]$ and $\rho(r) = \frac{1}{2}$, we have $\rho(x) = \frac{1}{2}\frac{dr}{dx}$ but $\frac{dx}{dr} = \varepsilon x t$, and hence

$$\rho(x) = \frac{1}{2\varepsilon x t} \quad \text{with} \quad x_- = e^{(k-\varepsilon)t} \le x \le e^{(k+\varepsilon)t} = x_+.$$

The mean is

$$\langle x \rangle = \int_{x_-}^{x_+} dx\, \frac{1}{2\varepsilon t}$$

$$= \frac{1}{2\varepsilon t}(x_+ - x_-)$$

$$= \frac{e^{kt}}{2\varepsilon t}(e^{\varepsilon t} - e^{-\varepsilon t}) = \frac{e^{kt}}{\varepsilon t}\sinh \varepsilon t.$$

The second moment is

$$M_2 = \frac{1}{2\varepsilon t} \int_{x_-}^{x_+} dx\, x$$

$$= \frac{1}{4\varepsilon t}(x_+^2 - x_-^2)$$

$$= \frac{e^{2kt}}{4\varepsilon t}(e^{2\varepsilon t} - e^{-2\varepsilon t}) = \frac{e^{2kt}}{2\varepsilon t}\sinh 2\varepsilon t.$$

The standard deviation is thus given by

$$\sigma^2 = \frac{e^{2kt}}{2\varepsilon t} \sinh 2\varepsilon t - \frac{e^{2kt}}{(\varepsilon t)^2} \sinh^2 \varepsilon t$$

$$= \frac{1}{2} \left(\frac{e^{kt}}{\varepsilon t} \right)^2 \sinh 2\varepsilon t \left(\varepsilon t - \frac{2\sinh^2 \varepsilon t}{\sinh 2\varepsilon t} \right)$$

$$= \frac{1}{2} \left(\frac{e^{kt}}{\varepsilon t} \right)^2 \sinh 2\varepsilon t \left(\varepsilon t - \tanh \varepsilon t \right),$$

where we have used the identity
$\sinh 2z = 2 \sinh z \cosh z$.

If $\varepsilon t \gg 1$, then $\varepsilon t \gg \tanh \varepsilon t \simeq 1$ and $\sinh 2\varepsilon t \simeq e^{2\varepsilon t}/2$, giving

$$\sigma \simeq \frac{1}{2\sqrt{\varepsilon t}} e^{(k+\varepsilon)t} \quad \text{and} \quad \langle x \rangle \simeq \frac{1}{2\varepsilon t} e^{(k+\varepsilon)t}$$

and hence $\sigma \simeq \langle x \rangle \sqrt{\varepsilon t}$.

Solution 1.54

See the Maple worksheet.

Solution 1.55

(**a**) Separating variables gives

$$bt = \int dN \, \frac{1}{N(1 - N/M)}$$

$$= \int dN \left(\frac{1}{N} + \frac{1}{M - N} \right)$$

$$= A + \ln \left(\frac{N}{M - N} \right),$$

where A is a constant determined by the initial conditions. Rearranging this relation gives

$$\frac{BN}{M - N} = e^{bt}, \quad \text{where } B = e^A,$$

hence

$$N(t) = \frac{M}{1 + Be^{-bt}}.$$

Initially $N = N_0$, so $N_0 = M/(1 + B)$, that is, $B = M/N_0 - 1$.

(**b**) See the Maple worksheet.

Solution 1.56

Since

$$\overline{x} = \frac{1}{N} \sum_{i=1}^{N} x_i, \quad \text{we have} \quad \overline{x}^2 = \frac{1}{N^2} \sum_{i=1}^{N} \sum_{j=1}^{N} x_i x_j.$$

The mean $\langle x_i x_j \rangle$ has different values depending on whether $i = j$ or $i \neq j$. For $i \neq j$, $\langle x_i x_j \rangle = \langle x_i \rangle \langle x_j \rangle = \langle x \rangle^2$, since the random variables x_i and x_j are independent. For $i = j$, $\langle x_i x_j \rangle = \langle x_i^2 \rangle = \langle x^2 \rangle$. Now, in the double sum for $\overline{x}^2$, there are N terms with $i = j$ and $N(N - 1)$ terms with $i \neq j$. Thus

$$\langle \overline{x}^2 \rangle = \frac{1}{N^2} \left(N(N - 1)\langle x \rangle^2 + N\langle x^2 \rangle \right)$$

$$= \langle x \rangle^2 + \frac{1}{N} \left(\langle x^2 \rangle - \langle x \rangle^2 \right),$$

giving the quoted result.

UNIT 2 Random walks and Monte Carlo integration

Study guide

This unit relies on the working knowledge of Maple developed in Block A. The sections should be studied in numerical order, and you will require access to a computer to study many of them. Apart from reading the text and understanding the examples, it is crucial that you work through as many of the exercises as time allows, because these are essential to learning the material.

For those solutions depending on generated random numbers, you may obtain slightly different numerical results from those given in the text.

Introduction

This unit explores aspects of finite sums of random numbers, so we first describe some examples of these sums in order to provide an idea of their significance. In Sections 2.1 and 2.2 we describe some of their general properties and, using Maple, explore some specific examples. Sections 2.3 and 2.4 use these ideas to develop efficient ways of evaluating certain types of integrals.

One of the simplest examples concerns two gamblers, A and B, who repeatedly toss an unbiased coin: if it falls heads, B pays A £1, and vice versa for a tail. After N tosses of any particular game the sum accumulated by A, which may of course be negative, is of the form

$$S_N = \varepsilon_1 + \varepsilon_2 + \cdots + \varepsilon_{N-1} + \varepsilon_N, \qquad (2.1)$$

where, for each k, $\varepsilon_k = +1$ (heads) or -1 (tails), with equal probability $\frac{1}{2}$. That is, ε_k, $k = 1, 2, \ldots, N$, are independent random numbers with the same density function. Thus the accumulated gain or loss of A is just a sum of **independent random numbers**, which simply means that for the kth toss the value of ε_k is independent of all previous tosses, that is, the values of $\varepsilon_1, \varepsilon_2, \ldots, \varepsilon_{k-1}$. Independent random numbers play an important role in this unit, and in many physical situations.

The sum (2.1) is a particular example of a **random walk**, which is defined to be the sum

$$S_N = x_1 + x_2 + \cdots + x_{N-1} + x_N \qquad (2.2)$$

of the N *independent* random variables $\{x_1, x_2, \ldots, x_N\}$; here we suppose the x_k to be identically distributed, that is, all have identical distribution functions, though this is not necessary for the general theory. The sum (2.2) can also be written in the form

$$S_k = S_{k-1} + x_k, \quad k = 1, 2, \ldots, N, \quad S_0 = 0, \tag{2.3}$$

so that each partial sum, S_k depends only upon the immediately preceding partial sum S_{k-1}, because x_k is independent of $\{x_1, x_2, \ldots, x_{k-1}\}$.

In the example of the gamblers, the distribution of ε was discrete with $P(1) = P(-1) = \frac{1}{2}$, which is a Bernoulli trial with $p = \frac{1}{2}$; see Subsection 1.1.2 of *Unit C1*. In many of the examples discussed here the distributions will be continuous.

In this reference we use the shortened form *Unit C1* to refer to *Unit 1* of Block C.

The sum is named a random walk because S_N may be visualised as the motion of a point particle moving along the x-axis in the following manner. At times $t = k$, $k = 1, 2, \ldots$, it jumps a distance x_k, to the right if $x_k > 0$ or the left if $x_k < 0$. Then, for a particle starting at $t = 0$ at the origin, just after the time $t = N$ the distance from the origin is S_N. Six particular realisations of the sum (2.1) are shown in Figure 2.1, where $\varepsilon_k = \pm 1$ with equal probability. In Figure 2.2 we show how the average, over 500 realisations, of the mean square $\langle S_k^2 \rangle$, $k = 1, 2, \ldots, N$, depends linearly upon k: you will observe that this increases in proportion to k. In fact, in this example $\langle S_k^2 \rangle \simeq k$, a result derived in Section 2.2.

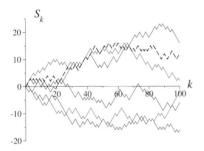

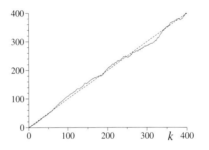

Figure 2.1   Graphs of six representative random walks, Equation (2.1), where $\varepsilon_k = \pm 1$ with equal probability

Figure 2.2   Graphs showing the average value $\langle S_k^2 \rangle$ over 500 realisations (solid red line) and the line $y = k$ (dashed line)

The random variables x_k in Equation (2.2) need not represent a physical distance; x_k may, for instance, be a momentum or the incremental change in a share price in a short time.

A random walk may also be a sum of vectors: for instance, if $\mathbf{r}_k = (x_k, y_k)$ is a vector in the xy-plane, where the Cartesian components x_k and y_k are independent random numbers, then the sum

$$\mathbf{S}_N = \mathbf{r}_1 + \mathbf{r}_2 + \cdots + \mathbf{r}_N \tag{2.4}$$

can be visualised as a particle moving in the xy-plane, with each component executing an independent random walk. Physical examples of random walks are common. The original application was in Brownian motion, which we describe next.

Brownian motion is the apparent jiggling motion of small particles of pollen dust suspended in still water. This motion is not visible to the naked eye, but can be seen with a microscope; it is interpreted as being due to the jostling of the particle by the random motion of liquid molecules. Brownian motion is named after Robert Brown (1773–1858), a Scottish botanist who in 1827 noticed the agitated motion of pollen grains in water. By the end of the nineteenth century this provided evidence that was consistent with the atomic theory of matter; later more careful observations helped end one of the controversies of that century.

Other circumstances where random motion is important include encounters between galaxies and the ejection of comets from the solar system.

Historically, the most significant application is the development of systematic treatments of the numerical values resulting from measurements of physical quantities: the evolution of this theory is very clearly described in the first few chapters of *The History of Statistics* by S.M. Stigler (1986, The Belknap Press). The story starts in the eighteenth century with an increased desire for a quantitative understanding of the world, fuelled partly by the need for accurate navigation, which required knowledge of astronomy, and by the need to make accurate maps; this, in turn, required understanding of the shape of the Earth. For example, in 1792 the metre was defined to be $1/1\,000\,000$ of the length of the meridian through Paris from the north pole to the equator; to be of practical use this required careful measurements along a sufficiently long arc of this meridian. Consequently, in 1795 the meridian arc through the observatory in Paris, close to the Jardin du Luxembourg, with coordinates $2°\,20'\,14''\,\text{E}$, $48°\,50'\,11''\,\text{N}$, was chosen as a suitable arc. This meridian was convenient because it passes through Dunkirk ($2°\,20'\,24''\,\text{E}$, $51°\,2'\,24''\,\text{N}$) and close to Barcelona ($2°\,10'\,12''\,\text{E}$, $41°\,24'\,0''\,\text{N}$), both at sea level. The distance between these points was measured to be $1074.6\,\text{km}$ (667.7 miles). In 1998 various French and Catalan societies combined to celebrate the 200th anniversary of this measurement by creating the *Green Meridian*, a line of trees and footpaths close to the actual meridian, and by putting commemorative plaques in several of the significant triangulation points.

The measurement of such a long arc required an understanding of the shape of the Earth, which had only just been determined. Newton (1643–1727), in the *Principia* (1687), suggested that the Earth had the shape of an oblate spheroid, that is, flattened at the poles, because of its rotation; further, he estimated that the ratio of the radii at the equator and the poles was $1 + 1/f$, where $f = 230$ – modern measurements give $f = 298.26$. But Domenico Cassini (1625–1712), director of the Royal Observatory of Paris from 1671 to 1712, claimed that, in fact, the Earth was a prolate spheroid, and early in the eighteenth century made meridian arc measurements with his son and successor, Jacques, which supported this notion, giving $f = -95$. In 1735 this conclusion was refuted by more accurate French measurements, which confirmed Newton's hypothesis. However, accurate measurements of the oblateness proved difficult because the effect was so small.

These and similar types of problems gave rise to the need for systematic methods of analysing numerical data. The simplest situation is where we have a set of N numerical values L_k, $k = 1, 2, \ldots, N$, resulting from N measurements of an observable; assume that an exact value L exists, and that each measurement $L_k = L + \varepsilon_k$ has an unknown error ε_k. The problem confronting the scientist is as follows: can these N measurements be combined to give better estimates of L, that is, with smaller uncertainties, and, if so, how should this be done?

Other, more complex situations give rise to equations of the form

$$a + bx_i + cy_i = 0, \quad i = 1, 2, \ldots, N > 3, \qquad (2.5)$$

where a, b and c are coefficients that need to be determined, and (x_i, y_i), $i = 1, 2, \ldots, N$, are measured quantities that if exact are assumed, or known from a theory, to satisfy the equation $a + bx + cy = 0$. For this problem it is necessary to find a systematic method of finding approximations to the coefficients that, in some sense, best fit this equation.

A good, but fairly advanced, description of encounters between galaxies is given in J. Binney and S. Tremaine (1987) *Galactic Dynamics*, Princeton University Press.

For the ejection of comets from the solar system, see D.G. Kendall (1961) 'Some problems in the theory of comets, I and II' in J. Neyman (ed.) *Proceedings of the 4th Berkeley Symposium on Mathematical Statistics and Probability*, University of California Press, Vol. 3, Part 1, pp. 99–147.

These coordinates are taken from `www.gaisma.com`; see also `www.world-gazetteer.com`.

By the middle of the eighteenth century, astronomers were combining measurements by taking averages, in various forms. But the applications were haphazard rather than systematic, and there was little theoretical underpinning for the methods. In particular, both Mayer (1723–62) and Maskelyne (1732–1811) appear to have assumed that the result of averaging N measurements reduced the error by a factor $1/N$, which is now known to be too optimistic.

On the other hand, Euler (1707–83) took a more conservative mathematician's view, that errors add: thus if we know that $L_1 = 100 \pm 2$ and $L_2 = 100 \pm 4$, then the average gives $(L_1 + L_2)/2 = 100 \pm 3$, so that averaging will not reduce the error. This notion is now known to be too pessimistic.

The resolution of this problem was eventually provided by Laplace (1749–1827) in 1810, but the first statement of the solution was given by Simpson (1710–61) in 1755: he explicitly stated that the arithmetic mean of a set of measurements of a single quantity is likely to have a smaller error than the individual measurements. Simpson's theory involved several unjustifiable assumptions, but made the crucial point that each estimate L_k comprises the sum of the exact (unknown) value L and the error ε_k (also unknown). After Simpson, the problem became one of understanding that the errors were random variables and then understanding the distribution of their sum, because the mean of N estimates is

$$\frac{1}{N}\sum_{k=1}^{N} L_k = L + \delta, \quad \delta = \frac{1}{N}\sum_{k=1}^{N}\varepsilon_k,$$

which involves the sum of the random numbers ε_k/N.

This problem was resolved in 1810 when Laplace published the *central limit theorem*. This theorem will be stated and examined in Section 2.2, but in essence it says that the distribution of δ is Gaussian regardless of the distribution of the individual components, which is a remarkable result.

The systematic method of dealing with Equations (2.5), now known as the method of least squares, was developed by Laplace and others towards the end of the eighteenth century in order to resolve the observational problems arising in astronomy and geodesy.

This unit is largely about random variables formed by summing independent random numbers, as in Equation (2.1); two important parameters characterising these sums are their mean and standard deviation. A general expression for the sum of any number of random numbers is derived in Section 2.2, but you should first attempt the following exercise which can be solved using the ideas introduced in *Unit C1* and which provides practice in using the type of algebra needed for this unit.

Exercise 2.1

(a) If x and y are independent random variables with means μ_x and μ_y and standard deviations σ_x and σ_y, as defined in Section 1.3 of *Unit C1*, show that the mean and standard deviation of the sum $z = x + y$ are, respectively, given by

$$\mu_z = \mu_x + \mu_y \quad \text{and} \quad \sigma_z^2 = \sigma_x^2 + \sigma_y^2.$$

It will be helpful to recall the result of Exercise 1.33 of *Unit C1* and to note that because x and y are independent random variables, the mean of their product is the product of their means, $\langle xy \rangle = \langle x \rangle \langle y \rangle$.

(b) For three independent random variables, x, y and z, with means μ_x, μ_y and μ_z and standard deviations σ_x, σ_y and σ_z, find the mean and standard deviation of the random variable $x + y + z$.

Note that $x + y$ and z are two independent variables.

2.1   The addition of two random variables

Here we consider the sum of two independent random variables x and y, with continuous density functions, not necessarily the same. If z is the random variable $z = x + y$, the aim is to obtain the density $\rho_Z(z)$ of z in terms of the densities of x and y, which we denote by $\rho_X(x)$ and $\rho_Y(y)$. This result is important and useful, particularly in the next section. Here it is convenient to assume that $\rho_X(x)$ and $\rho_Y(y)$ are defined on the whole real axis; this imposes no restrictions because either or both may be zero on a section of the axis, such as the negative part.

Recall that the probability that a random variable with density $\rho_X(x)$ lies in the interval $(x, x + \delta x)$ is, for small δx, $\rho_X(x)\,\delta x$.

Any pair of independent random variables x and y defines a point in the xy-plane, and the probability δP that such a point lies in the rectangle with corner (x, y) and sides of length δx and δy, as depicted in Figure 2.3, is the product of the probabilities of x being in the interval $(x, x + \delta x)$ and y being in the interval $(y, y + \delta y)$, because x and y are independent:

$$\delta P = \rho_X(x)\,\delta x \times \rho_Y(y)\,\delta y = \rho_X(x)\,\rho_Y(y)\,\delta x\,\delta y. \tag{2.6}$$

This is the product of the individual density functions and the area of the rectangle.

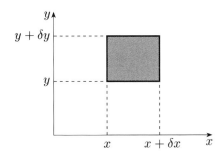

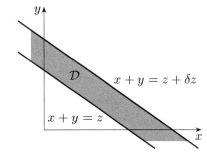

Figure 2.3   Diagram showing an elementary rectangle with area $\delta x\,\delta y$

Figure 2.4   Diagram showing the region in the xy-plane between the lines defined by $x + y = z$ and $x + y = z + \delta z$

The relation $x + y = z$, for a given value of z, defines a straight line in the xy-plane, as shown in Figure 2.4. It follows that the probability that z lies in the interval $(z, z + \delta z)$ is the integral of δP over the region $\mathcal{D}$ between the two lines $x + y = z$ and $x + y = z + \delta z$, the shaded region in Figure 2.4.

By definition, if $\rho_Z(z)$ is the density for z, this probability is $\rho_Z(z)\,\delta z$ for small δz, and on using Equation (2.6) we can relate the three densities:

$$\rho_Z(z)\delta z = \iint_{\mathcal{D}} dx\,dy\,\rho_X(x)\,\rho_Y(y), \quad z - x \le y \le z + \delta z - x,$$

$$= \int_{-\infty}^{\infty} dx\,\rho_X(x) \left[\int_{z-x}^{z+\delta z-x} dy\,\rho_Y(y) \right]. \tag{2.7}$$

Now use the general result, valid for any continuous function $g(y)$:

$$\int_{w}^{w+\delta w} dy\,g(y) = \delta w\,g(w + \theta\,\delta w) \quad \text{for some } \theta \text{ in } 0 \le \theta \le 1.$$

This result is known as the *mean value theorem*; it is not an assessed part of the course. Using this result on the term inside the square bracket of Equation (2.7), we obtain

$$\rho_Z(z) = \int_{-\infty}^{\infty} dx\,\rho_X(x)\,\rho_Y(z - x + \theta\,\delta z),$$

where θ depends upon x and y, but satisfies $0 \le \theta(x,y) \le 1$. Now let $\delta z \to 0$ to obtain the required result:

$$\rho_Z(z) = \int_{-\infty}^{\infty} dx\,\rho_X(x)\,\rho_Y(z - x). \tag{2.8}$$

Integrals of this form are named **convolution integrals**. Equation (2.8) shows how to determine the density function of the random variable $z = x + y$ in terms of the density functions of x and y.

As an example, consider the case where x and y have the exponential distributions

$$\rho_X(x) = \begin{cases} 0, & x < 0, \\ \mu_1 e^{-\mu_1 x}, & x \ge 0, \end{cases} \quad \text{and} \quad \rho_Y(y) = \begin{cases} 0, & y < 0, \\ \mu_2 e^{-\mu_2 y}, & y \ge 0, \end{cases}$$

where the constants μ_1 and μ_2 are both greater than zero. The fact that each distribution is non-zero only on the positive real axis limits the range of the integral (2.8): the component of the integrand $\rho_X(x)$ imposes the constraint $x \ge 0$, and the component $\rho_Y(y)$ gives $y = z - x \ge 0$, that is, $x \le z$. Thus the density for z is

$$\rho_Z(z) = \mu_1\mu_2 \int_0^z dx\,\exp(-\mu_1 x)\exp(-\mu_2(z - x)), \quad z \ge 0. \tag{2.9}$$

This integral simplifies to

$$\rho_Z(z) = \mu_1\mu_2 e^{-\mu_2 z} \int_0^z dx\,\exp(-(\mu_1 - \mu_2)x)$$

$$= \begin{cases} \dfrac{\mu_1\mu_2}{\mu_1 - \mu_2}\left(e^{-\mu_2 z} - e^{-\mu_1 z}\right), & \mu_1 \ne \mu_2, \\[2mm] \mu^2 z e^{-\mu z}, & \mu_1 = \mu_2 = \mu. \end{cases} \tag{2.10}$$

The density of $z = x + y$ is not an exponential distribution.

Exercise 2.2

If x and y are random variables defined on the positive real axis, with densities $\rho_X(x) = 2/(\pi \cosh x)$ and $\rho_Y(y) = e^{-y}$, show that the density of $z = x + y$ is

$$\rho_Z(z) = \frac{4}{\pi} e^{-z} \int_0^z dx\,\frac{e^{2x}}{e^{2x} + 1} = \frac{2}{\pi} e^{-z} \ln\left(\tfrac{1}{2} + \tfrac{1}{2} e^{2z}\right), \quad z \ge 0.$$

Exercise 2.3

What is wrong with the following argument?

Putting $y = x$ in Equation (2.8) gives $z = 2x$ and

$$\rho_Z(z) = \int_{-\infty}^{\infty} dx\, \rho_X(x)\, \rho_X(z - x).$$

But using Equation (1.27) in *Unit C1*, we also obtain $\rho_Z(z) = \rho_X(z/2)/2$, and hence

$$\rho_X(z/2) = 2 \int_{-\infty}^{\infty} dx\, \rho_X(x)\, \rho_X(z - x).$$

Exercise 2.4

Show that if $\rho_X(x)$ and $\rho_Y(y)$ are even functions, that is, $\rho_X(x) = \rho_X(-x)$ for all x, and $\rho_Y(y) = \rho_Y(-y)$ for all y, then the density of $z = x + y$ is also an even function of z.

Exercise 2.5

If $z = x + y$, where x and y are independent random variables both with density function

$$\rho(x) = \begin{cases} 1/2a, & |x| \le a, \\ 0, & |x| > a, \end{cases}$$

show that

$$\rho_Z(z) = \begin{cases} \dfrac{1}{2a}\left(1 - \dfrac{|z|}{2a}\right), & |z| \le 2a, \\ 0, & |z| > 2a. \end{cases}$$

2.1.1   The addition of Gaussian random variables

Here we find the distribution function for the sum of two or more random variables all with Gaussian distributions, not necessarily with the same parameters. The important result is that the sum of any number of such random variables also has a Gaussian distribution.

First consider the case of two variables, x_1 and x_2, with the distributions

$$\rho_k(x) = \frac{1}{\sigma_k \sqrt{2\pi}} \exp\left(-\frac{x^2}{2\sigma_k^2}\right), \quad k = 1, 2. \tag{2.11}$$

These have standard deviations σ_k, $k = 1, 2$, and both have zero mean value. The distribution of $z = x_1 + x_2$ is also Gaussian, with zero mean and standard deviation given by $\sigma^2 = \sigma_1^2 + \sigma_2^2$, as we now show.

Using the formula (2.8) gives the distribution of z:

$$\rho_Z(z) = \frac{1}{2\pi\sigma_1\sigma_2} \int_{-\infty}^{\infty} dx \exp\left(-\frac{x^2}{2\sigma_1^2} - \frac{(z - x)^2}{2\sigma_2^2}\right).$$

The argument of the exponential function is quadratic in x, so this integral can be evaluated, but first it is convenient to set $m_1 = 1/2\sigma_1^2$ and $m_2 = 1/2\sigma_2^2$ so the negative of the argument becomes

$$m_1 x^2 + m_2(z - x)^2 = (m_1 + m_2)\, x^2 - 2m_2 xz + m_2 z^2.$$

In order to cast the integrand in a suitable form we 'complete the square' by writing the right-hand side of this equation in the form

$$\left(x\sqrt{m_1+m_2} - \frac{m_2 z}{\sqrt{m_1+m_2}}\right)^2 + \frac{m_1 m_2 z^2}{m_1+m_2},$$

and define a new integration variable

$$u = x\sqrt{m_1+m_2} - \frac{m_2 z}{\sqrt{m_1+m_2}}.$$

Then the integral for $\rho_Z(z)$ becomes

$$\rho_Z(z) = \frac{1}{2\pi\sigma_1\sigma_2\sqrt{m_1+m_2}}\exp\left(-\frac{m_1 m_2 z^2}{m_1+m_2}\right)\int_{-\infty}^{\infty} du\, e^{-u^2}. \qquad (2.12)$$

But $\int_{-\infty}^{\infty} du\, e^{-u^2} = \sqrt{\pi}$ and

$$\sigma_1\sigma_2\sqrt{m_1+m_2} = \sqrt{\frac{\sigma_1^2+\sigma_2^2}{2}}, \quad \frac{m_1 m_2}{m_1+m_2} = \frac{1}{1/m_1+1/m_2} = \frac{1}{2(\sigma_1^2+\sigma_2^2)},$$

hence

$$\rho_Z(z) = \frac{1}{\sigma_z\sqrt{2\pi}}\exp\left(-\frac{z^2}{2\sigma_z^2}\right), \quad \text{where } \sigma_z^2 = \sigma_1^2 + \sigma_2^2. \qquad (2.13)$$

That is, if $z = x_1 + x_2$ and x_1 and x_2 have zero mean and Gaussian distributions, then z is also Gaussian distributed, with a variance which is the sum of the variances of x_1 and x_2.

This result is easily generalised to deal with the sum of any number of Gaussian variables with zero mean. For example, the sum of three such variables can be written in the form $w = x_1 + x_2 + x_3 = z + x_3$, where $z = x_1 + x_2$, so the previous result can be used again. This gives

$$\rho_W(w) = \frac{1}{\sigma_w\sqrt{2\pi}}\exp\left(-\frac{w^2}{2\sigma_w^2}\right), \quad \text{where } \sigma_w^2 = \sigma_1^2 + \sigma_2^2 + \sigma_3^2.$$

Proceeding in this way we see that if $z = x_1 + x_2 + \cdots + x_N$ is the sum of n random variables with the Gaussian distributions (2.11), then the density of z is

$$\rho(z) = \frac{1}{\sigma\sqrt{2\pi}}\exp\left(-\frac{z^2}{2\sigma^2}\right), \quad \text{where } \sigma^2 = \sum_{k=1}^{n}\sigma_k^2. \qquad (2.14)$$

It is important that you understand this result, and that derived in the next exercise, because they are used extensively in Section 2.3. Finally, we mention the converse result, that if the sum $w = x_1 + x_2$ of the two random variables x_1 and x_2 has a Gaussian distribution, then so do x_1 and x_2. This result was proved by Harald Cramér (1893–1985), but not until 1936.

H. Cramér (1936) 'Über eine Eigenschaft der normalen verteilungsfunktion', *Math. Zeit.*, **41**, 405–414.

Exercise 2.6

In this exercise the formula (2.14) is generalised to the case $\langle x_k\rangle \neq 0$ for all or some k.

If $z = x_1 + x_2 + \cdots + x_N$, where each x_k is a Gaussian random variable with mean μ_k and standard deviation σ_k, show that the density for z is

$$\rho_Z(z) = \frac{1}{\sigma\sqrt{2\pi}}\exp\left(-\frac{(z-\mu)^2}{2\sigma^2}\right), \quad \mu = \sum_{k=1}^{n}\mu_k, \quad \sigma^2 = \sum_{k=1}^{n}\sigma_k^2. \qquad (2.15)$$

[*Hint*: Use the random variables $y_k = x_k - \mu_k$, $k = 1, 2, \ldots, N$, to convert this problem to that dealt with in the text.]

2.2 Random walks

2.2.1 Statistics of random walks

Here we compute some statistics of the sum of N independent random variables x_k, $k = 1, 2, \ldots, N$,

$$S = x_1 + x_2 + \cdots + x_N = \sum_{k=1}^{N} x_k, \tag{2.16}$$

where all x_k have the same distribution, $\rho_X(x)$. Initially we assume that $\langle x \rangle = 0$, so the standard deviation of the parent distribution is $\sigma_X = \sqrt{\langle x^2 \rangle}$; this assumption is relaxed in Exercise 2.8.

The mean of S is zero, since $\langle x \rangle = 0$:

$$\langle S \rangle = \left\langle \sum_{k=1}^{N} x_k \right\rangle = \sum_{k=1}^{N} \langle x_k \rangle = 0. \tag{2.17}$$

The mean of S^2 is slightly more complicated because it requires squaring the sum of N terms. Thus

$$S^2 = \sum_{k=1}^{N} x_k^2 + 2 \sum_{k=1}^{N-1} \sum_{j=k+1}^{N} x_k x_j, \tag{2.18}$$

which is a generalisation of the formulae

$$(x_1 + x_2)^2 = x_1^2 + x_2^2 + 2x_1 x_2,$$
$$(x_1 + x_2 + x_3)^2 = x_1^2 + x_2^2 + x_3^2 + 2[x_1(x_2 + x_3) + x_2 x_3],$$
$$(x_1 + \cdots + x_4)^2 = x_1^2 + \cdots + x_4^2 + 2[x_1(x_2 + x_3 + x_4) + x_2(x_3 + x_4) + x_3 x_4].$$

But x_k and x_j, $k \neq j$, are independent random variables, so $\langle x_k x_j \rangle = \langle x_k \rangle \langle x_j \rangle$, because the choice of x_k does not affect x_j, and vice versa. Since $\langle x_k \rangle = 0$ for all k, $\langle x_k x_j \rangle = 0$ for all k and j, provided $k \neq j$. If $k = j$, then $\langle x_k x_j \rangle = \langle x_k^2 \rangle = \langle x^2 \rangle$ for all k, and hence

$$\langle S^2 \rangle = N \langle x^2 \rangle, \tag{2.19}$$

showing that the mean of S^2 is proportional to N, as seen in Figure 2.2 (page 58). The standard deviation of S is given by

$$\sigma_S^2 = \langle S^2 \rangle - \langle S \rangle^2 = N \langle x^2 \rangle = N \sigma_X^2, \tag{2.20}$$

so with increasing N, σ_S increases as $\sqrt{N}$, meaning that the density of S broadens.

Exercise 2.7

Compute the standard deviation of $S = x_1 + x_2 + \cdots + x_N$ when

$$\rho_X(x) = \begin{cases} 1/2a, & |x| \leq a, \\ 0, & |x| > a. \end{cases}$$

In this exercise you will generalise the results found in the text to deal with parent distributions, $\rho_X(x)$, with non-zero mean.

If the random variables x_k, $k = 1, 2, \ldots, N$, have identical densities with mean μ_X and standard deviation σ_X, show that the mean and standard deviation of S are $N\mu_X$ and $\sigma_X\sqrt{N}$.

[*Hint*: Use the random variables $y_k = x_k - \langle x_k \rangle$, which have zero mean.]

2.2.2   The central limit theorem

We now relax the condition that $\langle x \rangle = 0$, but continue with the assumption that the densities of the independent random variables x_k are identical, but not necessarily Gaussian.

Then it can be shown that if

$$S = \sum_{k=1}^{N} x_k, \tag{2.21}$$

and the first and second moments $\langle x \rangle$ and $\langle x^2 \rangle$ exist, then for any a and $b > a$, the density, $\rho_N(S)$, of S satisfies

$$\lim_{N \to \infty} \int_a^b dS \left(\rho_N(S) - \frac{1}{\sigma_X\sqrt{2\pi N}} \exp\left(-\frac{(S - N\langle x \rangle)^2}{2N\sigma_X^2} \right) \right) = 0, \tag{2.22}$$

where, for a continuous density,

$$\langle x \rangle = \int_{-\infty}^{\infty} dx\, x\, \rho_X(x) \quad \text{and} \quad \sigma_X^2 = \int_{-\infty}^{\infty} dx\, (x - \langle x \rangle)^2 \rho_X(x).$$

This is a formal statement of the **central limit theorem**, with the adjective 'central' to be understood as meaning 'fundamental'. This theorem is valid for a wider variety of density functions than just the continuous ones considered here.

In most cases when the density $\rho_X(x)$ is continuous, Equation (2.22) can be shown to give the approximation

$$\rho_N(S) \simeq \frac{1}{\sigma_X\sqrt{2\pi N}} \exp\left(-\frac{(S - N\langle x \rangle)^2}{2N\sigma_X^2} \right) \quad \text{if } N \gg 1. \tag{2.23}$$

Thus, provided the first and second moments of the parent distribution exist, the density of $S = x_1 + x_2 + \cdots + x_N$ is approximately Gaussian, regardless of the density of x. This is a remarkable and unexpected result.

When the parent distribution is Gaussian, this formula is exact, as shown in Equation (2.14) and Exercise 2.6. For other distributions, this approximation is often remarkably accurate for quite small values of N, even though the rigorous formulation, Equation (2.22), is expressed in terms of the limit $N \to \infty$. An example of the small N behaviour is given in Exercise 2.10: it is this aspect of the central limit theorem that makes the approximation (2.23) so useful.

The central limit theorem helps us to understand why a more accurate estimate is obtained from the average of several measurements, as shown in the next exercise.

Exercise 2.9

Consider a set of N independent measurements of the same quantity, yielding the results $m + \varepsilon_k$, $k = 1, 2, \ldots, N$, where m is the exact (unknown) value and ε_k is the error of the kth measurement. Assume that the ε_k are random variables, with zero mean and identical, but unknown, standard deviations σ. The sample average of these gives

$$\overline{m} = m + \delta, \quad \text{where } \delta = \frac{1}{N} \sum_{k=1}^{N} \varepsilon_k.$$

(a) Show that the density function of δ is

$$\rho(\delta) \simeq \frac{1}{\sigma} \sqrt{\frac{N}{2\pi}} \exp\left(-\frac{N\delta^2}{2\sigma^2}\right) \quad \text{if } N \gg 1.$$

(b) Show that the probability that $|\delta| < \alpha$ is $\frac{3}{4}$ when α satisfies the equation

$$\alpha = \sigma y_1 \sqrt{\frac{2}{N}}, \quad \text{where } y_1 \text{ is defined by } \quad \frac{3}{4} = \frac{2}{\sqrt{\pi}} \int_0^{y_1} dy \, e^{-y^2},$$

and use Maple to find the numerical value of y_1. Deduce that if two independent sets of N and $M > N$ measurements are made, then the spread in $|\delta|$, that is α, is halved if $M = 4N$.

The central limit theorem is an unexpected result: it was first proved in the form quoted in Equation (2.23) in 1810 by Laplace; this result was a generalisation of that published in 1718 by de Moivre (1667–1754) which was derived only for Bernoulli trials. But refinements and generalisations continued to be found for over a century after this. A short chronology is as follows. Bessel (1784–1846), Dirichlet (1805–59) and Cauchy (1789–1857) all contributed to the first stage of progress from 1810 to 1853, leading to a proof for distributions defined only on finite intervals. The second stage, 1870–1910, was dominated by Russian mathematicians Chebyshev (1821–94), Markov (1856–1922) and Lyapunov (1857–1918), who removed this restriction and made other advances. Yet further advances were made in the 20th century by Lindeberg (1876–1932), Lévy (1886–1971) and Feller (1906–70).

P.-S. Laplace (1810) 'Mémoire sur les approximations des formules qui sont fonctions de très grands nombres et sur leur application aux probabilités', *Mémoires de l'Académie des Sciences de Paris, 1809*, pp. 353–415, 559–565.

A. de Moivre (1718) *The Doctrine of Chance: A Method of Calculating the Probabilities of Events in Play.*

There is also a useful exact formula that expresses $\rho_N(S)$ in terms of integrals. We quote this result without proof:

$$\rho_N(S) = \frac{1}{2\pi} \int_{-\infty}^{\infty} dz \, e^{iSz} \left(\int_{-\infty}^{\infty} dx \, \rho_X(x) \, e^{-ixz} \right)^N. \tag{2.24}$$

There are not many densities $\rho_X(x)$ for which this equation yields a simple expression, but these cases help us to understand how the central limit theorem works. In Exercise 2.10 (overleaf) we use this formula to investigate how good the approximation (2.23) is for some small values of N.

Exercise 2.10

(a) For the density

$$\rho_X(x) = \begin{cases} 1/2a, & |x| \leq a, \\ 0, & |x| > a, \end{cases}$$

show that

$$\int_{-\infty}^{\infty} dx\, \rho_X(x)\, e^{-ixz} = \frac{\sin az}{az}.$$

Using the result of Exercise 2.5 (page 63), show that

$$\frac{1}{\pi a} \int_0^\infty dw \cos\left(\frac{S}{a}w\right)\left(\frac{\sin w}{w}\right)^2 = \begin{cases} \frac{1}{2a}\left(1 - \frac{|S|}{2a}\right), & |S| \leq 2a, \\ 0, & |S| \geq 2a. \end{cases}$$

(b) For the density $\rho_X(x)$, find $\langle x \rangle$ and $\langle x^2 \rangle$, and use Equation (2.23) to show that if $S = x_1 + x_2 + \cdots + x_N$, then

$$\rho_N(S) \simeq \frac{1}{a}\sqrt{\frac{3}{2N\pi}} \exp\left(-\frac{3S^2}{2Na^2}\right).$$

For $N = 2$ and $a = 1$, make a graphical comparison of this approximation with the result found in part (a).

(c) Use the result found in part (a) to show that

$$\rho_N(S) = \frac{1}{\pi a}\int_0^\infty dw \cos\left(\frac{S}{a}w\right)\left(\frac{\sin w}{w}\right)^N. \qquad (2.25)$$

In the case $a = 1$, use Maple to evaluate this integral for $N = 2, 3, \ldots, 8$, and make a graphical comparison of this exact result and the approximation given by the central limit theorem, obtained in part (b).

In Exercise 2.11, which is optional, we consider a density for which the first and second moments do not exist, discover that the central limit theorem fails and learn that $\rho_N(S)$ has a quite different form to that given in Equation (2.23).

Exercise 2.11

This question is about the *Cauchy* distribution, which has the density

$$\rho(x) = \frac{a}{\pi(a^2 + x^2)}, \qquad a > 0,$$

defined on the whole real line. For this distribution the central limit theorem fails, a fact first noted in 1827 by Poisson (1781–1840).

(a) Show that

$$f(x_1, x_2) = \int_{-x_1}^{x_2} dx\, x\, \rho(x) = \frac{a}{2\pi} \ln\left(\frac{a^2 + x_2^2}{a^2 + x_1^2}\right), \qquad x_1, x_2 > 0,$$

and by considering the value of $f(x_1, x_2)$ as either x_1 or x_2 becomes large, show that the first moment of the Cauchy distribution does not exist.

(b) Using the integral

$$\frac{a}{\pi} \int_{-\infty}^{\infty} dx \, \frac{e^{-ixz}}{a^2 + x^2} = e^{-a|z|},$$

show that if $S = x_1 + x_2 + \cdots + x_N$, where each x_k is identically Cauchy distributed, then the density of S is the Cauchy density

$$\rho_N(S) = \frac{aN}{\pi(S^2 + (aN)^2)}.$$

Find the value of S_1 such that the probability that $|S| \le S_1$ is $\frac{1}{2}$.

(c) Use Maple to construct the random walks

$$S_{k+1} = S_k + x_{k+1}, \quad S_0 = 0, \quad k = 0, 1, \ldots,$$

where the x_k are random variables drawn from a Cauchy distribution with $a = 1$. Plot graphs of the points (k, S_k), $k = 0, 1, \ldots, N$, for a number of realisations of this random walk and for suitable values of N.

Note that you should limit the size of N, but ensure that it is large enough to observe the characteristic features of this random walk and to see that it is quite different from the other examples given in this unit.

In the example of Brownian motion described in the introduction to this unit, the interval between collisions is very small, typically $\delta t = 10^{-10}$ seconds, so this process, if viewed over a timescale much larger than this, would appear to be continuous. Thus it is useful to develop a theory in which $\delta t \to 0$. This development leads to the theory of Wiener processes and to stochastic differential equations, both important, with many applications. Neither can be taught here, but the following two optional exercises explore an example of a random walk where δt is allowed to become very small; no new theory is required for these exercises, which involve a direct application of ideas already introduced. However, we shall see how a random walk can give rise to a function $y(x)$, continuous but nowhere differentiable on $0 \le x \le 1$, describing a curve with infinite length.

Exercise 2.12

Consider the motion of a particle along the x-axis which at each time $t_k = k \, \delta t$ has its position changed by a random amount according to the rule

$$x_{k+1} = x_k + \varepsilon_{k+1}\sqrt{\delta t}, \quad x_0 = 0, \quad k = 0, 1, \ldots, N-1,$$

where ε_k are a set of random numbers drawn from a distribution with zero mean and standard deviation σ, and $\delta t \, N = 1$ and $N \gg 1$.

(a) Show that

$$x_n = (\varepsilon_1 + \varepsilon_2 + \cdots + \varepsilon_n)\sqrt{\delta t}, \quad n = 1, 2, \ldots, N,$$

and that

$$\langle x_n \rangle = 0 \quad \text{and} \quad \langle x_n^2 \rangle = \sigma^2 t_n, \quad \text{where } t_n = \frac{n}{N}.$$

Use the central limit theorem to show that the density of x_n is approximately

$$\rho(x_n) \simeq \frac{1}{\sigma\sqrt{2\pi t_n}} \exp\left(-\frac{x_n^2}{2\sigma^2 t_n}\right), \quad t_n = \frac{n}{N}, \quad 1 \ll n \le N.$$

(b) Use Maple to construct representations of this random walk by plotting the points (t_n, x_n), $n = 1, 2, \ldots, N$, for various large values of N, for instance $N = 100$, 1000, or more, for the case that ε is uniform on $[-1, 1]$.

(c) A continuous line can be formed from each random walk by joining adjacent points (t_k, x_k) and (t_{k+1}, x_{k+1}) with a straight line. Show that the distance along this line is $s_{k+1} = \sqrt{\delta t^2 + \varepsilon_{k+1}^2 \delta t}$, and hence that the length of a particular realisation is

$$
s = \frac{1}{N} \sum_{k=1}^{N} \sqrt{1 + N \varepsilon_k^2}.
$$

Deduce that if ε is uniform on $[-1, 1]$ the mean length is

$$
\langle s \rangle = \left\langle \sqrt{1 + N \varepsilon^2} \right\rangle = \frac{1}{2} \int_{-1}^{1} d\varepsilon \sqrt{1 + N \varepsilon^2} \simeq \frac{\sqrt{N}}{2}, \quad \text{if } N \gg 1.
$$

These results show that this random walk with N steps can be used to construct a continuous line which is not differentiable at N points and has a mean length proportional to $\sqrt{N}$. As $N \to \infty$ we expect this construction to give a set of continuous lines which are nowhere differentiable and whose mean length is infinite.

In the following exercise we give an example of a random function $y(t)$, continuous on $(0, 1)$, yet with infinite length and such that the density of $y(t)$ at $t = n/N$, $1 \ll n \le N$, is approximately the same as the density of the random walk of length N discussed in the previous exercise.

Exercise 2.13

Consider the random function of the continuous variable t,

$$
y(t) = \frac{2\sqrt{2}}{\pi} \sum_{k=0}^{\infty} \frac{z_k}{2k + 1} \sin \left((k + \tfrac{1}{2})\pi t \right), \quad 0 \le t \le 1,
$$

where the z_k are independent Gaussian random variables with $\langle z \rangle = 0$ and $\langle z^2 \rangle = \sigma^2$. Note that $y(t)$ is a form of trigonometric series.

(a) Truncate the sum at $k = N$ to give a function $y_N(t)$ and, with $\sigma = 1$, plot several realisations of $y_N(t)$ for particular values of N, for instance $N = 10$, 100 and 1000. Note that for large N you will need to increase the numpoints option.

(b) Show that

$$
y(1) = \frac{2\sqrt{2}}{\pi} \sum_{k=0}^{\infty} \frac{(-1)^k z_k}{2k + 1},
$$

and deduce that $\langle y(1) \rangle = 0$.

Use the result $\sum_{k=0}^{\infty} (2k + 1)^{-2} = \pi^2/8$ to show that

$$
\langle y(1)^2 \rangle = \frac{8\sigma^2}{\pi^2} \sum_{k=0}^{\infty} \frac{1}{(2k + 1)^2} = \sigma^2.
$$

(c) By writing

$$y(t) = \sum_{k=0}^{\infty} s_k z_k, \quad s_k = \frac{2\sqrt{2}}{\pi} \frac{\sin((k+1/2)\pi t)}{2k+1},$$

and noting that $s_k z_k$ is a Gaussian random variable with zero mean, use the result quoted in Equation (2.14) (page 64) to show that the density of $y = y(t)$ is

$$\rho(y) = \frac{1}{\sigma(t)\sqrt{2\pi}} \exp\left(-\frac{y^2}{2\sigma(t)^2}\right),$$

where

$$\sigma(t)^2 = \frac{8\sigma^2}{\pi^2} \sum_{k=0}^{\infty} \frac{\sin^2((k+1/2)\pi t)}{(2k+1)^2}.$$

By noting that the Fourier series of $|t|$ is

$$|t| = \frac{1}{2} - \frac{4}{\pi^2} \sum_{k=0}^{\infty} \frac{\cos((2k+1)\pi t)}{(2k+1)^2}, \quad |t| \le 1,$$

and that $\sin^2 \theta = (1 - \cos 2\theta)/2$, show that $\sigma(t) = \sigma\sqrt{t}$, $0 < t \le 1$.

Deduce that at $t = n/N$, provided $1 \ll n \le N$, the density of $\rho(y)$ is approximately the same as the density of x_n in the random walk discussed in Exercise 2.12.

2.3   *Monte Carlo integration*

In this section we show how sums of random variables can be used to estimate the value of definite integrals. Because random variables are used, this is known as the **Monte Carlo method**. It is an important method because it is one of the most efficient means of evaluating multidimensional integrals with high dimension; by 'efficient' we mean that for a given accuracy it requires the least computational effort. We explain why this is so in Subsection 2.3.2.

In order to introduce this method we consider the one-dimensional integral

$$I = \frac{1}{b-a} \int_a^b dx\, f(x), \tag{2.26}$$

and hasten to add that normally, but not always, such integrals are best approximated by conventional numerical methods. The integral (2.26) can be interpreted as the mean value of $f(x)$, i.e. $\langle f \rangle$, on the interval (a, b), which is why the multiplicative factor $1/(b-a)$ has been included.

Now take a set of N random numbers $\{x_1, x_2, \ldots, x_N\}$, uniformly distributed in $[a, b]$, so the distribution function is $\rho_X(x) = 1/(b-a)$ for $a \le x \le b$ and zero otherwise. The mean value of $f(x)$ over this distribution is

$$\langle f \rangle = \int_a^b dx\, f(x)\, \rho_X(x) = \frac{1}{b-a} \int_a^b dx\, f(x), \tag{2.27}$$

which can be estimated by any finite realisation,

$$\langle f \rangle = I \simeq I_e = \frac{1}{N} \sum_{k=1}^{N} f(x_k). \tag{2.28}$$

The value of the random number I_e is named a **Monte Carlo estimate** of I, and is the basic approximation used here.

The estimate I_e for I is unlike that of conventional numerical methods because I_e is a random number with a value that depends upon the particular realisation of the sum, that is, the values chosen for $\{x_1, x_2, \ldots, x_N\}$. To be useful, we need estimates of the likely magnitude of the variation of I_e, which is given by the central limit theorem as shown below. The random number $z = N I_e = f(x_1) + f(x_2) + \cdots + f(x_N)$ has a density that can be approximated using the central limit theorem, Equation (2.23) (page 66), where $\langle x \rangle$ is replaced by $\langle f \rangle$, that is the required integral, and σ_X by σ, the standard deviation of $f(x)$:

$$\rho_Z(z) \simeq \frac{1}{\sigma\sqrt{2\pi N}} \exp\left(-\frac{(z - N\langle f \rangle)^2}{2N\sigma^2} \right), \quad N \gg 1.$$

Using the result given in Subsection 1.2.2 of *Unit C1* to change the variable from z to I_e, we see that $\rho(I_e) = \rho_Z(N I_e)\, dz/dI_e$, that is,

$$\rho(I_e) = \sqrt{\frac{N}{2\pi\sigma^2}} \exp\left(-\frac{N(I_e - I)^2}{2\sigma^2} \right). \tag{2.29}$$

In this formula σ is the standard deviation of $f(x)$, given by the mean of $(f(x) - \langle f \rangle)^2$, that is,

$$\sigma^2 = \frac{1}{b-a} \int_a^b dx\, (f(x) - I)^2, \quad I = \frac{1}{b-a} \int_a^b dx\, f(x), \tag{2.30}$$

$$= \left(\frac{1}{b-a} \int_a^b dx\, f(x)^2 \right) - I^2 = \langle f^2 \rangle - \langle f \rangle^2 .$$

From Equation (2.29) and the calculations of Subsection 1.3.2 of *Unit C1*, we see that the standard deviation of I_e is $\sigma/\sqrt{N}$; it is important to note that this decreases with increasing N, albeit rather slowly.

Leaving aside for one moment the problem that σ depends upon unknown integrals, we note that for large N the distribution of I_e is strongly peaked about $I_e = I$. More precisely, the probability that I_e lies in the interval $I - \alpha\sigma \le I_e \le I + \alpha\sigma$, for some positive α, is by definition

$$P(\alpha) = \int_{I-\alpha\sigma}^{I+\alpha\sigma} dI_e\, \rho(I_e) = \sqrt{\frac{2N}{\pi\sigma^2}} \int_0^{\alpha\sigma} ds\, \exp\left(-\frac{Ns^2}{2\sigma^2} \right), \tag{2.31}$$

where we have set $s = I_e - I$ and used the fact that the distribution (2.29) is even about $I_e = I$. Now make the variable change $s = u\sqrt{2\sigma^2/N}$ to put this expression in the form

$$P(\alpha) = \frac{2}{\sqrt{\pi}} \int_0^{\alpha\sqrt{N/2}} du\, e^{-u^2} = \mathrm{erf}\left(\alpha\sqrt{\frac{N}{2}} \right), \tag{2.32}$$

where $\mathrm{erf}(x)$ is the error function defined by the integral

$$\mathrm{erf}(x) = \frac{2}{\sqrt{\pi}} \int_0^x du\, e^{-u^2}.$$

You can determine what Maple knows about this function by typing `?erf` at the prompt; it may also be helpful to plot the graph of $\mathrm{erf}(x)$.

On setting $\alpha = N^{-1/2}$, since $\text{erf}(1/\sqrt{2}) \simeq 0.683$, we see that there is a 68% chance of an estimate I_e satisfying the inequality

$$I - \frac{\sigma}{\sqrt{N}} \le I_e \le I + \frac{\sigma}{\sqrt{N}}. \tag{2.33}$$

This means that of 100 independent estimates, about 68 will satisfy this inequality.

Also, since $\text{erf}(\sqrt{2}) \simeq 0.954$, on setting $\alpha = 2N^{-1/2}$ we see that there is a 95% chance of an estimate I_e satisfying the inequality

$$I - \frac{2\sigma}{\sqrt{N}} \le I_e \le I + \frac{2\sigma}{\sqrt{N}}.$$

A more useful version of this is

$$I_e - \frac{2\sigma}{\sqrt{N}} \le I \le I_e + \frac{2\sigma}{\sqrt{N}}, \tag{2.34}$$

showing that for a given single estimate there is a 95% chance of the exact (unknown) value of the integral lying in this interval. It is conventional to write this in the form

$$I = I_e \pm \frac{2\sigma}{\sqrt{N}} \quad (95\%), \tag{2.35}$$

which is often described by saying that with 95% confidence I is within two standard deviations of I_e. The interval (2.34) is named the **confidence interval**. Because $\sqrt{N}$ occurs in the denominator, the confidence interval is halved in length by increasing N by a factor of four.

For this method to be useful, we need an approximation to the standard deviation σ. In Equation (2.30) this is defined in terms an integral of $f(x)$, the value of which is unknown. It is therefore necessary to estimate the value of σ, using the same set of points used to estimate I. The natural way to do this is to use the procedure `Variance` which gives the **sample variance**, defined by

$$V_e = \frac{1}{N-1} \sum_{k=1}^{N} (f(x_k) - I_e)^2,$$

which was discussed in Subsection 1.3.1 of *Unit C1*, and which provides an estimate of the variance; recall that V_e is a random number and that the factor $1/(N-1)$ (rather than $1/N$) was chosen to ensure that $\langle V_e \rangle = \sigma^2$. In order to be consistent we also define the sample standard deviation σ_e, where $\sigma_e^2 = V_e$, and reserve the symbol σ for the distribution standard deviation which, in the present context, is defined in Equation (2.30). For large N it matters little whether we use the factor $1/(N-1)$ or $1/N$ in the calculation of V_e or σ_e.

Thus the Monte Carlo estimates of the average I and its standard deviation σ are

$$I \simeq I_e = \frac{1}{N} \sum_{k=1}^{N} f(x_k) \quad \text{and} \quad \sigma_e^2 = V_e = \frac{1}{N-1} \sum_{k=1}^{N} (f(x_k) - I_e)^2. \tag{2.36}$$

The standard deviation can be rewritten in the form (more convenient for computation)

$$\sigma_e^2 = \frac{N}{N-1} \left(\frac{1}{N} \sum_{k=1}^{N} f(x_k)^2 - I_e^2 \right).$$

Then Equation (2.35) can be cast in the form

$$I = I_e(1 \pm \varepsilon_N),$$

where

$$\varepsilon_N = \frac{2\sigma_e}{I_e\sqrt{N}} \tag{2.37}$$

is an estimate of the relative **statistical error**. This means that for 95% of the realisations of I_e, the relative error will be less than ε_N. It is reasonable to expect that both σ_e and I_e are relatively insensitive to N; that is, increasing N by a factor of 10 changes both by a much smaller factor. We use this idea to estimate the number of sample points needed to achieve a given accuracy, because it means that $\sqrt{N}\varepsilon_N \simeq$ constant. Thus to decrease the relative error by a factor of γ, we need to increase the number of sample points by a factor γ^2. This simple rule provides a strategy for systematically improving the accuracy until the desired result is obtained, which is illustrated in the next section.

The estimate I_e of the integral of $f(x)$, defined in Equation (2.28), is not like the approximations provided by the normal numerical procedures. For instance, with $a = 0$ and $b = 1$, the N-point trapezoidal rule gives

$$I = \int_0^1 dx\, f(x) = \frac{1}{N}\left[\tfrac{1}{2}\left(f(0) + f(1)\right) + \sum_{k=1}^{N-1} f\left(\frac{k}{N}\right)\right] + O(N^{-2}),$$

which provides an approximation differing from the exact result by a quantity approximately proportional to N^{-2}. Every evaluation of this rule produces the same value.

The Monte Carlo estimate I_e is different because I_e is a random number, the mean of which is the exact value of the integral. Making a single Monte Carlo estimate is the same as choosing a single number from the distribution (2.29) (page 72). Despite this, the method is useful for reasons that are discussed in Subsection 2.3.2. At this point, however, it is important to remember that the width of the distribution of I_e decreases as N increases, albeit rather slowly as $N^{-1/2}$. Also, it must be remembered that there is a finite probability that the exact value of the integral can lie outside the confidence interval.

Summary of results for one-dimensional integrals

Here we summarise the Monte Carlo method for estimating the value of

$$J = \int_a^b dx\, f(x). \tag{2.38}$$

Because J is the mean value of $(b - a)f(x)$, the random walk approximating J is related to that for $I = \langle f \rangle$ by the scale factor $(b - a)$, so the Monte Carlo estimate for J is

$$J \simeq J_e = \frac{b - a}{N} \sum_{k=1}^{N} f(x_k), \tag{2.39}$$

where x_k are N random numbers chosen from a distribution uniform in $[a, b]$. The standard deviation of the probability density of J_e is given by

$$\sigma^2 = (b - a) \int_a^b dx\, f(x)^2 - \left(\int_a^b dx\, f(x)\right)^2, \tag{2.40}$$

and the sample estimate of this is given by

$$\sigma_e \simeq (b-a)\sqrt{\frac{N}{N-1}}\sqrt{\frac{1}{N}\sum_{k=1}^{N} f(x_k)^2 - \left(\frac{1}{N}\sum_{k=1}^{N} f(x_k)\right)^2}, \qquad (2.41)$$

that is,

$$J = J_e \pm \frac{2\sigma_e}{\sqrt{N}} \quad \text{with } 95\% \text{ confidence.} \qquad (2.42)$$

2.3.1 Maple implementation

In this subsection we show how Maple can be used to provide Monte Carlo estimates of one-dimensional integrals. In order to be specific, we consider the integral

$$J = \int_0^{1/2} dx\, e^{x^2} \sin \pi x. \qquad (2.43)$$

For a Monte Carlo estimate with $N = 100$ random numbers uniformly distributed in $[0, \frac{1}{2}]$, we use the procedures defined in the Statistics package, introduced in *Unit C1*. First we need to load the package (note that all unnecessary Maple output has been suppressed):

```
> restart:  with(Statistics):
```

Next we need to define the integration limits $a = 0$, $b = \frac{1}{2}$, and the RandomVariable X that generates the random numbers

```
> a := 0:  b := 0.5:
> X := RandomVariable(Uniform(a,b)):
```

and then define the integrand as a Maple function

```
> f := x->exp(x^2)*sin(Pi*x):
```

and create a vector of $N = 100$ random numbers z, using X as described in Subsection 1.3.1 of *Unit C1*:

```
> N := 100:  z := Sample(f(X),N):
```

The Monte Carlo estimate of the integral is half the mean of $f(x)$, because $J = (b-a)I$, and this is given using the Mean procedure

```
> Je := (b-a)*Mean(z);
```
$$Je := 0.3757004636$$

and the variance is given by

```
> Ve := (b-a)^2*Variance(z);
```
$$Ve := 0.03818316862$$

so there is a probability of 0.95 that the exact value of the integral is in the interval $J_e \pm 2\sqrt{V_e/N} = 0.376 \pm 0.039$, that is, $0.337 \le J_e \le 0.415$. In this case a more precise approximation is provided by ordinary numerical integration,

```
> Ja := evalf[6](Int(f(x),x=a..b));
```
$$Ja := 0.358265$$

which is consistent with the Monte Carlo estimate. Obviously it would be more convenient to put all these statements in a procedure with arguments N, the number of points to be used, and a and b, the integration limits.

The output of this procedure is a list: the first entry is the Monte Carlo estimate; the second is the value of $\sigma_e = \sqrt{V_e}$; the third is a list giving the estimated 95% confidence limits. This procedure introduces the new, convenient Maple command uses, which allows one to use the contents of a package without first using the with() command. This command can be used only inside a procedure.

```
>   restart:
>   f := x->exp(x^2)*sin(Pi*x):
>   mc1 := proc(a,b,N)
>      local X,z,Je,sige,eps;
>      uses Statistics;
>      X := RandomVariable(Uniform(a,b)):
>      z := Sample(f(X),N);               # Define N random numbers
>      Je := (b-a)*Mean(z):               # The Monte Carlo estimate
>      sige := (b-a)*sqrt(Variance(z));   # The sample st. dev.
>      eps := evalf(2*sige/sqrt(N));      # The relative error
>      evalf[6]([Je,sige,[Je-eps,Je+eps]]);
>   end:
```

Three estimates for $N = 10$, 100 and 1000 are

```
>   mc1(0,0.5,10);
```
$$[0.430319,\ 0.221811,\ [0.290034,\ 0.570604]]$$

```
>   mc1(0,0.5,100);
```
$$[0.368670,\ 0.189602,\ [0.330750,\ 0.406590]]$$

```
>   mc1(0,0.5,1000);
```
$$[0.351335,\ 0.188810,\ [0.339394,\ 0.363276]]$$

These calculations confirm that the estimate of σ changes little as N increases from 10 to 1000. Using Equation (2.37) we see that the relative errors for $N = 10$ and $N = 100$ are

$$\varepsilon_{10} = \frac{2 \times 0.22}{0.43 \times \sqrt{10}} = 0.32 \quad \text{and} \quad \varepsilon_{100} = \frac{2 \times 0.19}{0.37 \times \sqrt{100}} = 0.10,$$

which suggest that $\varepsilon_N = 0.01$ if $\sqrt{N} = \sqrt{100}\varepsilon_{100}/\varepsilon_N$, that is, $N \simeq 10^4$. This value of N gives

```
>   mc1(0,0.5,10^4);
```
$$[0.359426,\ 0.190780,\ [0.355610,\ 0.363242]]$$

that is, $J = 0.359 \pm 0.0038 = 0.359(1 \pm 0.011)$, with 95% confidence, as predicted.

Exercise 2.14

Find a Monte Carlo estimate with a 95% confidence that the relative error is $\varepsilon_N \simeq 0.005$ for the following integrals.

(a) $J = \int_0^3 dx\, x^{1/3} \sin\left(\pi\sqrt{\dfrac{x}{3}}\right)$ (b) $J = \int_1^3 dx\, \dfrac{\exp(1/\sqrt{x})}{1 + \sin^2 \pi x}$

Exercise 2.15

Use the procedure `mc1` to produce 200 estimates of J, defined in Equation (2.43), and count how many of these lie within the 95% confidence limits.

Exercise 2.16

Consider the logistic map defined by the iteration sequence

$$x_{k+1} = a x_k (1 - x_k) \quad \text{with } x_0 = \eta,$$

and where $0 < \eta < 1$. For a in the interval $0 < a \le 4$, $x_k \le a/4$ for all k.

After the first few iterations $k = 0, 1, \ldots, n-1$, the sequence $(x_n, x_{n+1}, \ldots, x_{n+R})$ settles down into a pattern. We can define the mean time that $x > a/8$ for $n \le k \le n + R$ by the relation

$$T(a, \eta) = \frac{1}{R+1} \sum_{k=n}^{n+R} H(x_k - a/8),$$

where $H(w)$ is the Heaviside step function, defined by

$$H(w) = \begin{cases} 0, & w < 0, \\ 1, & w > 0. \end{cases}$$

Normally, $H(w)$ is not defined at $w = 0$.

(a) Write a procedure to compute $T(a, \eta)$ and plot the graph of $T(a, \eta)$ for $0 < \eta < 1$ and $a = 3.4$, 3.8 and 3.9, with $n = 10$ and $R = 1000$.

(b) Use the Monte Carlo method to compute

$$\overline{T}(a) = \int_0^1 d\eta \, T(a, \eta).$$

Plot the graph of $\overline{T}(a)$ for $3.4 \le a \le 4.0$ when $n = 10$ and $R = 1000$.

This computation takes a very long time, so you should choose the number of points used in the integration using a smaller interval for a, in a region where $\overline{T}(a)$ varies significantly, in order to estimate how many points can be used to produce an estimate in a reasonable time.

2.3.2   Two-dimensional integrals

Here we extend the method described in the previous subsection to deal with two-dimensional integrals. First we deal with integrals over a rectangular domain, and then we show how to extend the method to other shaped domains.

It is convenient to write the integral as the mean of $f(x, y)$,

$$I = \frac{1}{A} \int_{a_1}^{b_1} dx \int_{a_2}^{b_2} dy \, f(x, y), \quad A = (b_1 - a_1)(b_2 - a_2), \tag{2.44}$$

so I is the mean of $f(x, y)$ over the rectangle with area A.

The Monte Carlo estimate of f is just the average taken over a set of N points (x_k, y_k), $k = 1, 2, \ldots, N$, where x_k and y_k are uniformly distributed in (a_1, b_1) and (a_2, b_2), respectively. Thus

$$I \simeq I_e = \frac{1}{N} \sum_{k=1}^{N} f(x_k, y_k). \tag{2.45}$$

This is the two-dimensional equivalent of Equation (2.28) (page 72).

The sum in Equation (2.45) is another random walk, and I_e has the distribution given by Equation (2.29) (page 72), with the estimated standard deviation given by

$$\sigma_e^2 = \frac{1}{N-1} \sum_{k=1}^{N} (f(x_k, y_k) - I_e)^2$$

$$= \frac{N}{N-1} \left(\frac{1}{N} \sum_{k=1}^{N} f(x_k, y_k)^2 - \left(\frac{1}{N} \sum_{k=1}^{N} f(x_k, y_k) \right)^2 \right), \tag{2.46}$$

so with 95% confidence, $I = I_e \pm 2\sigma_e / \sqrt{N}$.

Maple implementation

The formulae (2.45) and (2.46) are identical to the one-dimensional formulae of Equation (2.36). Thus the Maple implementation is almost the same as procedure `mc1`, listed on page 76, and is given below: the only difference is that now two sets of random numbers are needed, one for the x-coordinate, in X, and one for the y-coordinate, in Y.

We illustrate this application by evaluating the integral

$$J = \int_1^2 dx \int_0^2 dy \, \sin \left(x^2 \cos y \right),$$

so here $J = 2I$, where I is the mean. The Maple function for the integrand is

```
>   restart:
>   f := (x,y)->sin(x^2*cos(y));
```

$$f := (x, y) \rightarrow \sin(x^2 \cos(y))$$

This double integral can be evaluated in the conventional Maple manner, using `Int`:

```
>   Ja:=evalf[6](Int(f(x,y),[x=1..2,y=0..2]));
```

$$Ja := 0.785271$$

The following procedure, `mc2`, is a version of `mc1`, with the following two differences.

1. The length $(b - a)$ is replaced by the area $A = (b_1 - a_1)(b_2 - a_2)$.
2. Two sets of random numbers are required, X for x and Y for y. Then the command `Sample(f(X,Y),N)` finds N values of the function in the rectangle.

```
>  mc2 := proc(a1,b1,a2,b2,N)
>     local X,Y,A,z,Je,sige,eps;
>     uses Statistics;
>     A := (b1-a1)*(b2-a2):            # Define area of rectangle
>     X := RandomVariable(Uniform(a1,b1)):
>     Y := RandomVariable(Uniform(a2,b2)):
>     z := Sample(f(X,Y),N);  # Define N random values of f(x,y)
>     Je := A*Mean(z):                 # The Monte Carlo estimate
>     sige := A*sqrt(Variance(z));       # The sample st. dev.
>     eps := 2*sige/sqrt(N);           # The statistical error
>     evalf[6]([Je,sige,[Je-eps,Je+eps]]);
>  end:
```

Thus for $N = 100$ and 1000 we obtain the following estimates:

```
>  mc2(1,2,0,2,100);  mc2(1,2,0,2,1000);
```
$$[0.695332, \ 1.16678, \ [0.461976, \ 0.928688]]$$
$$[0.838920, \ 1.13561, \ [0.767098, \ 0.910742]]$$

Again observe that the estimate of the standard deviation changes relatively little as N increases from 100 to 1000. These calculations show that the relative errors, defined in Equation (2.37) (page 74), are

$$\varepsilon_{100} \simeq \frac{2 \times 1.167}{0.695\sqrt{100}} \simeq 0.34 \quad \text{and} \quad \varepsilon_{1000} \simeq \frac{2 \times 1.136}{0.839\sqrt{1000}} \simeq 0.086,$$

suggesting that to obtain a relative error of 0.05 we need $N = 1000 \times (0.086/0.05)^2 \simeq 3000$. This value of N gives

```
>  mc2(1,2,0,2,3000);
```
$$[0.782946, \ 1.12916, \ [0.741715, \ 0.824177]]$$

thus $I = 0.783(1 \pm 0.053)$. The error is approximately halved by quadrupling N,

```
>  mc2(1,2,0,2,12000);
```
$$[0.794574, \ 1.12747, \ [0.773989, \ 0.815159]]$$

giving a relative error of 0.026.

Exercise 2.17

Find Monte Carlo estimates of

$$I_1 = \int_0^1 dx \int_1^2 dy \ \sqrt{x^2 y + \sqrt{xy}},$$

$$I_2 = \int_1^3 dx \int_3^5 dy \ \left(\frac{x^{3/2}}{y} + \frac{y^{1/4}}{x}\right) \sin\sqrt{xy},$$

using a sufficient number of points to obtain a relative accuracy of 0.01 for both integrals.

2.3.3   The many-dimensional case

The extension of the Monte Carlo method to the n-dimensional integral

$$I = \frac{1}{V_n} \int_{a_1}^{b_1} dx_1 \int_{a_2}^{b_2} dx_2 \cdots \int_{a_n}^{b_n} dx_n \, f(\mathbf{x}), \quad \mathbf{x} = (x_1, x_2, \ldots, x_n), \quad (2.47)$$

over the n-dimensional rectangle with volume $V_n = \prod_{j=1}^{n}(b_j - a_j)$, is identical to the two-dimensional case. The integral is the mean of $f(\mathbf{x})$ over V_n, so the Monte Carlo estimate for this is

$$I \simeq I_e = \frac{1}{N} \sum_{k=1}^{N} f(\mathbf{x}_k), \qquad (2.48)$$

where $\mathbf{x}_k$ are N points in the n-dimensional rectangle, with the component x_j uniformly distributed in (a_j, b_j), $j = 1, 2, \ldots, n$. The error estimate is given by the natural generalisation of Equation (2.46). Examples of the evaluation of many-dimensional integrals will be given after we have discussed methods of decreasing the statistical errors in the next section.

The advantages of the Monte Carlo method

The two significant advantages of a Monte Carlo method over conventional methods of integration are that it is more efficient for high-dimensional integrals and it is easier to apply to integration over awkward boundary shapes. Here we briefly explain why the first of these properties holds; the second is demonstrated later, with examples.

Typically, a conventional numerical method treats the integral (2.47) as a product of n one-dimensional integrals. Thus if M points are used for each variable, the computational time is roughly proportional to M^n, this being the number of function evaluations. The error is usually proportional to M^{-p} for some positive integer p, typically 2 or 4; an example of such a method is described in *Unit A4*, Section 4.2.

A Monte Carlo method using a total of N random numbers has statistical errors proportional to $N^{-1/2}$, *independent* of the dimension n. The computational time is proportional to N.

Thus for comparable accuracy, $N^{1/2} \sim M^p$, the Monte Carlo method will be faster if $N < M^n$, that is, if $M^{2p} < M^n$, that is, $n > 2p$, approximately.

An additional advantage for some applications is that Monte Carlo methods are easier to use if the integrand has many discontinuities; for an example of this type of problem see Exercise 2.23 (page 87).

2.4   Methods of decreasing the statistical errors

There are many ways of refining this simple Monte Carlo estimate for integrals, all of which decrease σ: the error still decreases as $N^{-1/2}$, but the multiplying factor is smaller. Here we describe two methods that are relatively easy to implement, yet significantly decrease the error.

2.4.1 Control functions

The integral

$$I = \int_a^b dx \, f(x) \tag{2.49}$$

can be written in the equivalent form

$$I = \int_a^b dx \, \big(f(x) - \phi(x)\big) + \int_a^b dx \, \phi(x), \tag{2.50}$$

where $\phi(x)$ is any integrable function. The Monte Carlo method can be made much more efficient by choosing any $\phi(x)$ satisfying the two criteria

1. $\phi(x) \simeq f(x)$ for $a \le x \le b$,

2. the **control function**, $\phi(x)$, has an integral $\int_a^b dx \, \phi(x)$ that is easily evaluated.

For any $\phi(x)$ satisfying these conditions, if

$$I_1 = \int_a^b dx \, \big(f(x) - \phi(x)\big), \tag{2.51}$$

then $|I_1| \ll |I|$ and the statistical error in the estimate of I_1 will be proportionally smaller than that of I. The effectiveness of this method clearly depends upon an appropriate choice of $\phi(x)$.

As an example we reconsider the integral

$$J = \int_0^{1/2} dx \, e^{x^2} \sin \pi x \tag{2.52}$$

from Subsection 2.3.1. Note that the Taylor expansion of $\sin \pi x$ is

$$\sin \pi x = \pi x - \tfrac{1}{6}(\pi x)^3 + \cdots$$

and that this is close to $\sin \pi x$ for $0 \le x \le \tfrac{1}{2}$, and also that

$$\int_0^{1/2} dx \, x e^{x^2} = \tfrac{1}{2}\left(e^{1/4} - 1\right) \quad \text{and} \quad \int_0^{1/2} dx \, x^3 e^{x^2} = \tfrac{1}{2} - \tfrac{3}{8}e^{1/4}.$$

Thus we can write the original integral in the form

$$I = \int_0^{1/2} dx \, e^{x^2} \left(\sin \pi x - \phi(x)\right) + \int_0^{1/2} dx \, e^{x^2} \phi(x), \quad \phi(x) = \pi x - \tfrac{1}{6}(\pi x)^3.$$

But the above integrals give $\int_0^{1/2} dx \, e^{x^2} \phi(x) \simeq 0.3506$, and hence

$$I = 0.3506 + I_1, \quad I_1 = \int_0^{1/2} dx \, e^{x^2} \left(\sin \pi x - \phi(x)\right).$$

A Monte Carlo estimate of I_1 using 100 points gives

$$\int_0^{1/2} dx \, e^{x^2} \left(\sin \pi x - \phi(x)\right) = 0.0089 \pm 0.0025,$$

so $I = 0.360 \pm 0.0025$ with 95% confidence: the exact value is 0.358. A Monte Carlo estimate of the original integral with 100 points gives 0.337 ± 0.040; thus for the same computational effort we have reduced the statistical error by a factor of about 16.

Exercise 2.18

Use Maple to find the first three terms of the Taylor series of $\tan x$ about $x = 0$, and use this as a control function to obtain a Monte Carlo estimate of

$$J = \int_0^{1/2} dx \, e^{x^2} \tan x$$

with a relative accuracy of 0.005.

2.4.2 Stratified sampling

The general idea of this method is to divide the region of integration into a sum of small regions, or strata, in each of which the variation of the integrand is small. Then the statistical errors for each region are small *and* they combine to give a smaller total error; this method almost always gives improved accuracy for the same effort. This seems counter-intuitive, but we shall show how it works using a simple example.

Consider the integral

$$I = \int_0^1 dx \, x = \tfrac{1}{2}. \tag{2.53}$$

Here I is the mean value of x, i.e. $I = \langle x \rangle$, on $[0,1]$, and the standard deviation on this interval is given by $\sigma^2 = \langle x^2 \rangle - \langle x \rangle^2 = 1/12$. Thus if we estimate the integral using a Monte Carlo method using N points, we obtain

$$I = I_e \pm \frac{1}{\sqrt{3N}} \quad \text{with 95\% confidence.} \tag{2.54}$$

Now split the integral into two parts, $I = I^{(1)} + I^{(2)}$, where

$$I^{(1)} = \int_0^{1/2} dx \, x \quad \text{and} \quad I^{(2)} = \int_{1/2}^1 dx \, x. \tag{2.55}$$

The standard deviations are obtained using Equation (2.40) (page 74), and are $\sigma_1^2 = \sigma_2^2 = 1/192$. These are smaller than the standard deviation on $[0,1]$ because on each of the intervals $[0, \tfrac{1}{2}]$ and $[\tfrac{1}{2}, 1]$ the function varies less. The Monte Carlo estimate of I is just $I_e = I_e^{(1)} + I_e^{(2)}$, but now we need to estimate the statistical errors of this sum: this is the important part of the analysis.

A Monte Carlo estimate of $I^{(1)}$ and $I^{(2)}$ using N_1 and N_2 points, respectively, gives estimates $I_e^{(k)}$, $k = 1, 2$, each with the approximate density, from Equation (2.29) (page 72),

$$\rho(z) = \frac{1}{\sqrt{2\pi \sigma_k^2/N_k}} \exp\left(-\frac{(z - I^{(k)})^2}{2(\sigma_k^2/N_k)}\right), \quad \text{where } z = I_e^{(k)}. \tag{2.56}$$

The required sum $I_e = I_e^{(1)} + I_e^{(2)}$ is just the sum of two random variables each with a Gaussian distribution, and from the formula (2.15) (page 64) we see that I_e also has a Gaussian distribution, with mean $I_e = I_e^{(1)} + I_e^{(2)}$ and standard deviation given by

$$\sigma^2 = \frac{\sigma_1^2}{N_1} + \frac{\sigma_2^2}{N_2}. \tag{2.57}$$

In the present example $\sigma_1^2 = \sigma_2^2 = 1/192$, and if we use equal numbers of points in each interval, $N_1 = N_2 = N/2$, we obtain

$$I = I_e^{(1)} + I_e^{(2)} \pm \frac{1}{2\sqrt{3N}} \quad \text{with 95\% confidence.} \tag{2.58}$$

Comparing this with Equation (2.54) we see that by using the same number of points, but two strata, we have halved the statistical error.

Exercise 2.19

(a) Derive the quoted values of σ_k^2, $k = 1, 2$.

(b) Derive Equation (2.58).

This suggests that dividing the interval $[0, 1]$ into $M > 2$ equal-length segments and using N/M points in each stratum will further decrease the statistical error. In the next exercise you will see that, in this example, such a ploy reduces the statistical error by a factor of M.

Exercise 2.20

(a) Divide the interval $[0, 1]$ into M subintervals $((k - 1)/M, k/M)$, $k = 1, 2, \ldots, M$, and show that on the kth interval the standard deviation σ_k is given by

$$\sigma_k^2 = \frac{1}{M}I_2 - I_1^2, \quad \text{where} \quad I_n = \int_{(k-1)/M}^{k/M} dx\, x^n,$$

and hence that $\sigma_k^2 = 1/(12M^4)$.

(b) If N/M points are used to find each of the estimates $I_e^{(k)}$, $k = 1, 2, \ldots, M$, show that

$$I = \sum_{k=1}^{M} I_e^{(k)} \pm \frac{1}{M\sqrt{3N}} \quad \text{with 95\% confidence.}$$

In this example we see that the statistical error decreases as $N^{-1/2}$, where N is the total number of points used, but as M^{-1}, where M is the number of subdivisions. This suggests that for a given N we should make M as large as possible. We now use Maple to investigate this possibility, first for one-dimensional integrals and then for many-dimensional integrals.

Stratification for one-dimensional integrals

Consider the one-dimensional example

$$J = \int_a^b dx\, f(x) \tag{2.59}$$

and divide the range of integration into M equal-length segments $(a + (k - 1)h, a + kh)$, $k = 1, 2, \ldots, M$, where $h = (b - a)/M$, so that

$$J = \sum_{k=1}^{M} J^{(k)}, \quad \text{where} \quad J^{(k)} = \int_{a+(k-1)h}^{a+kh} dx\, f(x). \tag{2.60}$$

Each of the integrals $J^{(k)}$ is estimated using a Monte Carlo method using N points which, to keep the notation as simple as possible, we make the same for each interval. If $J_e^{(k)}$ is an estimate for $J^{(k)}$, the estimate for J is just the sum

$$J_e = \sum_{k=1}^{M} J_e^{(k)}, \quad \text{where} \quad J_e^{(k)} = \frac{h}{N} \sum_{j=1}^{N} f(x_{kj}), \quad h = \frac{b-a}{M}, \quad (2.61)$$

where $x_{kj} = a + (k-1)h + hr_j$ with r_j, $j = 1, 2, \ldots, N$, being N random numbers uniformly distributed in $[0, 1]$.

The estimate for the standard deviation of $f(x)$ in the kth interval is, using Equation (2.41) (page 75),

$$\left(\sigma_e^{(k)} \right)^2 = \frac{Nh^2}{N-1} \left[\frac{1}{N} \sum_{j=1}^{N} f(x_{kj})^2 - \left(\frac{1}{N} \sum_{j=1}^{N} f(x_{kj}) \right)^2 \right]. \quad (2.62)$$

Each $J_e^{(k)}$ is a random variable with a Gaussian distribution with mean $J^{(k)}$ and standard deviation $\sigma_e^{(k)}/\sqrt{N}$, so the sum of these random numbers has the standard deviation Σ, the estimate of which is given by

$$\Sigma_e^2 = \frac{1}{N} \sum_{k=1}^{M} \left(\sigma_e^{(k)} \right)^2. \quad (2.63)$$

With 95% confidence, the value of J lies in the interval $J_e \pm 2\Sigma_e$. The formulae (2.62) and (2.63) are used in the Maple procedure mc3, listed below. But before describing this procedure we discuss some of the results obtained from it when applied to the following integral:

$$J = \int_0^{\pi/2} dx \, \exp\left(\sqrt{\sin x} \right) = 3.454\,39\ldots. \quad (2.64)$$

Estimated values of J obtained using a total of M strata and N points per strata, with the total number of points fixed at 1024, that is $MN = 1024$, are given in Table 2.1.

Table 2.1   Various Monte Carlo estimates of J, each using a total of $NM = 1024$ points, for the number of strata, M, increasing from 1 to 512. The exact value is $J = 3.454\,39\ldots.$

N	M	J_e	$2\Sigma_e$	N	M	J_e	$2\Sigma_e$
1024	1	3.481 68	0.044 66	32	32	3.452 99	0.001 86
512	2	3.474 16	0.024 56	16	64	3.454 57	0.000 88
256	4	3.450 69	0.012 99	8	128	3.454 29	0.000 52
128	8	3.453 98	0.006 87	4	256	3.454 33	0.000 23
64	16	3.453 95	0.003 61	2	512	3.454 42	0.000 15

From the values of J_e given in this table we see that the accuracy increases as M increases. This is expected because as the length of each stratum decreases, the variation of the integrand in each stratum decreases, so each integral can be accurately estimated using fewer points. Remember that only one point is needed for an exact result if the integrand is constant.

The following Maple procedure will provide a Monte Carlo estimate for the integral of a function $f(x)$ over the interval $a \leq x \leq b$, using M strata with N points in each.

This procedure is a straightforward application of Equations (2.61)–(2.63). It uses NM points to find a Monte Carlo estimate; we use the Maple procedure `Sample` only once to create NM random numbers, rather than M times to create N in each strata, because this is faster if there are many strata. It is essentially a complicated version of `mc1`, and part of the complication is because the Maple functions `Mean` and `Variance` need to be replaced by loops to perform these sums.

The output of this procedure is a list containing the estimate J_e, and the 95% confidence limit $2\Sigma_e$.

```
>   restart:
>   mc3 := proc(a,b,M,N)
>      local M1,M2,h,X,R,j,k,i,Je,sig2,sg2,xx,y,Sigmae;
>      uses Statistics;
>      h := evalf((b-a)/M);                    # Interval length
>      X := RandomVariable(Uniform(0,1));
>      R := Sample(X,N*M);
>      # Start loop round intervals
>      j := 1;                    # j is a counter, initialised to 1
>      Je := 0:  sig2 := 0;
>      for k from 1 to M do;    # Loop round each of the M strata
>         # Initialise moments on each stratum
>         M1 := 0:  M2 := 0:
>         # Loop round N points in each stratum
>         for i from 1 to N do:
>            xx := a+(k-1+R[j])*h;
>            y := evalf(f(xx));
>            M1 := M1+y;                        # First moment
>            M2 := M2+y*y;                      # Second moment
>            j := j+1;                          # Increment counter
>         od:                # End of integration over kth stratum
>         Je := Je+h*M1/N;           # Increment value of integral
>         # Compute square of standard deviation
>         sg2 := (N/(N-1))*h^2*(M2/N-(M1/N)^2);      # Eqn (2.62)
>         sig2 := sig2+sg2/N:    # Increment st. dev., Eqn (2.63)
>      od;
>      Sigmae := evalf(2*sqrt(sig2));      # 95% confidence limit
>      [Je,Sigmae];
>   end:
```

For the integral defined in Equation (2.64) we need

```
>   f:=x-> exp(sqrt(abs(sin(x))));
```
$$f := x \rightarrow e^{\sqrt{|\sin(x)|}}$$

Note that we have replaced $\sin x$ by $|\sin x|$ to avoid potential numerical problems if $\sin x < 0$ due to rounding errors. With 20 strata, $M = 20$, and $N = 4$ points per stratum, that is, a total of 80 points, this gives

```
>   mc3(0,Pi/2,20,4);
```
$$[3.451794594, 0.01097592964]$$

If you perform this calculation you are likely to obtain different estimates because different random numbers may be generated.

Table 2.1 can be reproduced using the following commands, the output of which is not given here.

```
>   printf("  %s        %s     %s    %s \n","N","M","Je","Error");
>   for k from 0 to 9 do:
>     M := 2^k:   N := 1024/M;
>     z := mc3(0,Pi/2,M,N):
>     printf(" %5.0f   %6.0f   %6.5f   %6.5f \n",N,M,z[1],z[2]);
>   od:
```

Here we use the printf command to obtain output that is easier to read. You do not need to know how to use this command, and can alternatively use print.

Since $\sigma_e^{(k)}$ is approximately independent of N, Σ_e is proportional to $N^{-1/2}$; this allows the error to be estimated when M is fixed and N varies. For example, if $M = 20$ we see, from the above result, that $2\Sigma_e \simeq 0.011 = 0.022N^{-1/2}$ $(N = 4)$, and hence to reduce $2\Sigma_e$ to 0.001 it is necessary to increase N to about 400. This gives

```
>   mc3(0,Pi/2,20,400);
```
$$[3.454275451, 0.001044569686]$$

Finally, we note that the combination of control functions with stratification gives greatly improved accuracy, but we leave this extension to be explored in exercises.

Exercise 2.21

(a) Use stratification with $M = 50$ to estimate the value of the integral defined in Exercise 2.18 (page 82), and using a suitable value of N, obtain a result with a relative error of about 0.001 with 95% confidence.

(b) In this part of the exercise we examine the effects of independently changing the number of strata M and the number of points per stratum N.

First, set $N = 4$, and compute the relative error ε for $M = 20 \times 2^k$, $k = 0, 1, \ldots, 6$, and plot the graph of $\ln \varepsilon$ against $\ln M$, to show that $\varepsilon M^{3/2}$ is approximately constant for this example.

Second, set $M = 10$ and $N = 10 \times 4^k$, $k = 0, 1, \ldots, 5$ and plot the graph of $\varepsilon\sqrt{N}$.

(c) Finally, set $NM = 512$, and in each of the cases $[N, M] = [2^k, 512 \times 2^{-k}]$, $k = 2, 3, \ldots, 8$, compute 200 realisations of J_e and the relative error ε, to confirm that in about 95% of cases the exact value of the integral is within the interval $(J_e(1 - \varepsilon), J_e(1 + \varepsilon))$. This calculation may take a long time.

Exercise 2.22

Use a combination of stratification and the control function suggested to find a Monte Carlo estimate, with relative accuracy 10^{-5}, of the following integrals.

(a) $J = \displaystyle\int_0^3 dx\, x^{1/3} \sin\left(\pi\sqrt{\dfrac{x}{3}}\right)$, a Taylor expansion about the origin

(b) $J = \displaystyle\int_1^4 dx\, \dfrac{\exp(1/\sqrt{x})}{1 + \sin^2 \pi x}$, $\phi(x) = 2/(1 + \sin^2 \pi x)$

Exercise 2.23

The function $P_T(\theta, K)$ is defined by the condition

$$P_T(\theta, K) = \begin{cases} 1, & X_j(\theta) > 3, \text{ for any } j \text{ satisfying } 1 \le j \le T, \\ 0, & X_j(\theta) \le 3, \text{ for all } j \in [1, T], \end{cases} \qquad (2.65)$$

where $X_j(\theta)$ are obtained by iterating the equations

$$\phi_{n+1} = \phi_n + X_n, \quad X_{n+1} = X_n + K \sin \phi_{n+1},$$

with $X_0 = 0$, $\phi_0 = \theta$, and K is a positive parameter.

Write a Maple procedure to compute $P_T(\theta, K)$ and plot the graphs of this function for a few values of K between 1 and 5, $0 \le \theta < \pi$ and $T = 50$.

Write another Maple procedure, to compute the value of

$$\overline{P}_T(K) = \frac{1}{2\pi} \int_0^{2\pi} d\theta \, P_T(\theta, K)$$

using a stratified Monte Carlo method. For $T = 50$ plot the graph of $\overline{P}_T(K)$ for $0.85 < K < 5$. This is a time-consuming calculation so use 100 subintervals with 4 points in each. This integral gives a measure of the proportion of trajectories starting on the line $X = 0$ which are unbounded.

The map defined in Equation (2.65) is known as the *standard map* and is one of the most studied nonlinear dynamical systems; it was introduced in *Unit B3*. For all $K > 0$ there is chaotic motion, but for $K < K_{\text{crit}} \simeq 0.972$ the motion starting at $X = 0$ is bounded.

Stratification for many-dimensional integrals

The idea of stratification is trivially generalised to many-dimensional integrals, but the practicalities of keeping track of all the variables requires some thought. For an n-dimensional integral the index k used to label the strata in the one-dimensional case becomes a list of n indices: for this reason the analysis given below is for two-dimensional integrals, as is the Maple procedure described later, though it is written to allow easy generalisation to higher dimensions.

Consider the two-dimensional integral

$$J = \int_{a_1}^{b_1} dx_1 \int_{a_2}^{b_2} dx_2 \, f(x_1, x_2) \qquad (2.66)$$

over a rectangular region – see Figure 2.5. The ith side of this rectangle, $a_i \le x_i \le b_i$, $i = 1, 2$, is divided into M_i equal-length subintervals, with length $h_i = (b_i - a_i)/M_i$: an example with $M_1 = 3$ and $M_2 = 2$ is shown in Figure 2.5.

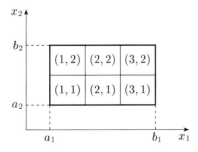

Figure 2.5   Illustration of the stratification of a rectangle into 6 strata, each labelled by the indices (k_1, k_2), where in this case $k_1 = 1, 2, 3$ and $k_2 = 1, 2$

Each elementary rectangle is labelled by the indices $k_1 = 1, 2, \ldots, M_1$ and $k_2 = 1, 2, \ldots, M_2$, so that in the rectangle (k_1, k_2) the variables lie in the intervals

$$a_1 + (k_1 - 1)h_1 < x_1 < a_1 + k_1 h_1, \quad a_2 + (k_2 - 1)h_2 < x_2 < a_2 + k_2 h_2.$$

The integral $J^{(k_1 k_2)}$ over each elementary rectangle is estimated by the usual Monte Carlo method using N sample points, so Equation (2.45) (page 78) becomes

$$J_e^{(k_1 k_2)} = \frac{h_1 h_2}{N} \sum_{j=1}^{N} f(x_{1j}, x_{2j}), \tag{2.67}$$

where

$$x_{1j} = a_1 + (k_1 - 1 + r_{1j})h_1 \quad \text{and} \quad x_{2j} = a_2 + (k_2 - 1 + r_{2j})h_2,$$

and where r_{1j} and r_{2j} are each a set of N random numbers uniformly distributed in $[0, 1]$. Similarly, the sample standard deviation is given by

$$\left(\sigma_e^{(k_1 k_2)}\right)^2 = \frac{N(h_1 h_2)^2}{N - 1} \left[\frac{1}{N} \sum_{j=1}^{N} f(x_{1j}, x_{2j})^2 - \left(\frac{1}{N} \sum_{j=1}^{N} f(x_{1j}, x_{2j}) \right)^2 \right], \tag{2.68}$$

which is the appropriate generalisation of Equation (2.46). As for the one-dimensional case, $J_e^{(k_1 k_2)}$ is a random variable with mean equal to the integral over the rectangle (k_1, k_2) and with estimated standard deviation $\sigma_e^{(k_1 k_2)}/\sqrt{N}$. The sum of these random variables provides a Monte Carlo estimate of the required integral J, and has standard deviation Σ, the estimate of which is given by (see Equation (2.14))

$$\Sigma_e^2 = \frac{1}{N} \sum_{k_1=1}^{M_1} \sum_{k_2=1}^{M_2} \left(\sigma_e^{(k_1 k_2)}\right)^2. \tag{2.69}$$

Apart from the complication of summing over all elementary rectangles, this is exactly the same as the method described for one-dimensional integrals, and is implemented in the following procedure mc4. This has three arguments.

1. Lim is a list of the lists of the integration limits. For the two-dimensional integral (2.66) it is $[[a_1, b_1], [a_2, b_2]]$, but in general it would be $[[a_1, b_1], [a_2, b_2], \ldots, [a_N, b_N]]$.

2. M is a list of two positive integers $[M_1, M_2]$ defining the number of partitions in each direction. For an n-dimensional integral it would be $[M_1, M_2, \ldots, M_N]$.

3. N is a scalar defining the number of sample points used to evaluate the integrals over each elementary rectangle. The total number of sample points used is $N_T = N M_1 M_2$ for a two-dimensional integral, and $N_T = N \prod_{j=1}^{n} M_j$ in general.

The variable n is the dimension of the integral and here is set to $n = 2$; for higher-dimensional integrals only a few lines of this procedure need to be changed. As in mc3, the output is a list of J_e and $2\Sigma_e$.

```
>  restart:
>  mc4 := proc(Lim,M,N)
>     local z,zz,a,b,h,Nt,z1,z2,X,i,j,k,Je,sig2,sige,x,
            M1,M2,n,jj;
>     uses Statistics;
>     n := 2:            # Parameter defining the integral dimension
>     a := [seq(Lim[k][1],k=1..n)];   # Lower integration limits
>     b := [seq(Lim[k][2],k=1..n)];   # Upper integration limits
>     h := [seq((b[k]-a[k])/M[k],k=1..n)];
>     Nt := N*mul(M[k],k=1..n); # Total number of sample points
>     for k from 1 to n do:
>       X[k] := RandomVariable(Uniform(0,1));
>     od:
>     for k from 1 to n do:
>       z[k] := Sample(X[k],Nt):
>     od:
>     j := 1:                    # Initialise random number counter
>     Je := 0:                   # Initialise estimate for integral
>     sig2 := 0:    # Initialise estimate for standard deviation
>     # Loop round strata in direction 1
>     for k[1] from 1 to M[1] do:
>       # Loop round strata in direction 2
>       for k[2] from 1 to M[2] do:
>         M1 := 0:  M2 := 0:              # Initialise moments
>         # Now loop round N points of each stratum
>         for i from 1 to N do:
>           # Loop round number of dimensions
>           for jj from 1 to n do:
>             x[jj] := a[jj]+(k[jj]-1+z[jj][j])*h[jj];
>           od:
>           zz := evalf(f(x[1],x[2]));
>           M1 := M1+zz;
>           M2 := M2+zz*zz;
>           j := j+1;
>         od;
>         # End of loop for integration in stratum
>         Je := Je+h[1]*h[2]*M1/N;                 # Eqn (2.67)
>         sige := N*(h[1]*h[2])^2*(M2/N-(M1/N)^2)/(N-1);
                                                   # Eqn (2.68)
>         sig2 := sig2+sige/N;                     # Eqn (2.69)
>       od;
>     od;
>     [Je,evalf(2*sqrt(sig2))];
>  end:
```

For the first example of the use of `mc4` we evaluate the integral

$$J = \int_1^2 dx \int_1^4 dy\, x^y y^x \qquad (2.70)$$

using the Maple commands

```
>  f := (x,y)->x^y*y^x;
```

$$f := (x,\, y) \rightarrow x^y\, y^x$$

```
>  J := evalf(Int(f(x,y),[x=1..2,y=1..4]));
```

$$J := 60.67632012$$

On the other hand, with various values of M_1, M_2 and N, with $N_T = 1024$, the procedure `mc4` gives the values generated with the following commands and listed in Table 2.2.

```
>  printf(" %s     %s      %s       %s    %s \n",
          "M1","M2","N","Je","Error");
>  Lim := [[1,2],[1,4]]:
>  for k from 1 to 4 do:
>     M1 := 2^k;  M2 := 2*M1;  N := 1024/(M1*M2);
>     z := mc4(Lim,[M1,M2],N);
>     printf("%4.0f  %4.0f %6.0f  %6.4f  %6.4f\n",
              M1,M2,N,z[1],z[2]);
>  od:
```

Table 2.2   Monte Carlo estimate of the integral (2.70) using a total of $N_T = 1024$ points with various types of stratification. The exact value is $J = 60.676\ldots$.

M_1	M_2	N	J_e	$2\Sigma_e$
2	4	128	58.679	2.77
4	8	32	60.889	1.61
8	16	8	60.528	0.89
16	32	2	60.655	0.42

A more interesting example, not so easily evaluated using conventional methods, is the integral

$$J = \iint_{\mathcal{D}} dx\, dy\, x^y y^x, \qquad (2.71)$$

where $\mathcal{D}$ is the rectangle $1 \le x \le 2$, $1 \le y \le 4$, as in Equation (2.70), but excluding the circle of radius $\frac{1}{2}$ with centre at $x = \frac{3}{2}$, $y = \frac{5}{2}$. A simple method of evaluating this integral is to define the function

$$f(x,y) = \begin{cases} x^y y^x, & \left(x - \frac{3}{2}\right)^2 + \left(y - \frac{5}{2}\right)^2 > \frac{1}{4}, \\ 0, & \text{otherwise}, \end{cases} \qquad (2.72)$$

which is zero inside the circle. A Maple procedure for this function is

```
>  f := proc(x,y)
>     local t;
>     t := evalf((x-3/2)^2+(y-5/2)^2-1/4);
>     if t>0 then x^y*y^x else 0 fi;
>  end:
```

and then `mc4` gives, for the same values of M_1, M_2 and N as before, the values given in Table 2.3.

Table 2.3   Monte Carlo estimate of the integral (2.71) using a total of $N_T = 1024$ points with various types of stratification

M_1	M_2	N	J_e	$2\Sigma_e$
2	4	128	49.876	3.75
4	8	32	50.388	1.87
8	16	8	50.904	1.10
16	32	2	50.523	0.69

Exercise 2.24

Using a stratified Monte Carlo method, write a Maple procedure that evaluates the integral

$$J(u,v) = \iint_{\mathcal{D}} dx\, dy \, \frac{\exp(xy)}{1+x^2},$$

where $\mathcal{D}$ is the unit square in the first quadrant, with one side along Ox and another along Oy, excluding the circle of radius $\frac{1}{4}$, centre at (u,v), with equation

$$(x-u)^2 + (y-v)^2 = \tfrac{1}{16}.$$

Plot the graphs of $J(w,w)$ with $-0.5 \le w \le 1.5$ and $J(w, 1-w)$ with $-0.5 \le w \le 1.5$.

Exercise 2.25

The centre of gravity $\bar{\mathbf{r}}$ of a two-dimensional plate with density $\rho(x,y)$ occupying a region $\mathcal{D}$ in the xy-plane is defined by the equation

$$\bar{\mathbf{r}} = \iint dx\, dy\, \mathbf{r}\, \rho(x,y) \Big/ \iint dx\, dy\, \rho(x,y).$$

A square steel plate with density $\rho = 1 + \sqrt{x^2 + y^2}$, with two sides along Ox and Oy and of unit length, has two holes. One hole is circular with centre at $(\frac{1}{4}, \frac{3}{4})$ and radius $\frac{1}{8}$, with equation

$$\left(x - \tfrac{1}{4}\right)^2 + \left(y - \tfrac{3}{4}\right)^2 = \tfrac{1}{64}.$$

The other hole is elliptical with equation

$$16\left(x - \tfrac{2}{3}\right)^2 + 64\left(y - \tfrac{1}{4}\right)^2 = 1.$$

(a) Use `plot3d` to plot the graph of the density function, which is zero inside these holes.

(b) Use a suitable modification of `mc4` to find the coordinates of the centre of gravity with relative statistical errors of less than 0.01. Note that efficiency is improved if all the integrals are evaluated together.

Exercise 2.26

A cuboid block of steel, of uniform density, has three sides aligned along the xyz coordinate axes, so its interior is in the region $x > 0$, $y > 0$ and $z > 0$. It has unit length along Ox and Oy, and length $c > 0$ along Oz. A hole of radius r is drilled completely through it from the origin to the diagonally opposite corner: it can be shown that the interior of this hole is the region defined by

$$(c^2 + 1)(x^2 + y^2) + 2z^2 - 2x(y + cz) - 2cyz < (2 + c^2)r^2$$

and $0 \le x \le 1$, $0 \le y \le 1$, $0 \le z \le c$.

(a) Use `implicitplot3d` (in the `plots` package) to confirm that this equation is that of the hole.

(b) Generalise `mc4` to deal with three-dimensional integrals to compute the mass of this shape for any r and c. Use your procedure to plot a graph of the ratio of the mass of this shape to the undrilled cuboid for $0 < r < 1.2$ and $c = 3$.

2.5   End of unit exercises

Exercise 2.27

This is an optional exercise that derives the expressions for the mean and standard deviation for the sum of two independent random variables $z = x + y$.

Using the expression (2.8) for the density function of z, obtain the formulae for the mean and standard deviation of z.

Exercise 2.28

(a) Show that if $w = x_1 + x_2 + x_3$, where the x_k, $k = 1, 2, 3$, have identical exponential density functions defined in Equation (1.23) with parameter μ, then the density function for w is

$$\rho_3(w) = \begin{cases} 0, & w < 0, \\ \frac{1}{2}\mu^3 w^2 e^{-\mu w}, & w \geq 0. \end{cases}$$

[*Hint*: Use the density of $x_1 + x_2$ given in Equation (2.10) (page 62).]

(b) Use induction, or otherwise, to show that if $w = x_1 + x_2 + \cdots + x_n$, where all the random variables x_k have the density given in part (a), to show that

$$\rho_n(w) = \begin{cases} 0, & w < 0, \\ \frac{1}{(n-1)!}\mu^n w^{n-1} e^{-\mu w}, & w \geq 0. \end{cases}$$

(c) Show that $\rho_n(w)$ has a single maximum at $w = (n-1)/\mu$.

(d) Show that the central limit theorem gives, for large n,

$$\rho_n(w) \simeq \frac{\mu}{\sqrt{2\pi n}} \exp\left(-\frac{(\mu w - n)^2}{2n}\right).$$

Make a graphical comparison of this approximation with the exact result found in part (b) with $\mu = 1$ and for $n = 2, 3, \ldots, 20$, in steps of 2.

Exercise 2.29

If $\rho_X(x)$ is an even function, show that Equation (2.24) (page 67) simplifies to

$$\rho_N(S) = \frac{1}{\pi}\int_0^\infty dz \left(2\int_0^\infty dx\, \rho_X(x)\cos xz\right)^N \cos Sz.$$

Exercise 2.30

In this exercise we use the bimodal even distribution with density

$$\rho(x) = \begin{cases} \dfrac{1}{2(b-a)}, & -b \le x \le -a \text{ or } a \le x \le b, \ b > a > 0, \\ 0, & \text{otherwise}, \end{cases}$$

to show that the passage to the central limit theorem is not always as fast or smooth as for some of the examples considered in the main text.

(a) Show that

$$\int_{-\infty}^{\infty} dx \, \rho(x) \, e^{-ixz} = \frac{\sin zb - \sin za}{(b-a)z},$$

and, using Equation (2.24) (page 67), show that the density of $S = x_1 + x_2 + \cdots + x_N$ is given by

$$\rho_N(S) = \frac{1}{\pi} \int_0^{\infty} dz \, \cos Sz \left(\frac{\sin zb - \sin za}{(b-a)z} \right)^N.$$

(b) Show that

$$\langle x \rangle = 0 \quad \text{and} \quad \langle x^2 \rangle = \tfrac{1}{3} \left(a^2 + ab + b^2 \right),$$

and hence that an approximation to $\rho_N(S)$ is

$$\rho_N(S) \simeq \sqrt{\frac{3}{2N\pi(a^2 + ab + b^2)}} \exp \left(-\frac{3S^2}{2N(a^2 + ab + b^2)} \right).$$

(c) Use Maple to evaluate the integral expression for $\rho_N(S)$ found in part (a) for $a = 1$, $b = 2$ and various values of N, and compare this exact result with the approximation given in part (b) by the central limit theorem.

(d) With $a = 1$ and $b = 2$ use Maple to estimate $\rho_N(S)$ by evaluating the sum $S = x_1 + x_2 + \cdots + x_N$ many times in order to construct a numerical approximation to the density. Use the exact result for $N = 6$ to check that your procedure is correct, then for $N = 10, 15, \ldots, 30$ compare, graphically, your results with the central limit theorem approximation.

Exercise 2.31

Consider the integral

$$J = \int_0^2 dx \, e^x,$$

which evaluates exactly to $J = e^2 - 1$.

(a) Use Equation (2.40) (page 74) to show that the standard deviation is given by $\sigma^2 = 2J$.

(b) Find 1000 realisations of the simple Monte Carlo estimate J_e using $N = 1000$ sample points, and find the proportion of values that lie in the intervals J_1, J_2 and J_3, where $J_k = J \pm k\sigma/\sqrt{N}$. Show that these proportions are consistent with the estimates given by Equation (2.32) (page 72).

Exercise 2.32

Use a stratified Monte Carlo method to estimate the value of

$$J(x) = \int_0^x du \, \sin(u + 3\exp(f(u))),$$

where

$$f(u) = \begin{cases} u, & \text{if floor}(\exp(u)) \text{ is odd}, \\ 1, & \text{if floor}(\exp(u)) \text{ is even}. \end{cases}$$

Use a sufficient number of points to ensure that your estimate differs from the exact result by a relative error of less than 0.005 with a probability of 95%, and plot the graph of $J(x)$ for $0.1 < x < 4$.

Exercise 2.33

The following type of approximation was developed by Laplace in his investigation of the central limit theorem. Here we revisit the problem considered in Exercise 2.10 (page 68).

(a) Compare, graphically, the functions

$$y_1(z) = \left(\frac{\sin z}{z}\right)^N \quad \text{and} \quad y_2(z) = \exp\left(-\frac{Nz^2}{6}\right)$$

for $|z| < 6/\sqrt{N}$ and $2 \leq N \leq 15$.

(b) Using the fact that $y_1(z) \simeq y_2(z)$ for small $|z|$ and large N, show that the density $\rho_N(S)$ of the random variable $S = x_1 + x_2 + \cdots + x_N$, defined in Exercise 2.10, is approximately

$$\rho_N(S) \simeq \frac{1}{2\pi}\int_{-\infty}^{\infty} dz \, \exp\left(iSz - \tfrac{1}{6}Na^2z^2\right) = \frac{1}{a}\sqrt{\frac{3}{2N\pi}}\exp\left(-\frac{3S^2}{2Na^2}\right),$$

which agrees with the formula derived using the central limit theorem.

You will find the following result useful:

$$\int_{-\infty}^{\infty} dx \, e^{iAx - Bx^2} = \sqrt{\frac{\pi}{B}}\exp\left(-\frac{A^2}{4B}\right), \quad B > 0, \quad A \text{ real}.$$

Note that the approximation discussed in part (a) follows from one of the definitions of the exponential function, namely

$$e^x = \lim_{n\to\infty}\left(1 + \frac{x}{n}\right)^n,$$

so we assume that

$$e^x \simeq \left(1 + \frac{x}{n}\right)^n \quad \text{if } n \gg 1.$$

Then

$$\left(\frac{\sin z}{z}\right)^N \simeq \left(1 - \tfrac{1}{6}z^2 + \cdots\right)^N \simeq \left(1 - \tfrac{1}{6}Nz^2\frac{1}{N}\right)^N$$

$$\simeq \exp\left(-\tfrac{1}{6}Nz^2\right),$$

which is a reasonable approximation for $Nz^2 < 6$.

Learning outcomes

After studying this unit you should understand all the concepts and ideas introduced, and in particular be able to:

- compute the probability distribution of a sum of two independent random variables in simple situations;
- compute the mean and standard deviation of a sum of N random variables with identical probability distributions;
- understand the central limit theorem, and in those cases where it applies, use Equation (2.23) to compute the limiting probability distribution of a sum of independent random variables;
- apply Equation (2.24) in simple situations to compute the exact probability distribution of a sum of independent random variables;
- use Maple to perform numerical simulations of random walks and obtain approximations to their distributions;
- use Maple to compute Monte Carlo estimates of certain definite integrals, accurate to within a given confidence;
- use control functions and stratification to improve Monte Carlo estimates of definite integrals;
- compute Monte Carlo estimates of multidimensional integrals over awkward boundaries such as those given in the text.

Solutions to Exercises

Solution 2.1

(a) If $z = x + y$ then, since the operation of taking the mean is linear, $\langle z \rangle = \langle x + y \rangle = \langle x \rangle + \langle y \rangle$, and $z^2 = x^2 + y^2 + 2xy$, so $\langle z^2 \rangle = \langle x^2 \rangle + \langle y^2 \rangle + 2 \langle xy \rangle$. Also,

$$\sigma_z^2 = \langle z^2 \rangle - \langle z \rangle^2$$
$$= \langle x^2 \rangle - \langle x \rangle^2 + \langle y^2 \rangle - \langle y \rangle^2 + 2 \langle xy \rangle - 2 \langle x \rangle \langle y \rangle.$$

But x and y are independent, so $\langle xy \rangle = \langle x \rangle \langle y \rangle$ and hence $\sigma_z^2 = \sigma_x^2 + \sigma_y^2$.

(b) Define $v = x + y + z$ and $w = x + y$, so $v = w + z$. Now v is the sum of two independent random variables and the result found in part (a) gives

$$\langle v \rangle = \langle w \rangle + \langle z \rangle = \langle x \rangle + \langle y \rangle + \langle z \rangle$$

and

$$\sigma_v^2 = \sigma_w^2 + \sigma_z^2 = \sigma_x^2 + \sigma_y^2 + \sigma_z^2.$$

Solution 2.2

Using Equation (2.8) we obtain

$$\rho_Z(z) = \frac{2}{\pi} \int_0^z dx \, \frac{1}{\cosh x} \, e^{-(z-x)}.$$

Since $x > 0$ and $z - x > 0$,

$$\rho_Z(z) = \frac{4}{\pi} e^{-z} \int_0^z dx \, \frac{e^{2x}}{e^{2x} + 1}$$
$$= \frac{2}{\pi} e^{-z} \left[\ln \left(1 + e^{2x} \right) \right]_{x=0}^z$$
$$= \frac{2}{\pi} e^{-z} \ln \left(\tfrac{1}{2} + \tfrac{1}{2} e^{2z} \right), \quad z \geq 0.$$

Solution 2.3

Equation (2.8) is derived by assuming that x and y are independent random variables, so we cannot set $y = x$.

Solution 2.4

From Equation (2.8),

$$\rho_Z(-z) = \int_{-\infty}^{\infty} dx \, \rho_X(x) \, \rho_Y(-z - x)$$
$$= \int_{-\infty}^{\infty} dx' \, \rho_X(-x') \, \rho_Y(-z + x'), \quad x' = -x,$$
$$= \int_{-\infty}^{\infty} dx' \, \rho_X(x') \, \rho_Y(z - x') = \rho_Z(z),$$

where we have used the facts that $\rho_X(-x') = \rho_X(x')$ and $\rho_Y(-z + x') = \rho_Y(z - x')$.

Solution 2.5

First note that $\rho(x)$ is even, hence $\rho_Z(z)$ is even, and we may assume that $z \geq 0$. Equation (2.8) gives

$$\rho_Z(z) = \int_{-\infty}^{\infty} dx \, \rho(x) \, \rho(z - x) = \frac{1}{2a} \int_{-a}^{a} dx \, \rho(z - x).$$

But $\rho(z - x) > 0$ only if $|z - x| \leq a$, that is $-a \leq z - x \leq a$, which gives $z - a \leq x \leq z + a$. For $z \geq 0$, the region where $\rho(z - x) > 0$ is shown by the shaded region in Figure 2.6.

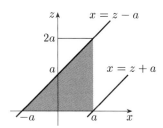

Figure 2.6 Region of integration where $\rho(z - x) > 0$

Hence the integral becomes

$$\rho_Z(z) = \left(\frac{1}{2a} \right)^2 \int_{z-a}^{a} dx = \frac{1}{2a} \left(1 - \frac{z}{2a} \right), \quad 0 \leq z \leq 2a.$$

Since $\rho_Z(z)$ is even, the quoted result follows.

Solution 2.6

The trick is to convert the problem to that solved in the text. Let $y_k = x_k - \mu_k$, so $\langle y_k \rangle = 0$ for all k. Then $z = \mu + \sum_{k=1}^{n} y_k$, where $\mu = \sum_{k=1}^{n} \mu_k$. Now define $w = z - \mu$, so $w = \sum_{k=1}^{n} y_k$. The density of w is, from Equation (2.14),

$$\rho_W(w) = \frac{1}{\sigma \sqrt{2\pi}} \exp \left(-\frac{w^2}{2\sigma^2} \right), \quad \text{where } \sigma^2 = \sum_{k=1}^{n} \sigma_k^2,$$

and where σ_k is the standard deviation of y_k, which is the same as that of x_k, because the transformation from x to y is simply a translation. Since $z = w + \mu$, the density of z is $\rho_Z(z) = \rho_W(z - \mu)$, which gives the result.

Solution 2.7

The mean, $\langle x \rangle$, is zero, since $\rho_X(-x) = \rho_X(x)$, and hence

$$\sigma^2 = \langle x^2 \rangle = \frac{1}{2a} \int_{-a}^{a} dx \, x^2 = \tfrac{1}{3} a^2 \quad \text{and} \quad \sigma_S = a \sqrt{\frac{N}{3}}.$$

Solution 2.8

The method is the same as used in Exercise 2.6. Define new random variables $y_k = x_k - \mu_X$, with zero mean and standard deviation σ_X^2, and $W = S - N\mu_X = \sum_{k=1}^{N} y_k$, which has has zero mean, giving $\langle S \rangle = N\mu_X$ and $\sigma_S^2 = \sigma_W^2 = N\sigma_X^2$.

Solution 2.9

(a) Since δ is the sum of N random variables ε_k / N with zero mean and standard deviation σ / N, the central limit theorem, Equation (2.23), gives, on replacing σ_X with σ / N,

$$\rho(\delta) \simeq \frac{1}{\sigma} \sqrt{\frac{N}{2\pi}} \exp \left(-\frac{N\delta^2}{2\sigma^2} \right), \quad \text{if } N \gg 1.$$

(b) The probability that $|\delta| < \alpha$ is, by definition,

$$p = \frac{1}{\sigma}\sqrt{\frac{N}{2\pi}} \int_{-\alpha}^{\alpha} dx \, \exp\left(-\frac{Nx^2}{2\sigma^2}\right).$$

Putting

$$y = \frac{x}{\sigma}\sqrt{\frac{N}{2}},$$

we obtain

$$p = \frac{2}{\sqrt{\pi}} \int_0^{y_1} dy \, e^{-y^2}, \quad \text{where } y_1 = \frac{\alpha}{\sigma}\sqrt{\frac{N}{2}}.$$

Putting $p = \frac{3}{4}$ gives the equation for y_1; the associated Maple worksheet shows that $y_1 = 0.813\ldots$.

The spread of the sample average is proportional to $N^{-1/2}$, so is halved if $M^{-1/2} = \frac{1}{2}N^{-1/2}$, that is, $M = 4N$.

Solution 2.10

(a) The integral is

$$\int_{-\infty}^{\infty} dx \, \rho_X(x) \, e^{-ixz} = \frac{1}{2a} \int_{-a}^{a} dx \, e^{-ixz}$$

$$= \frac{1}{-2iaz}\left(e^{-iaz} - e^{iaz}\right)$$

$$= \frac{\sin az}{az}.$$

Hence, using Equation (2.24),

$$\rho_2(S) = \frac{1}{2\pi} \int_{-\infty}^{\infty} dz \, e^{iSz} \left(\frac{\sin az}{az}\right)^2$$

$$= \frac{1}{\pi} \int_0^{\infty} dz \, \cos Sz \left(\frac{\sin az}{az}\right)^2$$

since the imaginary part of the integrand is odd and the real part is even. Now put $w = az$ to give

$$\rho_2(S) = \frac{1}{\pi a} \int_0^{\infty} dw \, \cos\left(\frac{S}{a}w\right) \left(\frac{\sin w}{w}\right)^2,$$

which is a product of a function of S/a and $1/a$. This density is derived in Exercise 2.5 (page 63) and gives the alternative representation of $\rho_2(z)$.

(b) Since $\langle x \rangle = 0$ and $\langle x^2 \rangle = a^2/3$, $\sigma_X^2 = a^2/3$ and Equation (2.23) becomes

$$\rho_N(S) \simeq \frac{1}{a}\sqrt{\frac{3}{2\pi N}} \exp\left(-\frac{3S^2}{2Na^2}\right).$$

The graphs of this approximation for $N = 2$ and the exact value of $\rho_2(S)$ are shown in Figure 2.7 (see also the Maple worksheet).

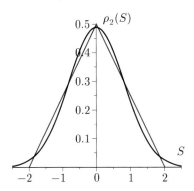

Figure 2.7 Graphs showing the exact density $\rho_2(S)$ (red line) and the central limit theorem approximation (black line)

(c) The derivation of $\rho_N(S)$ is the same as that of $\rho_2(S)$, except that $((\sin w)/w)^2$ is replaced with $((\sin w)/w)^N$. See the Maple worksheet for the remainder of the solution.

Solution 2.11

(a) The function is

$$f(x_1, x_2) = \frac{a}{\pi} \int_{-x_1}^{x_2} dx \, \frac{x}{a^2 + x^2}$$

$$= \left[\frac{a}{2\pi} \ln(a^2 + x^2)\right]_{-x_1}^{x_2}$$

$$= \frac{a}{2\pi} \ln\left(\frac{a^2 + x_2^2}{a^2 + x_1^2}\right).$$

Now, for $x > a$,

$$\ln(a^2 + x^2) = \ln\left(x^2\left(1 + \frac{a^2}{x^2}\right)\right)$$

$$= 2\ln x + \ln\left(1 + \frac{a^2}{x^2}\right)$$

$$= 2\ln x + \frac{a^2}{x^2} - \frac{a^4}{2x^4} + \cdots,$$

so for large x_1 and x_2,

$$f = \frac{a}{2\pi}\left(2\ln x_2 - 2\ln x_1 + \frac{a^2}{x_2^2} - \frac{a^2}{x_1^2} + \cdots\right).$$

As either $x_1 \to \infty$ or $x_2 \to \infty$, $|f(x_1, x_2)| \to \infty$. Hence $\langle x \rangle$ does not exist.

(b) Using the given integral in Equation (2.24), we see that

$$\rho_N(S) = \frac{1}{2\pi} \int_{-\infty}^{\infty} dz \, e^{iSz - Na|z|}$$

$$= \frac{1}{2\pi} \int_0^{\infty} dz \, e^{-z(Na - iS)}$$

$$\quad + \frac{1}{2\pi} \int_0^{\infty} dw \, e^{-w(Na + iS)} \quad (w = -z)$$

$$= \frac{1}{2\pi}\left(\frac{1}{Na - iS} + \frac{1}{Na + iS}\right)$$

$$= \frac{Na}{\pi((Na)^2 + S^2)}.$$

The probability, p, that $|S| \le S_1$ is given by

$$p = \frac{2aN}{\pi} \int_0^{S_1} dS \, \frac{1}{S^2 + (Na)^2}.$$

Put $S = aN \tan\phi$ to give

$$p = \frac{2}{\pi} \tan^{-1}\left(\frac{S_1}{aN}\right),$$

and if $p = \frac{1}{2}$, then $S_1 = aN$.

(c) See the Maple worksheet.

Solution 2.12

(a) Adding all the realisations $x_{k+1} = x_k + \varepsilon_{k+1}\delta t$ for $k = 0$ to $n - 1$ gives the required expression. Since $\langle \varepsilon \rangle = 0$, the mean of x_n is zero. Using Equation (2.19) gives, since the variables ε_i and ε_j are independent if $i \ne j$,

$$\langle x_n^2 \rangle = n\langle \varepsilon^2 \rangle \, \delta t = \sigma^2 t_n \quad \text{since} \quad \sigma^2 = \langle \varepsilon^2 \rangle.$$

The central limit theorem, in the form of Equation (2.23), gives by replacing σ_X with $\sigma\sqrt{\delta t}$

$$\rho(x_n) = \frac{1}{\sigma\sqrt{2\pi n \delta t}} \exp\left(-\frac{x_n^2}{2\sigma^2 n \delta t}\right).$$

But $\delta t = 1/N$ and $n/N = t_n$, hence the required result.

(b) See the Maple worksheet.

(c) The distance between the two points (t_k, x_k) and (t_{k+1}, x_{k+1}) is, using Pythagoras's theorem,

$$s_{k+1} = \sqrt{(t_{k+1} - t_k)^2 + (x_{k+1} - x_k)^2}$$
$$= \sqrt{(\delta t)^2 + \varepsilon_{k+1}^2 \delta t},$$

and the total length of the line is

$$s = \delta t \sum_{k=1}^{N} \sqrt{1 + \varepsilon_k^2/\delta t} = \frac{1}{N}\sum_{k=1}^{N} \sqrt{1 + N\varepsilon_k^2}.$$

The mean of this random number is

$$\langle s \rangle = \frac{1}{N}\sum_{k=1}^{N} \left\langle \sqrt{1 + N\varepsilon_k^2} \right\rangle = \left\langle \sqrt{1 + N\varepsilon^2} \right\rangle.$$

But ε is uniformly distributed in $[-1, 1]$, so

$$\left\langle \sqrt{1 + N\varepsilon^2} \right\rangle = \tfrac{1}{2}\int_{-1}^{1} d\varepsilon\, \sqrt{1 + N\varepsilon^2}$$
$$= \int_{0}^{1} d\varepsilon\, \sqrt{1 + N\varepsilon^2}$$
$$\simeq \sqrt{N}\int_{0}^{1} d\varepsilon\, \varepsilon = \tfrac{1}{2}\sqrt{N} \quad \text{if } N \gg 1.$$

Alternatively, evaluate the integral and expand in inverse powers of N.

Solution 2.13

(a) See the Maple worksheet.

(b) Since $\sin((n + 1/2)\pi) = (-1)^n$,

$$y(1) = \frac{2\sqrt{2}}{\pi}\sum_{k=0}^{\infty} \frac{(-1)^k z_k}{2k + 1},$$

and since $\langle z \rangle = 0$, $\langle y(1) \rangle = 0$.

Consider the finite sum

$$y_N(1) = \frac{2\sqrt{2}}{\pi}\sum_{k=0}^{N} \frac{(-1)^k z_k}{2k + 1},$$

and use Equation (2.18) to obtain

$$\langle y_N(1)^2 \rangle = \frac{8}{\pi^2}\sum_{k=0}^{N} \frac{\langle z_k^2 \rangle}{(2k + 1)^2} = \frac{8\sigma^2}{\pi^2}\sum_{k=0}^{N} \frac{1}{(2k + 1)^2}.$$

Take the limit to obtain

$$\langle y(1)^2 \rangle = \frac{8\sigma^2}{\pi^2}\sum_{k=0}^{\infty} \frac{1}{(2k + 1)^2} = \sigma^2$$

since

$$\sum_{k=0}^{\infty} \frac{1}{(2k + 1)^2} = \frac{\pi^2}{8}.$$

The last identity can be obtained by putting $t = 0$ in the Fourier series for $|t|$ (given in part (c) of the question), or by using Maple or using standard tables for series and products.

(c) Because $\langle s_k z_k \rangle = 0$ and $\langle s_k^2 z_k^2 \rangle = \sigma^2 s_k^2$, using Equation (2.14) we find that the density of $y = y(t)$ is

$$\rho(y) = \frac{1}{\sigma(t)\sqrt{2\pi}} \exp\left(-\frac{y^2}{2\sigma(t)^2}\right),$$

where

$$\sigma(t)^2 = \frac{8\sigma^2}{\pi^2}\sum_{k=0}^{\infty} \frac{\sin^2(k + 1/2)\pi t}{(2k + 1)^2}$$
$$= \frac{4\sigma^2}{\pi^2}\sum_{k=0}^{\infty}\left(\frac{1}{(2k + 1)^2} - \frac{\cos(2k + 1)\pi t}{(2k + 1)^2}\right)$$
$$= \frac{4\sigma^2}{\pi^2}\left(\frac{\pi^2}{8} - \frac{\pi^2}{4}\left(\frac{1}{2} - |t|\right)\right) = |t|\sigma^2.$$

Hence $\sigma(t) = \sigma\sqrt{t}$ if $0 \le t \le 1$, and at the times $t = n/N$, the density $\rho(y(t))$ is the same as the density $\rho(x_n)$ derived in Exercise 2.12.

Solution 2.14 – 2.18

See the Maple worksheet.

Solution 2.19

(a) The two standard deviations are given by using Equation (2.40):

$$\sigma_1^2 = \frac{1}{2}\int_{0}^{1/2} dx\, x^2 - \left(\int_{0}^{1/2} dx\, x\right)^2$$
$$= \frac{1}{3 \cdot 2^4} - \left(\frac{1}{2^3}\right)^2 = \frac{1}{192},$$

$$\sigma_2^2 = \frac{1}{2}\int_{1/2}^{1} dx\, x^2 - \left(\int_{1/2}^{1} dx\, x\right)^2$$
$$= \frac{7}{3 \cdot 2^4} - \left(\frac{3}{2^3}\right)^2 = \frac{1}{192}.$$

(b) If $N_1 = N_2 = N/2$ then $\sigma^2 = 4/(192N)$, and with 95% confidence limits the Monte Carlo estimate is

$$I = I_e^{(1)} + I_e^{(2)} \pm 2\sigma = I_e^{(1)} + I_e^{(2)} \pm \frac{1}{2\sqrt{3N}}.$$

Solution 2.20

(a) The original integral can be written in the form

$$I = \int_{0}^{1} dx\, x = \sum_{k=1}^{M}\int_{(k-1)/M}^{k/M} dx\, x.$$

For the kth interval, $J_k = \int_{(k-1)/M}^{k/M} dx\, x$, use the formula (2.40) (page 74) with $b - a = 1/M$ for the standard deviation; this gives

$$\sigma_k^2 = \frac{1}{M}\int_{(k-1)/M}^{k/M} dx\, x^2 - \left(\int_{(k-1)/M}^{k/M} dx\, x\right)^2.$$

But if

$$I_N = \int_{(k-1)/M}^{k/M} dx\, x^n$$
$$= \frac{1}{(n + 1)}\left(\left(\frac{k}{M}\right)^{n+1} - \left(\frac{k - 1}{M}\right)^{n+1}\right),$$

it follows that

$$\sigma_k^2 = \frac{1}{M}I_2 - I_1^2$$
$$= \frac{1}{3M^4}\left(3k^2 - 3k + 1\right) - \frac{(2k-1)^2}{4M^4}$$
$$= \frac{1}{12M^4}.$$

(b) On each interval we use N/M sample points, so the square of the standard deviation of the sum of the M estimates is

$$\sigma_e^2 = \sum_{k=1}^{M}\frac{1}{12M^4}\times\frac{M}{N} = \frac{1}{12M^2N}.$$

This is a generalisation of Equation (2.57). Hence a 95% confidence range for I_e is

$$I = \sum_{k=1}^{M}I_e^{(k)} \pm 2\sigma_e, \quad 2\sigma_e = \frac{1}{M\sqrt{3N}}.$$

Solution 2.21 – 2.26

See the Maple worksheet.

Solution 2.27

The mean is

$$\langle z \rangle = \int_{-\infty}^{\infty} dz\, z \int_{-\infty}^{\infty} dx\, \rho_X(x)\,\rho_Y(z-x)$$
$$= \int_{-\infty}^{\infty} dx\, \rho_X(x) \int_{-\infty}^{\infty} dz\, (z-x+x)\,\rho_Y(z-x).$$

But

$$\int_{-\infty}^{\infty} dz\, \rho_Y(z-x) = 1$$

and

$$\int_{-\infty}^{\infty} dz\, (z-x)\rho_Y(z-x) = \langle y \rangle,$$

so

$$\langle z \rangle = \int_{-\infty}^{\infty} dx\, \rho_X(x)\,(\langle y \rangle + x) = \langle y \rangle + \langle x \rangle.$$

Similarly, since $z^2 = (z-x)^2 + 2x(z-x) + x^2$ and $\langle z^2 \rangle =$

$$\int_{-\infty}^{\infty} dx\, \rho_X(x) \int_{-\infty}^{\infty} dz\, \left((z-x)^2 + 2x(z-x) + x^2\right)\rho_Y(z-x),$$

we have

$$\langle z^2 \rangle = \int_{-\infty}^{\infty} dx\, \rho_X(x)\,\left(\langle y^2 \rangle + 2x\langle y \rangle + x^2\right)$$
$$= \langle y^2 \rangle + 2\langle x \rangle\langle y \rangle + \langle x^2 \rangle,$$

and hence $\sigma_Z^2 = \sigma_X^2 + \sigma_Y^2$.

Solution 2.28

(a) Put $w = x_3 + z$, where $z = x_1 + x_2$ has the density given in Equation (2.10) (page 62). Equation (2.8) then gives

$$\rho_W(w) = \int_{-\infty}^{\infty} dz\, \rho_Z(z)\,\rho(w-z)$$
$$= \mu^3 \int_0^w dz\, ze^{-\mu z}e^{-\mu(w-z)} = \tfrac{1}{2}\mu^3 w^2 e^{-\mu w}.$$

(b) Results already obtained show that the formula is valid for $n = 1, 2, 3$. Assume it to be true for n. Let $z = x_1 + x_2 + \cdots + x_n$ and $w = z + x_{n+1}$, so the density of w is

$$\rho_{n+1}(w) = \int_{-\infty}^{\infty} dz\, \rho(w-z)\,\rho_n(z)$$
$$= \frac{1}{(n-1)!}\mu^{n+1}e^{-\mu w}\int_0^w dz\, z^{n-1}$$
$$= \frac{1}{n!}\mu^{n+1}w^n e^{-\mu w}, \quad w \geq 0,$$

with $\rho_{n+1}(w) = 0$ for $w < 0$, which proves the result.

(c) For $w \geq 0$,

$$\frac{d\rho_n}{dw} = \frac{\mu^n}{(n-1)!}w^{n-2}e^{-\mu w}(n - 1 - \mu w)$$

so ρ_n has a single stationary point at $w = (n-1)/\mu$. Since $\rho_n(0) = 0$ and $\rho_n(w) \to 0$ as $w \to \infty$, it follows that the stationary point is a maximum.

(d) For the exponential distribution $\langle x \rangle = 1/\mu$ and $\sigma = 1/\mu$ (see Exercise 1.47), so Equation (2.23) gives

$$\rho_n(w) = \frac{\mu}{\sqrt{2\pi n}}\exp\left(-\frac{\mu^2(w-n/\mu)^2}{2n}\right), \quad n \gg 1,$$

which gives the required result.

See the Maple worksheet for the remainder of the solution.

Solution 2.29

We have

$$\int_{-\infty}^{\infty} dx\, \rho(x)e^{-ixz} = \int_{-\infty}^{\infty} dx\, \rho(x)\,(\cos xz - i\sin xz)$$
$$= 2\int_0^{\infty} dx\, \rho(x)\cos xz$$
$$= f(z),$$

since $\rho(-x) = \rho(x)$. The function $f(z)$ is also even, because $\cos xz$ is even in z, and hence on using the same method as above,

$$\rho_N(S) = \frac{1}{2\pi}\int_{-\infty}^{\infty} dz\, e^{iSz}f(z)^N$$
$$= \frac{1}{\pi}\int_0^{\infty} dz\, f(z)^N \cos Sz.$$

Solution 2.30

(a) Since $\rho(x)$ is an even function, as in the previous exercise,

$$\int_{-\infty}^{\infty} dx\, \rho(x)\,e^{-ixz} = 2\int_0^{\infty} dx\, \rho(x)\cos xz$$
$$= \frac{1}{b-a}\int_a^b dx\, \cos xz$$
$$= \frac{\sin zb - \sin za}{(b-a)z}.$$

Then the quoted result follows on using the result from the previous exercise because $(\sin z)/z$ is an even function.

(b) The density is even and hence $\langle x \rangle = 0$, and

$$\langle x^2 \rangle = 2 \int_a^b dx \, x^2 \rho(x) = \frac{b^3 - a^3}{3(b-a)} = \tfrac{1}{3}(b^2 + ab + a^2).$$

Then since $\sigma = \sqrt{\langle x^2 \rangle}$, the central limit theorem, Equation (2.23), gives

$$\rho_N(S) \simeq \frac{1}{\sqrt{2 \langle x^2 \rangle \, \pi N}} \exp \left(-\frac{S^2}{2N \langle x^2 \rangle} \right),$$

which is the result quoted.

(c) and **(d)** See the Maple worksheet.

Solution 2.31

(a) Equation (2.40) gives

$$\sigma^2 = 2 \int_0^2 dx \, e^{2x} - J^2 = e^4 - 1 - J^2,$$

and since $e^2 = J + 1$, we obtain $\sigma^2 = 2J$.

(b) See the Maple worksheet.

Solution 2.32

See the Maple worksheet.

Solution 2.33

(a) See the Maple worksheet.

(b) Using the first result found in Exercise 2.10, Equation (2.24) becomes

$$\rho_N(S) \simeq \frac{1}{2\pi} \int_{-\infty}^{\infty} dz \, e^{iSz} \exp \left(-\tfrac{1}{6} N a^2 z^2 \right)$$

$$= \frac{1}{a} \sqrt{\frac{3}{2\pi N}} \exp \left(-\frac{3S^2}{2Na^2} \right),$$

where we have used the given integral with $A = S$ and $B = Na^2/6$.

UNIT 3 Simulations: standard map and disease spreading

Study guide

In this unit, we develop Maple programs to investigate properties of the standard map and models that describe the spreading of infectious diseases. The unit contains some background information and motivation for the equations, but you are not expected to derive such equations on your own, and should concentrate on the methods and their implementation in Maple.

The first section connects to material you met earlier in the course. The models and corresponding Maple programs in the second section are built up gradually, starting from simple situations and adding additional features or new parameters as the models become more complex. Part of the development is done in the form of exercises, which form an integral part of the text. You should attempt all the exercises in the text, at first without consulting the solutions, to gain practice in programming in Maple.

You may find that your solutions look different from the sample solutions. This is not surprising because there are many different ways to program in Maple. The given solutions aim to provide simple programs, not necessarily the most elegant or efficient ones. In addition, for those solutions which depend on generating random numbers, you may obtain slightly different numerical results from those given in the text.

The final exercise introduces random matrices. This is meant to provide you with more practice in Maple programming, using an example that has not been discussed in much detail before. If you feel confident using Maple, you can also try to develop your own approach to any of the exercises. Playing around with different ways to address the same problem, and consulting the Maple help facility if required, is a good way to gain more experience with Maple.

Introduction

In this unit, we are going to use Maple to explore properties of particular dynamical systems. The first section concerns the standard map, which was introduced in *Unit B3*. In this short section, we show that in the chaotic regime, the behaviour of this dynamical system can be approximated by a random walk.

The second, more substantial, section considers models of infectious diseases. We start with a simple model describing a single outbreak of a disease, and proceed to more complex models that yield semi-realistic models of recurrent epidemics. The models are based on rate equations, which describe the changes in populations of susceptible, infected and immune (recovered) individuals. We solve the corresponding systems of differential equations with Maple, and discuss general properties using the theory developed in *Unit B1*. We then introduce a different approach, where the spreading of a disease is considered as a random process, and an individual is infected with a probability that depends on the number of infected individuals in the population. While for large populations both approaches show the same behaviour, similar to what was shown for a population growth model in *Unit 1* of this block, stochastic effects are important for small populations.

3.1   Stochastic behaviour in the standard map

The **standard map** was introduced in *Unit B3* as the map describing the motion of a periodically kicked rotor. More generally, it serves as a good approximation to periodically driven nonlinear systems, and has been studied in much detail.

The standard map is given by

$$\begin{pmatrix} x_n \\ y_n \end{pmatrix} \longmapsto \begin{pmatrix} x_{n+1} \\ y_{n+1} \end{pmatrix} = \begin{pmatrix} (x_n + y_n + K \sin x_n) \bmod 2\pi \\ y_n + K \sin x_n \end{pmatrix}, \tag{3.1}$$

where K is the only parameter. Phase portraits of the map were considered in *Unit B3*, and it was demonstrated that for $K > K_c \simeq 0.97$ the magnitude of the angular momentum variable y can become arbitrarily large, and for $K \gg 1$ the phase portraits show no regular features.

When K is large, the changes in x_n are large, and as a consequence $x_n \bmod 2\pi$ varies in the interval $[0, 2\pi)$ approximately according to a uniform random distribution. This means that the equation for y can be approximated by a random walk, introduced in *Unit 2*, with increments $K \sin x_n$ in the interval $[-K, K]$. As shown in Subsection 2.2.1 of *Unit 2*, this approximation implies that the mean $\langle (y_n - y_0)^2 \rangle$ grows linearly with n, with a coefficient

$$\langle (K \sin x)^2 \rangle = \frac{1}{2\pi} \int_0^{2\pi} K^2 \sin^2 x \, dx = \frac{K^2}{2}.$$

To test the predicted relation $\langle (y_n - y_0)^2 \rangle \simeq K^2 n/2$, we are going to perform a calculation of a sample average. This is done by following a finite number of orbits of the dynamical system. We choose a number of randomly located values $x_0 \in [0, 2\pi)$, and start iterating with $y_0 = 0$, calculate the values of $(y_n - y_0)^2 = y_n^2$ along each orbit, and finally average over the trajectories at each iteration. In the following example, we provide a procedure that performs this calculation.

Example 3.1

Write a Maple procedure `smdiff` that computes the sample average of $(y_n - y_0)^2$ for a number of randomly chosen start positions $(x_0, 0)$ up to a given n, taken over a specified number of orbits.

Solution

The following procedure has three arguments: the parameter K, the number of orbits `norb`, and the length of each orbit `lorb`.

```
>   smdiff := proc(K,norb,lorb)                              #1
>     local i,j,xi,dy,xc,yc;                                 #2
>     uses Statistics;                                       #3
>     xi := Sample(Uniform(0,2*Pi),norb);     # Values of x0 #4
>     dy := Array(1..lorb):                                  #5
>     for j to norb do                   # Loop over orbits  #6
>       xc := xi[j];                                         #7
>       yc := 0;                                             #8
>       for i to lorb do               # Calculate an orbit  #9
>         yc := yc+K*sin(xc);                               #10
>         xc := xc+yc;                                      #11
>         dy[i] := dy[i]+yc^2;                              #12
>       end do:                                             #13
>     end do:                                               #14
>     [[0,0],seq([i,dy[i]/norb],i=1..lorb)];               #15
>   end proc:                                               #16
```

On line **#3** in this procedure, the `uses` command tells Maple which modules or packages the procedure uses, here the `Statistics` package. The advantage of doing this is that you do not need to worry whether or not you loaded the `Statistics` package during the Maple session – Maple will automatically load the necessary definitions within the procedure.

Using the `Sample` command, the x-coordinates of the start points are drawn randomly from a uniform distribution on the interval $[0, 2\pi]$ and collated in a vector `xi` (line **#4**). The initial y-coordinates are 0 (line **#8**). This means that we need to compute the average over y_n^2. To do this, we add up the values of y_n^2 over the orbits, separately for each n, in an `Array` called `dy` (line **#12**). At the end, each element of the `Array` `dy` is divided by the number of orbits `norb` to obtain the sample average (line **#15**). The data are returned as a list in a form that is suitable for plotting.

There are two loops in the procedure. The inner loop (on `i`) calculates the orbit of one start point (lines **#7** and **#8**); in each step the standard map is applied to the current point with coordinates `xc` and `yc` (lines **#10** and **#11**), and the corresponding value of y_n^2 is added to the appropriate element in the array `dy` (line **#12**). Note that because we are only interested in the evolution of the y variable, and x only enters via the function $\sin x$, we do not need to calculate $x \bmod 2\pi$. The outer loop runs over the different start points in `xi`, corresponding to the different realisations of the orbit. ♦

Exercise 3.1

(a) Use the procedure `smdiff` to calculate the sample average for $K = 5$, for an orbit length of up to 10. Compare the results obtained for averaging over 100 and 1000 orbits.

(b) Plot the result of the same calculation for $K = 5$, now for orbits of length up to 50, averaged over 1000 orbits.

The plot obtained in Exercise 3.1 shows the expected linear behaviour. To quantify this observation, we fit the data with a linear function and calculate the slope in the following example.

Example 3.2

Write a Maple procedure `smfitplot` which calls `smdiff` to calculate the sample average, performs a least squares fit of the data to a linear function, and produces a plot of the data and the fit function. Use this to plot the result of a simulation for $K = 5$ for orbits of length up to 50, averaged over 1000 orbits.

Solution

To fit data we use the Maple `Fit` command, which requires the `Statistics` package. The following procedure performs this task, and the comments indicate what each line does.

```
>   smfitplot := proc(K,norb,lorb)
>     local data,xd,yd,i,fitfun,fp,dp;
>     uses plots,Statistics;
>     data := smdiff(K,norb,lorb);      # Calc. (n,<yn-y0>) data
>     xd := <seq(data[i,1],i=1..lorb+1)>;              # n data
>     yd := <seq(data[i,2],i=1..lorb+1)>;         # <yn-y0> data
>     fitfun := Fit(a+b*n,xd,yd,n);          # Fit data to a+b*n
>     print(evalf[6](fitfun));    # Print fitting function a+b*n
>     fp := plot(fitfun(n),n=0..lorb);
>     dp := plot(data,style=point,colour=black,symbol=circle);
>     display(dp,fp);            # Plot fitting function and data
>   end proc:
```

Here, we use the output data of our procedure `smdiff`, and collect the coordinates of data points in two vectors `xd` and `yd`. The function obtained from the `Fit` command is printed, and a plot of the data with the fit function superimposed is returned.

The fit and the corresponding plot are obtained from

```
>   smfitplot(5,1000,50);
```
$$6.00461 + 11.5597\,n$$

The plot is shown in Figure 3.1. The average slope in this case was 11.6, which is close to the expected value $K^2/2 = 12.5$.

Note that repeating the calculation will always lead to slightly different results for the slope (unless you restart Maple) because the procedure `smdiff` uses random initial values for the x-coordinate. Also, the intercept on the y-axis (constant a) can differ quite significantly between calculations. ◆

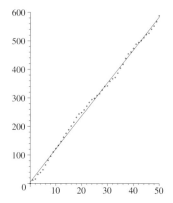

Figure 3.1 Sample average $\langle (y_n - y_0)^2 \rangle$ for $n \leq 50$ and linear fit obtained in Example 3.2

In the following exercise, we collect data for various values of K, and compare the result with the predicted value $K^2/2$ of the slope.

(a) By removing the plot commands, simplify procedure `smfitplot` to a procedure `smfit` returning just the measured slope.

(b) Use this procedure `smfit` to accumulate data for the slope for $5 \leq K \leq 30$, in steps of 0.25, using 100 orbits with lengths up to 50. Plot the ratio of the measured slope to the predicted value $K^2/2$ as a function of K.

(c) Plot these ratios together with the function $1 - 2J_2(K)$, where J_2 denotes a Bessel function of the first kind. In Maple, the function $J_2(K)$ is obtained with the command `BesselJ(2,K)`.

As shown by the example of the standard map, the behaviour of a deterministic dynamical system in the chaotic regime can be described by statistical methods; in this sense the system behaves as if it were stochastic. This is an example of a very powerful approach to understanding complex dynamical systems. In Exercise 3.37 at the end of this unit, we consider the effect of adding randomness to the dynamical system, by introducing random variations of the parameter K.

3.2   Dynamics of infectious diseases

Historic accounts tell of disastrous epidemics of infectious diseases in human populations, such as the bubonic plague (black death) which caused an estimated 25 million deaths (out of a population of about 100 million) in 14th-century Europe. While today some major diseases of the past, such as smallpox, have been completely or virtually eradicated, some threats persist, such as that of a major influenza epidemic. Also, new infectious diseases such as AIDS (acquired immune deficiency syndrome), new variant CJD (Creutzfeldt–Jakob disease) and SARS (severe acute respiratory syndrome) have emerged in recent decades. Infectious diseases affect not only humans, but also animals. For instance, farm stock may suffer from infectious diseases, such as foot-and-mouth disease, with potentially large economic impact on the food industry, and the survival of endangered species in wild animal populations may be threatened by epidemics. Animal diseases such as avian influenza ('bird flu') and BSE (bovine spongiform encephalopathy or 'mad cow disease', which has been linked to a variant of CJD) also pose potential risks for humans, so it is important to understand and predict their dynamics.

There are, therefore, plenty of reasons to study the dynamics of infectious diseases, both in humans and in animals. This is not only important for the understanding of the dynamics of an epidemic, but more crucially it is required for any efficient control of a disease by measures such as vaccination, provided that these are available.

Given the devastating impact of epidemics in history, it is not surprising that the first attempts at a quantitative understanding of the dynamics of epidemics date back to the 18th century. The Swiss mathematician Daniel Bernoulli estimated the effectiveness of variolation against smallpox using mathematical methods. There has been ongoing research activity since the early 20th century, increasingly employing probabilistic rather than deterministic models in recent decades.

There exist many different infectious diseases, which are caused by different micro-organisms such as viruses, bacteria and parasites. Clearly, different models will be appropriate for different diseases, depending on the method of transmission and on other properties of the disease, and numerous examples can be found in the scientific literature. In this section, we are going to consider simple models that concentrate on general properties. For more details see R.M. Anderson and R.M. May (1991) *Infectious diseases of humans*, Oxford University Press.

Variolation is a method of purposefully infecting a person with smallpox (variola) in a controlled manner so as to minimise the severity of the infection and also to induce immunity against further infection.

For a recent appreciation of Bernoulli's results, see K. Dietz and J.A.P. Heesterbeek (2000) 'Bernoulli was ahead of modern epidemiology', *Nature*, **408**, pp. 513–514.

3.2.1   A simple model of an epidemic outbreak

We consider a population consisting of N individuals, and for simplicity assume for now that N is constant. We wish to describe the dynamics of an **epidemic** that is started by a few infected individuals in a completely susceptible population, which means that no individuals have acquired **immunity** against the disease. To keep matters simple, we only distinguish between individuals who are **susceptible** (those who have not been infected in the past), **infected** (those who currently carry the disease and are able to pass it on) and **recovered** (those who have recovered from the disease and are immune to further infection). We denote the number of susceptible individuals at time t by $X(t)$, the number of infected individuals by $Y(t)$, and the number of individuals who have recovered from the disease by $Z(t)$. Since the total number of individuals is fixed, these variables have to satisfy the constraint

By an epidemic, we mean an outbreak of a disease affecting a considerable part of the total population.

$$X(t) + Y(t) + Z(t) = N. \tag{3.2}$$

Implicitly, we have already made a number of simplifying assumptions. In particular, we assume that all individuals eventually recover, so no deaths result from the disease. We also neglect any additional stages, such as incubation and latent periods where individuals are infected but do not yet show symptoms of the disease, or are not yet infectious to other individuals. Furthermore, we assume that recovered individuals have acquired perfect immunity and cannot be re-infected.

We considered a simple population model in *Unit 1*. There it was shown how a deterministic approximation in terms of a rate equation is related to a stochastic description that considers births as random events occurring with a given probability. Here, we shall follow a similar approach – we first discuss a deterministic approach based on rate equations for infection and recovery of individuals, and then simulate a stochastic process where infections occur randomly.

Rate equations

We start with a simple model with two possible events: a susceptible individual can become infected through contact with a currently infected individual, and an infected individual can recover from the disease. We consider a **mixed population** where spatial distribution is not taken into account, so at any time each susceptible individual is equally likely to get infected. The presence of infected individuals gives rise to a **force of infection** that is proportional to the number of infected individuals $Y(t)$. Denoting the proportionality constant by β, the force of infection is $\lambda(t) = \beta Y(t)$. As there are $X(t)$ susceptible individuals, the rate of infections in the population is then $\lambda(t) X(t) = \beta X(t) Y(t)$.

Infections decrease the number of susceptible individuals. As we did in Subsection 1.4.1 of *Unit 1* for the population growth model, we consider the populations to be continuous variables and express the changes in the population in terms of differential equations. The change in the susceptible population X is then given by

$$\dot{X} = -\beta XY. \tag{3.3}$$

Here and in what follows we frequently drop the explicit dependence on the time variable t to simplify the notation.

Individuals who have been infected are added to Y, so we have a term βXY for the change $\dot{Y}$ in the number of infected individuals. However, there is also a second contribution, since infected individuals can recover from the disease, by which we mean that an individual ceases to be infectious. We assume that this happens at a constant **recovery rate** ν, so the total change in infected individuals becomes

$$\dot{Y} = \beta XY - \nu Y. \tag{3.4}$$

The inverse $1/\nu$ is the **recovery time**, which is the time it takes an infected individual to recover from the disease.

Finally, the recovered individuals contribute to the change in Z, so we obtain a third equation,

$$\dot{Z} = \nu Y. \tag{3.5}$$

In summary, we have a dynamical system of differential equations for X, Y and Z, which is nonlinear due to the presence of the term βXY. Its solutions describe the dynamics of the epidemic, which depend on the values of the two positive parameters β and ν. Like the birth and death rates in the population growth model of *Unit 1*, these have units of $(\text{Time})^{-1}$.

Exercise 3.3

Using Equations (3.3)–(3.5), show that the total change is $\dot{X} + \dot{Y} + \dot{Z} = 0$, so the differential equations are compatible with the condition that $N = X(t) + Y(t) + Z(t)$ is constant.

The dynamics of an epidemic

Before we study the dynamical system in more detail, we are going to write a Maple procedure to solve the model for given parameter values. This serves to show us that solutions of the model qualitatively describe what we expect, and will also be of use for later comparison with the stochastic process.

Example 3.3

(a) Write a Maple procedure `dsmodel1` that numerically solves the set of ordinary differential equations (3.3)–(3.5) for given parameters β and ν and initial conditions $X(0)$, $Y(0)$ and $Z(0)$ at time $t = 0$.

(b) We measure time in years, and use a recovery rate $\nu = 12$, which corresponds to a recovery time $1/\nu = 1/12$, i.e. one month. For a parameter $\beta = 10^{-3}$, and initial number of infected individuals $Y(0) = 10$ in a completely susceptible population of $N = 10^5$, plot the solution over the period of one year.

Solution

(a) From Equation (3.2) for $t = 0$, we have $X(0) + Y(0) + Z(0) = N$, so we only need to specify three out of these four numbers in the procedure.

A procedure using `dsolve` to solve the initial-value problem for the three differential equations is

```
>   dsmodel1 := proc(beta,nu,X0,Y0,Z0)
>      local dseqs;
>      global X,Y,Z,t;
>      unassign('X','Y','Z','t');
>      dseqs := {diff(X(t),t)+beta*X(t)*Y(t)=0,
                 diff(Y(t),t)-(beta*X(t)-nu)*Y(t)=0,
                 diff(Z(t),t)-nu*Y(t)=0,
                 X(0)=X0, Y(0)=Y0, Z(0)=Z0};
>      dsolve(dseqs,{X(t),Y(t),Z(t)},numeric);
>   end proc:
```

The `global` command allows variables to be accessed outside a procedure (cf. `local`). It is used here because we want to use X, Y and Z outside the procedure. To ensure that any previous use of these variables does not have unwanted effects, we use an `unassign` statement to clear any predefined values.

(b) There are various ways of plotting numerical solutions of differential equations obtained by `dsolve`. Here, we use `odeplot` which was introduced in Subsection 4.6.1 of *Unit A4*, and requires the `plots` package. The following Maple code produces a plot of the graphs of the three functions $X(t)$, $Y(t)$ and $Z(t)$ for $0 \le t \le 1$, with initial values $X(0) = 10^5 - 10$, $Y(0) = 10$, $Z(0) = 0$.

For other methods see Subsection 2.6.3 of *Unit A2*.

```
>   with(plots):
>   dssol := dsmodel1(1e-3,12,10^5-10,10,0):
>   odeplot(dssol,[[t,X(t),colour=black],
             [t,Y(t),colour=red],[t,Z(t),colour=black]],
             0..1,numpoints=200);
```

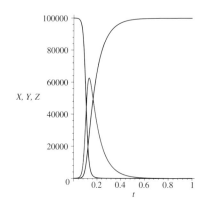

The plot is shown in Figure 3.2. Note that we have used the plot option `numpoints=200`. This option tells Maple to calculate the function at a given number of points in preparing the plot.

We observe that as time increases, almost all susceptible individuals become infected and eventually recover. ◆

Figure 3.2 Plot of susceptible (black, decreasing), infected (red) and recovered (black, increasing) populations obtained in Example 3.3(b)

In Example 3.3, all three differential equations are solved simultaneously. However, the constraint in Equation (3.2) means that only two of the three equations are independent. Solving Equations (3.3) and (3.4) for $X(t)$ and $Y(t)$, we can obtain $Z(t)$ from $Z(t) = N - X(t) - Y(t)$. So, in effect, we are dealing with a two-dimensional dynamical system only. You are asked to modify the procedure `dsmodel1` accordingly in the following exercise.

Exercise 3.4

(a) Write a Maple procedure `dsmodel2` that solves Equations (3.3) and (3.4), and for given β, ν, N, $X(0)$ and $Y(0)$ returns a plot of the functions X, Y and $Z = N - X - Y$, with the plot range and the number of plot points specified as additional variables `plran` and `np`, respectively.

(b) Produce plots for the same parameter values and initial conditions as in Example 3.3.

The basic reproductive rate R_0

We are going to rewrite the dynamical system (3.3)–(3.5) in a standard form by introducing rescaled variables

$$x(t) = \frac{X(t)}{N}, \quad y(t) = \frac{Y(t)}{N}, \quad z(t) = \frac{Z(t)}{N}. \tag{3.6}$$

The new variables x, y and z denote the proportions (or fractions) of the population that are susceptible, infected and recovered, respectively. They can take values in the interval $[0, 1]$, and Equation (3.2) becomes

$$x(t) + y(t) + z(t) = 1. \tag{3.7}$$

Differential equations for x, y and z are obtained by dividing Equations (3.3)–(3.5) by N. This gives

$$\dot{x} = \frac{\dot{X}}{N} = -\frac{\beta XY}{N} = -\beta N xy,$$

$$\dot{y} = \frac{\dot{Y}}{N} = \frac{\beta XY - \nu Y}{N} = \beta N xy - \nu y,$$

$$\dot{z} = \frac{\dot{Z}}{N} = \frac{\nu Y}{N} = \nu y.$$

Any solution starting out with admissible values, i.e. satisfying $x, y, z \in [0, 1]$ and $x + y + z = 1$, will always stay in that region of phase space, because $\dot{x} = 0$ if $x = 0$ and $\dot{y} = 0$ if $y = 0$, so if at any time either x or y vanishes, they will remain at zero thereafter, and hence cannot become negative. This means that x always decreases and thus cannot exceed its initial value. If $y = 1$ then $x = 0$ and the equation for y becomes $\dot{y} = -\nu y$, so y decreases exponentially and hence can never exceed 1 either.

Noting that the parameter β and the population size N always occur as the product βN, we introduce a new dimensionless parameter R_0 defined as

$$R_0 = \frac{\beta N}{\nu}. \tag{3.8}$$

Substituting for βN with $R_0 \nu$ then gives the system of differential equations in the form that we would like to use in what follows, namely

$$\dot{x} = -\nu R_0 xy, \tag{3.9}$$

$$\dot{y} = \nu(R_0 x - 1)y, \tag{3.10}$$

$$\dot{z} = \nu y. \tag{3.11}$$

What is the meaning of the new parameter R_0? It turns out that this number is a characteristic quantity for the dynamics of the disease, called the **basic reproductive rate**. It was introduced by George MacDonald in 1952 in connection with models of the spread of malaria. The basic reproductive rate R_0 corresponds to the number of infections arising from a single infected individual, during the time they remain infectious, in a

G. MacDonald (1952) 'The analysis of equilibrium in malaria', *Tropical Diseases Bulletin*, **49**, pp. 813–829.

fully susceptible population of size N. The numerator βN is the force of infection by a single infected individual in a population of N susceptible individuals. This is multiplied by the recovery time $1/\nu$ to obtain R_0. The value of R_0 determines whether and how fast a disease spreads in a population. This will become clearer when we consider some examples and properties of the solutions obtained below.

Exercise 3.5

(a) Calculate the value of R_0 for the parameter values in Example 3.3.

(b) Change the population size N to 10^3, 10^4 and 2×10^4. Calculate the corresponding values of R_0. Use the procedure dsmodel2 to investigate the solutions for X, Y and Z for these cases. What do you observe?

Exercise 3.6

(a) Write a Maple procedure dsmodel3 that solves Equations (3.9) and (3.10) for $x(t)$ and $y(t)$, and plots the solutions for $x(t)$, $y(t)$ and $z(t)$, given the parameters R_0 and ν, and the initial conditions $x(0) = 1 - y_0$, $y(0) = y_0$, $z(0) = 0$, which we specify by a single parameter for y_0, the initial fraction of infected individuals.

(b) Plot the solutions for parameter values that correspond to those used in Exercise 3.5, and check by inspection that the solutions for $x(t)$ and $y(t)$ are consistent with the respective solutions for $X(t)$ and $Y(t)$ obtained in Example 3.3 and Exercise 3.5.

As seen in Exercises 3.5 and 3.6, the value of R_0 has a crucial influence on the dynamics. For $R_0 < 1$, the disease affects only a small proportion of the susceptible population, so no epidemic occurs. For sufficiently large R_0, however, the disease spreads through the population, spreading more quickly and affecting a larger part of the population as R_0 increases.

To understand this behaviour, consider Equation (3.10) for $y(t)$, the proportion of infected individuals. If, for any t, we have $R_0\, x(t) - 1 > 0$, the derivative $\dot{y}(t) > 0$ and the solution grows, while it decreases if $R_0\, x(t) - 1 < 0$. So the condition for an epidemic is that initially this term is positive, hence $R_0\, x(0) - 1 > 0$, or $R_0 > 1/x(0)$. Since we are interested in the situation where only a small number of infected individuals enter a fully susceptible population, we have $x(0) \simeq 1$, and the condition becomes $R_0 > 1$, in accordance with the observations in Exercise 3.5.

For an epidemic outbreak, initially $R_0\, x(0) > 1$. Individuals become infected, which means that x decreases while y increases. At some time $t_{\max}$, there are so few susceptible individuals left that $R_0\, x(t_{\max}) = 1$, and $\dot{y}(t_{\max}) = 0$. At this point, the fraction of infected individuals is maximal, and starts decreasing as $R_0\, x(t) < 1$ for $t > t_{\max}$, approaching an equilibrium where $\lim_{t \to \infty} y(t) = 0$.

Vaccination acts by reducing the number of susceptible individuals. In Equation (3.8), N is the size of the (fully susceptible) population, which in a vaccinated population has to be replaced by the number of non-vaccinated individuals (assuming all vaccinated individuals are protected). Thus the effective value of R_0 is reduced compared to its value in a fully susceptible population of the same size. The following exercise calculates the fraction of the population that needs to be vaccinated to prevent an infectious disease from spreading.

Exercise 3.7

(a) What is the minimum fraction of the population that you should vaccinate against a disease with $R_0 > 1$ (for the unprotected population) to prevent it from spreading?

(b) The data for measles epidemics in England in the 1950s put the value of R_0 at about 15. What fraction of the population needs to be vaccinated to prevent measles epidemics in England?

Maximum fraction of infected individuals

From the preceding remarks, it follows that during an epidemic outbreak (so initially $R_0 > 1/x(0)$) there exists a particular time instant $t_{max} > 0$ when a maximum number of individuals are infected. This maximum occurs when the right-hand side of Equation (3.10) changes sign. Initially, it is positive, so $\dot{y} > 0$ and $y(t)$ increases, while $x(t)$ decreases. This changes at $t = t_{max}$ defined by $R_0 x(t_{max}) - 1 = 0$, so for $t > t_{max}$ we have $\dot{y} < 0$ and hence $y(t)$ decreases. We are now going to calculate the maximum fraction of infected individuals $y_{max} = y(t_{max})$.

To do this, we derive a differential equation for $y(x)$, which is implicitly defined by the system of differential equations for $x(t)$ and $y(t)$. The derivative of this function is given by

$$y'(x) = \frac{dy}{dx} = \frac{dy}{dt}\frac{dt}{dx} = \frac{dy}{dt}\left(\frac{dx}{dt}\right)^{-1} = \frac{\dot{y}}{\dot{x}}.$$

It makes sense to define a single function $y(x)$ since $x(t)$ is monotonically decreasing, because in the case of interest the right-hand side of Equation (3.9) is negative.

Using Equations (3.9) and (3.10), we express the derivatives $\dot{x}(t)$ and $\dot{y}(t)$ in terms of x and y, which yields

$$\frac{dy}{dx} = \frac{\nu(R_0 x - 1)y}{-\nu R_0 xy} = -\frac{R_0 x - 1}{R_0 x} = \frac{1}{R_0 x} - 1.$$

We thus obtain the differential equation

$$y'(x) = \frac{1}{R_0 x} - 1, \tag{3.12}$$

which can be solved by integration.

Note that $y'(x) = 0$ for $x = 1/R_0$, and since $y'(x) = \dot{y}/\dot{x}$ this implies that $\dot{y}(t) = 0$ for $t = t_{max}$ with $x(t_{max}) = 1/R_0$. This proves that the heuristic argument given above gave the correct result.

Example 3.4

(a) Solve the differential equation (3.12) for $y(x)$, and determine $y_{max} = y(t_{max})$ from the condition $x(t_{max}) = 1/R_0$ for an epidemic starting at time $t = 0$ from a number of infected individuals in a fully susceptible population, so $z(0) = 0$.

(b) Derive an approximate result for the case where the epidemic is started by a small number of infected individuals, so $y(0)$ is very small.

Solution

(a) Integrating both sides of Equation (3.12) gives

$$\int dy = \int \left(\frac{1}{R_0 x} - 1\right) dx,$$

hence

$$y = \frac{\ln(x)}{R_0} - x + C,$$

where C is a constant. Remembering that both x and y are functions of time t, we can calculate C from the initial values by inserting $t = 0$ in the equation above, which yields $C = x(0) + y(0) - \ln(x(0))/R_0$. Inserting this value of C in the solution, we find

$$y(t) = x(0) + y(0) - x(t) + \frac{\ln(x(t))}{R_0} - \frac{\ln(x(0))}{R_0}$$

$$= x(0) + y(0) - x(t) - \frac{1}{R_0} \ln\left(\frac{x(0)}{x(t)}\right).$$

Equation (3.7) and the initial condition $z(0) = 0$ imply that $x(0) + y(0) = 1$, so we obtain the solution

$$y(t) = 1 - x(t) - \frac{1}{R_0} \ln\left(\frac{x(0)}{x(t)}\right), \tag{3.13}$$

which gives us the desired relation between $x(t)$ and $y(t)$.

Now we calculate $y_{\max}$ as

$$y_{\max} = y(t_{\max}) = 1 - x(t_{\max}) - \frac{1}{R_0} \ln\left(\frac{x(0)}{x(t_{\max})}\right).$$

With $x(t_{\max}) = 1/R_0$ this yields

$$y_{\max} = 1 - \frac{1 + \ln(R_0 \, x(0))}{R_0}, \quad R_0 > \frac{1}{x(0)}. \tag{3.14}$$

(b) If we start with a small number of infected individuals, $y(0) \simeq 0$ and $x(0) \simeq 1$, so

$$y_{\max} \simeq 1 - \frac{1 + \ln(R_0)}{R_0}, \quad R_0 > 1, \tag{3.15}$$

within this approximation.   ◆

We compare this result with our numerical solutions in the following exercise.

Exercise 3.8

Calculate $y_{\max}$ for the cases with $R_0 > 1/x(0)$ which were considered in Exercise 3.6, and compare with the plots of $y(t)$ obtained in that exercise.

Exercise 3.9

(a) Calculate the limiting values of $y_{\max}$ for $R_0 \to 1/x(0)$ and, separately, for $R_0 \to \infty$.

(b) Use the Maple `limit` command (use `?limit` to find out how it works) to check your result.

(c) Use Maple to plot $y_{\max}$ as a function of R_0, for $x(0) \simeq 1$.

Exercise 3.10

From the discussion of the meaning of R_0, what value of $y_{\max}$ would you expect for $R_0 < 1/x(0)$? Why does our calculation in Example 3.4 give a wrong result for this case?

As Exercise 3.10 shows, we have to be rather careful to interpret the solution of Equation (3.13) correctly. It is instructive to look at the graph of the function $y(x)$, which we shall do in the following example.

Example 3.5

Plot the solution y of Equation (3.13) as a function of x, for $R_0 = 4$ and $x(0) = 0.99$.

Solution

The following Maple code produces such a plot.

```
>  x0 := 0.99:   R0 := 4.0:
>  plot(1-x-ln(x0/x)/R0,x=0.01..x0,labels=[x,y]);
```

The resulting plot is shown in Figure 3.3.   ◆

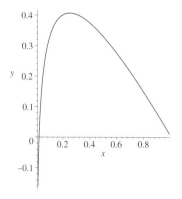

Figure 3.3   Plot of $y(x)$ obtained in Example 3.5

The example shows that, for the given values of the parameters, $y(x)$ becomes negative for small values of x, which is not permitted for our model. So what does this solution mean? The answer is as follows. We start off at $x(0) = 0.99$, $y(0) = 1 - 0.99 = 0.01$. Then, with increasing time t, x decreases, and y increases, until $x = 1/R_0 = 0.25$ where $y = y_{\max} = 1 - (1 + \ln(3.96))/4 \simeq 0.406$. For larger t, y decreases, and tends to zero as $t \to \infty$; the left part of the graph where y becomes negative is therefore never reached, and only the part of the solution $y(x)$ where $y \geq 0$ is of interest to us. The point x_f where y vanishes is then the value that $x(t)$ approaches for large t, so x_f is a fixed point of the system. This means that the interesting part of the solution is the function y for $x \in [x_f, x(0)]$.

For $R_0 \leq 1/x(0)$, the function $y(t)$ decreases for all t, and $y_{\max} = y(0)$. There is no epidemic in this case as the disease disappears, and only a small number of individuals are infected before this happens. So the interval $[x_f, x(0)]$ becomes rather small, but $x_f < x(0)$ as long as $y(0) > 0$ and $R_0 > 0$. In the following exercise, we consider an example of this case.

Exercise 3.11

Plot the solution y of Equation (3.13) as a function of x, for $R_0 = 0.9$ and $x(0) = 0.99$. Adjust the plot range such that you can see the part of the curve where $y > 0$. From the graph, what is the approximate value of x_f?

We now take a closer look at the behaviour of the model for large times.

Fixed points and asymptotic behaviour

After the initial epidemic outbreak, the system approaches a **fixed point**, corresponding to a solution with $\dot{x}(t) = \dot{y}(t) = \dot{z}(t) = 0$. This amounts to an equilibrium solution with constant fractions x_f, y_f and z_f of susceptible, infected and recovered individuals, respectively.

From Equation (3.11), we deduce (assuming $\nu \neq 0$) that $y_f = 0$, and this suffices to ensure that $\dot{x}(t) = \dot{y}(t) = 0$ by Equations (3.9) and (3.10). So any values of x_f and z_f, subject to the constraint $x_f + z_f = 1$ that follows from Equation (3.7), correspond to a fixed point of the dynamical system.

Which fixed point the system approaches for large time t depends on the parameters and on the initial conditions. For the case $z(0) = 0$, we can use the relation between $y(t)$ and $x(t)$ derived in Example 3.4. Inserting the fixed point solution $x(t) = x_f$, $y(t) = y_f = 0$ into Equation (3.13), we obtain

$$0 = 1 - x_f - \frac{1}{R_0} \ln \left(\frac{x(0)}{x_f} \right) = 0, \tag{3.16}$$

which, for given values of R_0 and $x(0)$, determines x_f, and then $z_f = 1 - x_f$. Equation (3.16) can be solved numerically for the value of x_f.

Exercise 3.12

Using the Maple command `solve`, calculate x_f for $x(0) = 1 - y(0) = 0.99$, for $R_0 = 4$ and $R_0 = 0.9$.

Exercise 3.13

(a) Based on the Maple procedure `dsmodel3` of Exercise 3.6, write a procedure `dsmodel4` which, in addition to solving Equations (3.9)–(3.10), computes the value of y_{max} and the asymptotic values for $x(t)$ and $z(t)$. Again, you can assume that $z(0) = 0$, so it suffices to specify a single initial condition, the fraction $y(0)$ of infected individuals.

(b) Test your procedure on a few choices of parameters, and compare the results with those of earlier examples and exercises.

To compare this with the general theory for two-dimensional dynamical systems as presented in Subsection 1.4.2 of *Unit B1*, we set $\dot{x} = f(x, y)$ with $f(x, y) = -\nu R_0 xy$, and $\dot{y} = g(x, y)$ with $g(x, y) = \nu(R_0 x - 1)y$. This gives the Jacobian at the fixed point $(x_f, y_f) = (x_f, 0)$ as

$$\mathbf{J}(x_f, y_f) = \begin{pmatrix} f_x(x_f, y_f) & f_y(x_f, y_f) \\ g_x(x_f, y_f) & g_y(x_f, y_f) \end{pmatrix} = \nu \begin{pmatrix} 0 & -R_0 x_f \\ 0 & R_0 x_f - 1 \end{pmatrix}$$

which is *singular*, so the classification of Subsection 1.4.2 of *Unit B1* does not apply. This property is linked to the existence of fixed points for any value of $x_f \in [0, 1]$.

3.2.2 Repeated epidemics in regenerating populations

So far, we have modelled a single epidemic outbreak, after which the disease disappears, because the fraction of susceptible individuals becomes too small to sustain an epidemic. In reality, diseases usually recur, and one reason for this is that a population regenerates, via the birth of new individuals who are susceptible to the disease.

The simplest way to model a regenerating population is by assuming constant **birth** and **death** (mortality) rates, as in the population growth model discussed in *Unit 1*. Choosing both rates equal will keep the total population constant; if the rates are not the same, we model epidemics in a growing or declining population. Here, we assume that births and deaths occur at a constant rate μ, and that all newborn individuals are susceptible to the disease. The model we consider here describes a behaviour that was observed, for instance, in measles epidemics in various countries before widespread immunisation programmes were introduced.

We disregard the possibility of a temporary immunity due to maternal antibodies, i.e. antibodies that are passed from mother to child, which protect a child from infection for a time; it is possible to include this in a more generalised model. We also disregard the possibility that the disease is lethal or that it weakens the population, i.e. it affects μ.

Rate equations

Our original Equations (3.3)–(3.5) are modified by this addition as follows:

$$\dot{X} = \mu N - \beta XY - \mu X, \tag{3.17}$$
$$\dot{Y} = \beta XY - \nu Y - \mu Y, \tag{3.18}$$
$$\dot{Z} = \nu Y - \mu Z. \tag{3.19}$$

Here, the term $\mu N = \mu(X + Y + Z)$ corresponds to the births in the susceptible population X, and the terms $-\mu X$, $-\mu Y$ and $-\mu Z$ represent the deaths which are assumed to occur with the same rate in all three populations. Note that for $\mu = 0$, we recover the original Equations (3.3)–(3.5).

Exercise 3.14

Verify that Equations (3.17)–(3.19) preserve the total population $X + Y + Z$.

Introducing again the normalised variables $x(t) = X(t)/N$, $y(t) = Y(t)/N$ and $z(t) = Z(t)/N$, Equations (3.17)–(3.19) become

$$\dot{x} = \mu(1 - x) - \beta N xy, \tag{3.20}$$
$$\dot{y} = (\beta N x - (\nu + \mu))y, \tag{3.21}$$
$$\dot{z} = \nu y - \mu z. \tag{3.22}$$

We can write Equation (3.21) in the form of Equation (3.10) if we introduce the basic reproductive rate R_0, but now defined as

$$R_0 = \frac{\beta N}{\nu + \mu}, \tag{3.23}$$

which reduces to Equation (3.8) for $\mu = 0$. The differential equations become

$$\dot{x} = \mu(1 - x) - (\nu + \mu)R_0 xy, \tag{3.24}$$
$$\dot{y} = (\nu + \mu)(R_0 x - 1)y, \tag{3.25}$$
$$\dot{z} = \nu y - \mu z, \tag{3.26}$$

which is the set of equations we are going to consider now.

Numerical problems with solution of rate equations

If you compare Equations (3.24)–(3.26) with their counterparts (3.9)–(3.11), the only changes are due to the presence of the parameter μ. Again, we need $R_0 x(0) > 1$ to start off with an epidemic initially; however, there is now a growth term $\mu(1 - x)$ in Equation (3.24), which means that the fraction of susceptible individuals can grow as a result of births, and thus epidemics may possibly recur. We shall investigate this behaviour in the following example.

Example 3.6

(a) Based on the Maple procedure `dsmodel3` of Exercise 3.6, write a procedure `dsmodel5` which solves Equations (3.24)–(3.26), assuming $z(0) = 0$.

(b) Plot the solution for $R_0 = 25/3$, $\nu = 12$, $\mu = 1/70$ (corresponding to a life expectancy of 70 years) and $y(0) = 10^{-4}$, over periods of 1 and 100 years. What do you observe?

(c) Plot the solution for the same parameters ν, μ and initial condition $y(0)$, but for $R_0 = 4$. Explain what happens.

(d) Write an improved Maple procedure `dsmodel6` to address the problem identified in part (c).

Solution

(a) Starting from the procedure `dsmodel3`, we add an additional parameter μ which enters the differential equations. This gives

```
>    dsmodel5 := proc(R0,nu,mu,y0,plran,np)
>        local dseqs,dssol,x,y,t;
>        uses plots;
>        dseqs := {diff(x(t),t)-mu*(1-x(t))
                     +R0*(nu+mu)*x(t)*y(t)=0,
                  diff(y(t),t)-(nu+mu)*(R0*x(t)-1)*y(t)=0,
                  x(0)=1-y0, y(0)=y0};
>        dssol := dsolve(dseqs,{x(t),y(t)},numeric);
>        odeplot(dssol,[[t,x(t),colour=black],
                     [t,y(t),colour=red],
                     [t,1-x(t)-y(t),colour=black]],
                 plran,numpoints=np);
>    end proc:
```

(b) The plots are obtained by

```
>    dsmodel5(25/3,12,1/70,1e-4,0..1,1000);
>    dsmodel5(25/3,12,1/70,1e-4,0..100,1000);
```

The resulting plots are shown in Figures 3.4 and 3.5. As expected from our previous investigation of the system with $\mu = 0$, there is an initial epidemic, which involves nearly the entire population by $t \simeq 0.4$ years, due to the large value of R_0 (see Figure 3.4). However, after that epidemic has ceased, the number of susceptible individuals slowly recovers due to births, over a number of years, until a second epidemic is triggered, which happens when $x(t)$ becomes large enough again, such that $R_0 \, x(t) > 1$ (at $t \simeq 15$ in Figure 3.5).

This then repeats, but the amplitude of the curve decreases, which means that the epidemics become less pronounced, until the system once more settles into an equilibrium state where $x(t) \to x_f$ and $z(t) \to z_f$ approach constant values, and $y(t) \to 0$, as $t \to \infty$.

(c) Using the same command as above with $R_0 = 4$ produces the warning message shown below and the plot shown in Figure 3.6.

```
>    dsmodel5(4,12,1/70,1e-4,0..100,1000);
```

```
Warning, cannot evaluate the solution further right of 28.381888,
probably a singularity
```

Obviously, something went wrong here – the solution starts off as expected, but where we might expect a second epidemic to occur, the solution shoots off in the 'wrong' direction, and obviously is not correct because y becomes negative. So what is at fault here – is it the model or an artifact of Maple? In fact, it is a problem of numerical accuracy, caused by the very small value of $y(t)$ between epidemics. The problem is that y may, by numerical error, become negative, and if this happens at a place where the factor $R_0 \, x(t) - 1$ becomes positive, $y(t)$ takes off in the negative rather than positive direction. We thus expect that this problem becomes worse the lower $y(t)$ drops between epidemics, that is, the longer the time between two successive

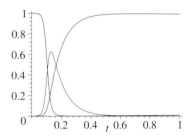

Figure 3.4

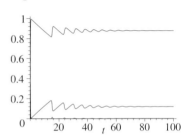

Figure 3.5   Plot of the populations $x(t)$, $y(t)$ (red) and $z(t)$ of Example 3.6(b). The initial epidemic is hardly visible due to the large time interval – choosing a short time interval will show it clearly. Note that you may obtain a different plot from that shown here. This is due to a problem in the procedure which will be explained in a moment.

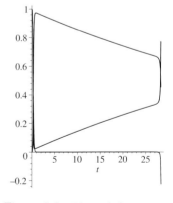

Figure 3.6   Plot of the solution obtained by `dsmodel5` for $x(t)$, $y(t)$ (red) and $z(t)$ in Example 3.6(c)

epidemics. This time is governed by the birth rate μ – the larger μ is, the quicker the population regenerates.

(d) We can cure the problem by sufficiently increasing the accuracy goal of the calculation, which can be done by adding an optional argument `abserr=eps` in the `dsolve` command, which specifies the absolute error that we wish to achieve to be at most `eps`. However, setting a very small error margin may increase the computation time considerably.

Use the Maple help facility to investigate the various options of the `dsolve` command.

An improved procedure `dsmodel6` differs from `dsmodel5` only by including `eps` on lines #1 and #2.

```
>   dsmodel6 := proc(R0,nu,mu,y0,eps,plran,np)          #1
>      local dseqs,dssol,x,y,t;
>      uses plots;
>      dseqs := {diff(x(t),t)-mu*(1-x(t))
                    +R0*(nu+mu)*x(t)*y(t)=0,
                  diff(y(t),t)-(nu+mu)*(R0*x(t)-1)*y(t)=0,
                  x(0)=1-y0,  y(0)=y0};
>      dssol := dsolve(dseqs,{x(t),y(t)},
                    numeric,abserr=eps);                 #2
>      odeplot(dssol,[[t,x(t),colour=black],
                     [t,y(t),colour=red],
                     [t,1-x(t)-y(t),colour=black]],
                plran,numpoints=np);
>   end proc:                                            ◆
```

How small does `eps` have to be? Before addressing this question, we ask you to experiment in the following exercise.

Exercise 3.15

Experiment with the procedure call

```
>   dsmodel6(4,12,1/70,10^(-4),eps,0..200,1000)
```

for various values of the parameter `eps`, and try to recover the oscillating solution.

As Exercise 3.15 shows, we were lucky to obtain the correct result in our first calculation for $R_0 = 25/3$. In fact, you need to calculate the solution very precisely, as will become apparent from the following exercise.

Exercise 3.16

(a) Write a Maple procedure `dsmodel7` which plots $\log_{10}(|y(t)|)$.

(b) Starting from $n = 1$, produce plots for error limits eps $= 10^{-10n}$, for parameter values $R_0 = 4$, $\nu = 12$, $\mu = 1/70$ and initial condition $y(0) = 10^{-4}$, until it becomes evident that the solution is correct.

(c) Use the required accuracy in the procedure `dsmodel6` to verify that the oscillating behaviour persists.

(d) Looking at the values of $y(t)$ between epidemics, do you think that the model can account for recurrent epidemics in finite populations?

This exercise shows that there is a problem with an unacceptably low fraction of infected individuals between epidemics, which would mean that in any finite population the disease would be eradicated after the first outbreak. In such situations, where small numbers of individuals are involved, rate equations do not really apply as they require a suitably large population limit. We shall return to this point later, but first consider properties of our present model.

Equilibrium populations and frequency of epidemics

The fixed points x_f, y_f and z_f are obtained by setting $\dot{x} = \dot{y} = \dot{z} = 0$ in Equations (3.24)–(3.26). This yields

$$0 = \mu(1 - x_f) - (\nu + \mu)R_0\, x_f\, y_f,$$
$$0 = (\nu + \mu)(R_0\, x_f - 1)\, y_f,$$
$$0 = \nu\, y_f - \mu\, z_f.$$

We ask you to solve this system of equations in the following exercise.

Exercise 3.17

Use Maple to show that there are two fixed points,

$$x_f = 1, \quad y_f = z_f = 0, \tag{3.27}$$

and

$$x_f = \frac{1}{R_0}, \quad y_f = \frac{\mu(R_0 - 1)}{R_0(\nu + \mu)}, \quad z_f = \frac{\nu(R_0 - 1)}{R_0(\nu + \mu)}. \tag{3.28}$$

Verify the result by performing the calculation by hand.

The first fixed point corresponds to the scenario where the disease disappears from the population, which is what we expect to happen if $R_0 < 1$: eventually all recovered individuals die out and the population becomes completely susceptible. The second fixed point is more interesting, and we expect this to govern the large-time behaviour for $R_0 > 1$. The value $x_f = 1/R_0$ lies exactly at the boundary of the onset of an epidemic. What happens is that if you start at this value, the number of infected individuals stays constant over time, and the disease has become **endemic** in the population. The non-susceptible population $1 - x_f = 1 - 1/R_0$ is distributed on y_f and z_f according to the ratio of the constants ν and μ. A larger recovery rate ν leads to a higher z_f, while a larger death rate μ results in a larger value of y_f. Usually μ is much smaller than ν, so y_f will be much smaller than z_f in the equilibrium population, which means that only a small fraction of the population is affected by the disease at a given time.

In epidemiology, an infectious disease is said to be endemic in a population when it is maintained without the need for external inputs.

In contrast to the $\mu = 0$ case, there are now isolated fixed points determined by the parameters ν, μ and R_0. We can therefore apply the methods of *Unit B1* to classify the fixed points. For this, we again consider the two-dimensional dynamical system $\dot{x} = f(x, y)$ and $\dot{y} = g(x, y)$, with f and g the functions given in Equations (3.24) and (3.25).

For the fixed point $(x_f, y_f) = (1, 0)$ of Equations (3.27), we find

$$f_x(x_f, y_f) = -\mu - (\nu + \mu)R_0\, y_f = -\mu,$$
$$f_y(x_f, y_f) = -(\nu + \mu)R_0\, x_f = -(\nu + \mu)R_0,$$
$$g_x(x_f, y_f) = (\nu + \mu)R_0\, y_f = 0,$$
$$g_y(x_f, y_f) = (\nu + \mu)(R_0\, x_f - 1) = (\nu + \mu)(R_0 - 1),$$

so the corresponding Jacobian is

$$\mathbf{J}(x_f, y_f) = \begin{pmatrix} -\mu & -(\nu + \mu)R_0 \\ 0 & (\nu + \mu)(R_0 - 1) \end{pmatrix}. \tag{3.29}$$

This is a triangular matrix, so the eigenvalues are the diagonal elements, $\lambda_1 = -\mu$ and $\lambda_2 = (\nu + \mu)(R_0 - 1)$. So for $R_0 < 1$, this fixed point is a **stable node**, while for $R_0 > 1$ it becomes a **saddle point**. For $\mu = 0$ or $R_0 = 1$ the matrix is *singular*, and the classification of *Unit B1* does not apply.

Example 3.7

(a) For the fixed point of Equations (3.28), calculate the Jacobian $\mathbf{J}(x_f, y_f)$ and its eigenvalues.

(b) For parameter values $R_0 = 25/3$, $\nu = 12$ and $\mu = 1/70$ (per year), compute the populations at the fixed point (to three decimal places), and determine the nature of the fixed point.

(c) Near the fixed point, what is the frequency of the epidemics, and hence the time between two epidemics?

Solution

(a) For the fixed point of Equations (3.28), the derivatives are

$$\begin{aligned} f_x(x_f, y_f) &= -\mu - (\nu + \mu)R_0\, y_f = -\mu - \mu(R_0 - 1) = -\mu R_0, \\ f_y(x_f, y_f) &= -(\nu + \mu)R_0\, x_f = -(\nu + \mu), \\ g_x(x_f, y_f) &= (\nu + \mu)R_0\, y_f = \mu(R_0 - 1), \\ g_y(x_f, y_f) &= (\nu + \mu)(R_0\, x_f - 1) = 0, \end{aligned}$$

so the corresponding Jacobian is

$$\mathbf{J}(x_f, y_f) = \begin{pmatrix} -\mu R_0 & -(\nu + \mu) \\ \mu(R_0 - 1) & 0 \end{pmatrix}, \tag{3.30}$$

which is nonsingular for $\mu \neq 0$. Using Equation (1.33) of *Unit B1*, we calculate the eigenvalues as

$$\begin{aligned} \lambda_{1,2} &= \tfrac{1}{2}\,\mathrm{tr}\,\mathbf{J} \pm \tfrac{1}{2}\sqrt{(\mathrm{tr}\,\mathbf{J})^2 - 4\det\mathbf{J}} \\ &= \frac{-\mu R_0 \pm \sqrt{\mu^2 R_0^2 - 4\mu(\nu + \mu)(R_0 - 1)}}{2}. \end{aligned} \tag{3.31}$$

(b) Inserting the parameter values into Equations (3.28) gives

$$x_f = \tfrac{3}{25} = 0.120, \quad y_f \simeq 0.001, \quad z_f \simeq 0.879$$

for the fixed point populations. The eigenvalues are

$$\lambda_{1,2} \simeq -0.060 \pm 1.120i,$$

so the fixed point is a stable spiral.

(c) Near the fixed point the motion is oscillatory, with angular frequency $\omega \simeq 1.120$ (per year). The frequency is thus $f = \omega/(2\pi) \simeq 0.178$ per year.

The time T between two epidemics is the period of the oscillation, so $T = 1/f \simeq 5.608$. So, asymptotically, epidemics occur every 5.6 years, but since we have a stable spiral, the amplitude of the oscillations decreases, and the system approaches the fixed point populations of part (b). This looks roughly in agreement with Figure 3.5. ◆

Equation (3.31) shows that the nature of the fixed point depends on the parameter values, because the term under the square root can be positive or negative (or zero). In most cases, the parameter ν is much larger than μ or μR_0; consequently the term under the square root is negative and the eigenvalues are complex. Because their real part, $-\mu R_0/2$, is always negative, this leads to a stable spiral as in Example 3.7.

Exercise 3.18

If the parameters satisfy $\nu \gg \mu$, what, approximately, are the fixed point populations x_f, y_f and z_f in the stable fixed point for $R_0 > 1$?

Exercise 3.19

(a) For parameter values $R_0 = 4$, $\nu = 12$ and $\mu = 1/70$ (per year), compute the fixed point populations (to three significant figures) and the time between two epidemics near the fixed point.

(b) Use the procedure `dsmodel7` to plot $\log_{10}(|y(t)|)$ for sufficiently large t, estimate the period of the decaying oscillations, and compare with the result obtained in part (a).

3.2.3 Infections by external contacts

Earlier we identified a serious problem with our model, namely that the fraction of infected individuals becomes so small between epidemics that in a finite population the disease will be eradicated after one epidemic. Rate equations cease to be applicable if we consider small populations; once the number of infected individuals becomes small, we need to model the spreading of the disease as a random process, which allows for the disease to be eradicated. This will be done in Subsection 3.2.4 below.

However, this will not change the fact that, with the given parameters, the disease is most likely to disappear after the first outbreak, which is not what has been observed, for instance in measles epidemics. How could we explain this? A possible answer is as follows. So far, we have only considered one isolated population, but for a realistic simulation you might, for example, study the dynamics of measles epidemics in the United Kingdom, taking into account contacts and exchanges of individuals with neighbouring countries. With widespread long-haul air traffic this has become even more important. One example was the spreading of SARS in 2002/3, a viral disease that originated in China and was spread as far as Canada by travellers before it was successfully contained.

We can include infections arising from external contacts in our model, in the simplest case by infecting susceptible individuals at a constant rate $\kappa \geq 0$, representing an assumed constant threat of infection by contacts with the external world. To this end, we add a term $\kappa X(t)$ to the equation for $\dot{Y}(t)$, representing the externally infected individuals, and subtract the same number from $\dot{X}(t)$ to keep the total population constant.

In the equations for the rescaled variables, this produces terms $\mp \kappa x(t)$ in Equations (3.24) and (3.25). Including these terms, Equations (3.24)–(3.26) become

$$\dot{x} = \mu(1 - x) - \kappa x - (\nu + \mu)R_0 xy, \qquad (3.32)$$

$$\dot{y} = \kappa x + (\nu + \mu)(R_0 x - 1)y, \qquad (3.33)$$

$$\dot{z} = \nu y - \mu z. \qquad (3.34)$$

These equations are the subject of the following exercises.

Exercise 3.20

(a) Modify procedure `dsmodel6` to obtain a procedure `dsmodel8` that solves Equations (3.32)–(3.34).

(b) Use procedure `dsmodel8` to produce graphs of the solutions for parameter values $R_0 = 4$, $\nu = 12$, $\mu = 1/70$, $y(0) = 10^{-4}$, and `eps` $= 10^{-50}$ for $\kappa = 0$, $\kappa = 10^{-16}$, $\kappa = 10^{-8}$, $\kappa = 10^{-4}$ and $\kappa = 10^{-2}$. What do you observe?

(c) Create a sequence of plots for $\kappa = 10^{-20}, 10^{-19}, 10^{-18}, \ldots, 10^{-1}$, and produce an animation using the `insequence=true` option of the `display` command.

Depending on your computer specification, this calculation may take a while. If you find that it takes too long, try to use a smaller range of values, or plot every second graph.

Exercise 3.21

To check whether the inclusion of external contacts resolves the problem of a too low fraction of infected individuals, modify the procedure `dsmodel7` accordingly, and use the new procedure `dsmodel9` to plot $\log_{10}(|y(t)|)$ for the parameter values used in part (b) of the previous exercise.

As seen in the above exercises, the effect of the additional term κx is that the oscillations are damped. With increasing κ, the periods between epidemics decrease, and their amplitude decreases (so that the minimum values of $|y|$ are increased), until for large κ the populations tend to an equilibrium state.

3.2.4 Stochastic modelling of epidemics

In Subsection 1.4.3 of *Unit 1*, the connection between a stochastic model of population growth and the deterministic rate equations was discussed, and it was shown that rate equations describe the average behaviour (where the average is over many realisations of the stochastic process) in a large population limit.

So far, we have used rate equations to model disease dynamics. At the level of a single individual, however, it is natural to consider disease spreading as a stochastic process, with a given probability that an infected individual will infect one or more susceptible individuals. In this section, we will consider such models, and we will use Maple to simulate their behaviour. As in the population growth model of *Unit 1*, the models discussed here can be shown to give rise to the rate equations discussed above for the average behaviour in large populations, but we shall not prove this result.

Before discussing the simulation, we briefly remind you about the Maple `Statistics` package.

The Maple Statistics package

In this subsection we will make use of the Maple `Statistics` package, which was introduced in *Unit 1*. Recall that this package provides random numbers with various distributions. For example, the command `RandomVariable(Uniform(0,1))` defines a random variable which is uniformly distributed over the interval $[0, 1]$, while `RandomVariable(Exponential(1/lambda))` defines a random variable with an exponential distribution with rate λ, i.e. with probability distribution function

$$\rho(t) = \lambda\, e^{-\lambda t}, \quad t \geq 0. \tag{3.35}$$

In the following example, we draw a set of random numbers from the exponential distribution, using the `Sample` command (which can be used with the distribution as its argument – the commands `Sample(RandomVariable(Exponential(1/lambda)))` and `Sample(Exponential(1/lambda))` give the same result), and show that their distribution is indeed exponential.

The uniform and exponential distributions were introduced in Unit 1.

It is customary to use the verb 'to draw' when referring to a sample of random numbers.

Example 3.8

For an exponential distribution with rate $\lambda = 1$, draw $100\,000$ random numbers, plot their distribution with the `Histogram` command of the `Statistics` package, and compare this with the distribution function $\rho(t) = \exp(-t)$.

Solution

We load the `Statistics` and `plots` packages, draw random numbers and plot the histogram against the distribution function $\rho(t) = \exp(-t)$:

```
>   with(Statistics):  with(plots):
>   data := Sample(Exponential(1),100000):
>   display(plot(exp(-t),t=0..8,colour=black),
            Histogram(data,binwidth=0.2,colour=red));
```

The resulting plot is shown in Figure 3.7. The `binwidth` option determines the bin width, i.e. the width of each histogram bar or column. It has been adjusted to show that the distribution of the $100\,000$ random numbers agrees with $\rho(t)$. ◆

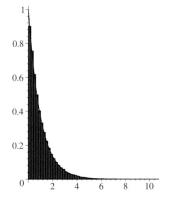

Figure 3.7 Histogram of exponentially distributed random numbers obtained in Example 3.8

A histogram representation of data displays columns with heights corresponding to the number of data points that lie within certain intervals (bins). You can experiment by adjusting the `binwidth` parameter and observe how the histogram changes.

We are now ready to discuss the stochastic modelling of epidemics. As with the rate equation approach, we start with the simulation of a simple model without births and deaths.

Stochastic model of an epidemic outbreak

As above, we consider a total population of N individuals, and denote the number of susceptible, infected and recovered individuals by X, Y and Z, respectively, so $N = X + Y + Z$. Since we do not consider births or deaths at the moment, we assume that N is constant.

We consider two processes that occur randomly. An individual can become infected, which means he moves from the susceptible population X to the infected population Y. Hence an infection event corresponds to a process

Infection: $\begin{cases} X \to X - 1 \\ Y \to Y + 1 \end{cases}$

which does not change the total population N. The second process is that an individual recovers from the disease, and is no longer infectious to other individuals. This means that the individual moves from the population Y to the population Z of recovered individuals. A recovery event corresponds to the process

$$\text{Recovery:} \quad \begin{cases} Y \to Y - 1 \\ Z \to Z + 1 \end{cases}$$

which, again, keeps the total population constant.

For the population growth model of *Unit 1*, we used a fixed time interval and modelled the process as a Bernoulli trial. Here, we are going to consider time as a continuous variable, with the infection and recovery events occurring at random times $\{\tau_0, \tau_1, \tau_2, \ldots\}$ and with given probabilities, as shown schematically in Figure 3.8.

Figure 3.8

When the number of events is large, such a process in which events occur randomly in continuous time is called a **Poisson process**, named after the French mathematician Siméon-Denis Poisson (1781–1840).

However, rather than considering the values of τ_i, we will consider the time interval between two successive events $t_i = \tau_{i+1} - \tau_i$, also called the **waiting time**. It can be shown that if the τ_i are uniformly randomly distributed, then the waiting time $t_i = \tau_{i+1} - \tau_i$ is distributed according to the exponential distribution. This is demonstrated in the following example.

An example of a Poisson process is the emission of particles from a radioactive source with a given half-life, which is caused by atoms decaying randomly and independently of each other.

Example 3.9

(a) If you select M (with M large) random times $\tau_1, \tau_2, \ldots, \tau_M$ from the uniform distribution on the unit interval $0 \le \tau_i \le 1$, and consider the differences between adjacent times (i.e. the waiting times), argue that the average or mean waiting time is approximately $1/M$.

(b) Draw $M = 10\,000$ uniformly distributed random times in the interval $[0, 1]$ and order them using `sort`. Compute the list of waiting times and use `Histogram` to plot their distribution, and compare with the density function $M \exp(-Mt)$.

Type `?sort` to see how this command works.

Solution

(a) The $M - 1$ waiting times have to add up to 1 (apart from small boundary effects). The times τ_i are uniformly distributed, so will on average fill the unit interval uniformly. This means that the average waiting time is $1/(M - 1) \simeq 1/M$.

(b) The following Maple code performs the required task:

```
>  with(Statistics):  with(plots):  M := 10000:
>  tim := sort(Sample(Uniform(0,1),M)):
>  waittim := [seq((tim[k+1]-tim[k]),k=1..M-1)]:
>  display(plot(M*exp(-M*t),t=0..5/M,colour=black),
           Histogram(waittim,binwidth=1/(5*M),
                     colour=red));
```

The resulting plot is shown in Figure 3.9. ◆

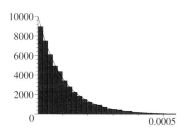

Figure 3.9

The exponential distribution

Example 3.9 demonstrates that for a Poisson process, when the number of events M becomes large, the waiting time, i.e. the time interval between two successive events, is distributed according to the exponential distribution. This means that the waiting time is a continuous random variable t with density given by Equation (3.35), with $\lambda = M$, i.e.

$$\lambda = (\text{average waiting time})^{-1}.$$

So λ has units of inverse time, and corresponds to a rate. The larger the value of λ, the closer one expects events to occur. The next example derives this result using probability arguments.

Example 3.10

Calculate the mean of the exponential distribution $\rho(t)$ of Equation (3.35).

Solution

The mean is obtained by an integration by parts,

$$\langle t \rangle = \int_0^\infty t\,\rho(t)\,dt = \int_0^\infty t\,\lambda\,e^{-\lambda t}\,dt$$

$$= \left[(t)(-e^{-\lambda t}) \right]_0^\infty - \int_0^\infty (1)(-e^{-\lambda t})\,dt$$

$$= \int_0^\infty e^{-\lambda t}\,dt = \frac{1}{\lambda}.$$

So, as expected, the mean time between two successive events is the inverse rate λ^{-1}. ♦

Exercise 3.22

Consider the exponential distribution $\rho(t)$ of Equation (3.35).

(a) Show that $\rho(t)$ is normalised such that $\int_0^\infty \rho(t)\,dt = 1$.

(b) Calculate the probability that no event has occurred within time T.

Minimum waiting time distribution

For the simple model outlined above we have *two* processes, infection and recovery, that will occur randomly with, in general, different rates (Figure 3.10).

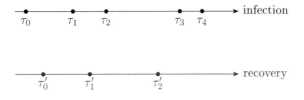

Figure 3.10   Schematic depiction of infections (black) and recoveries (red) occurring at different rates

Suppose that in a given time we have M_{inf} infection and M_{rec} recovery events. Then the waiting times of these two processes will be exponentially distributed with two rates $M_{\text{inf}} = \lambda_{\text{inf}}$ and $M_{\text{rec}} = \lambda_{\text{rec}}$. (If we include birth and death processes, more exponentially distributed processes are added.)

Now suppose that we combine these processes (as depicted in Figure 3.11) and ask, what is the waiting time distribution of the combined process, and with what probabilities do infections and recoveries occur in the new distribution?

Figure 3.11

We expect the times of the combined events to be uniformly distributed with an average waiting time $1/(M_{\text{inf}} + M_{\text{rec}})$. Hence the waiting times of the combined process will be exponentially distributed, with rate $\lambda = M_{\text{inf}} + M_{\text{rec}} = \lambda_{\text{inf}} + \lambda_{\text{rec}}$, and for each event there will be a probability of $M_{\text{inf}}/(M_{\text{inf}} + M_{\text{rec}}) = \lambda_{\text{inf}}/\lambda$ that it will be an infection, and a probability of $M_{\text{rec}}/(M_{\text{inf}} + M_{\text{rec}}) = \lambda_{\text{rec}}/\lambda$ that it will be a recovery.

A derivation of this result using probability arguments, valid for any number of processes, is obtained by considering the **minimum waiting time** distribution, which is the distribution of waiting times between any of the events from the various exponentially distributed processes.

An example of minimum waiting time would be the distribution of time intervals between signals in a Geiger counter caused by radioactive decay of a mixture of two radioactive substances with different half-lives.

Minimum waiting time result

Consider n random processes with exponential distributions $\rho_i(t)$ with rates λ_i, for $i = 1, 2, \ldots, n$. Then the distribution of the minimum waiting time from these processes is again an exponential distribution, with rate $\lambda = \lambda_1 + \lambda_2 + \cdots + \lambda_n$, and the probability that a particular event arises from the process with rate λ_i is λ_i/λ, $i = 1, 2, \ldots, n$.

To see why the distribution of minimum waiting times is again exponential, consider an example of two processes with exponential distributions $\rho_1(t)$ and $\rho_2(t)$, with respective rates λ_1 and λ_2. The probabilities that, within time T, no event has occurred from each process are $\exp(-\lambda_1 T)$ and $\exp(-\lambda_2 T)$, respectively; compare Exercise 3.22(b). So the probability that no event has occurred at all is given by the product $\exp(-\lambda_1 T)\exp(-\lambda_2 T) = \exp(-\lambda T)$ with $\lambda = \lambda_1 + \lambda_2$. This corresponds to an exponential distribution with rate λ. The argument can be generalised to more than two processes. The proof of the second part of the above statement requires conditional probabilities, which are outside the scope of this course. Instead, we consider a couple of examples in Example 3.11 and Exercise 3.23 below.

Example 3.11

(a) Draw 100 000 random numbers from two exponential distributions with rates $\lambda_1 = \lambda_2 = 1$, and compare the distribution of the minimum waiting time of these data with an exponential distribution with rate $\lambda = 2$.

(b) Calculate the frequencies of events from each process, and compare with the expected frequencies.

Solution

(a) This can be done as follows:

```
>  with(Statistics):  with(plots):
>  d1 := Sample(Exponential(1),100000):
>  d2 := Sample(Exponential(1),100000):
>  d12 := [seq(min(d1[i],d2[i]),i=1..100000)]:
>  display(plot(2*exp(-2*t),t=0..5,colour=black),
           Histogram(d12,binwidth=0.1,colour=red));
```

The resulting plot is shown in Figure 3.12.

(b) We use two counters, n1 and n2, to count the number of times that the random variable in the first set is smaller than the corresponding variable in the second set, and vice versa:

```
>  n1 := 0:  n2 := 0:
>  for i to 100000 do
>    if d1[i]<d2[i] then
>      n1 := n1+1;
>    else
>      n2 := n2+1;
>    end if;
>  end do:
>  evalf[6]([n1,n2]/100000);
```

$$[0.501650, 0.498350]$$

The actual result will depend on the sample. However, it should also be very close to 0.5 in both cases, which is the expected outcome since the events occur at equal rates. ♦

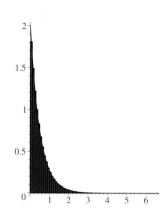

Figure 3.12 Histogram obtained in Example 3.11(a), verifying that the minimum waiting time of two exponentially distributed data sets is again exponentially distributed

---

Exercise 3.23

(a) Draw 100 000 random numbers from three exponential distributions with rates $\lambda_1 = 1$, $\lambda_2 = 2$ and $\lambda_3 = 3$, and compare the distribution of the minimum waiting time of these data with an exponential distribution with rate $\lambda = \lambda_1 + \lambda_2 + \lambda_3$.

(b) Calculate the frequencies of events from each of the three processes, and compare with the expected frequencies λ_i/λ.

The rates of infection and recovery

Figure 3.11 depicts the essence of the stochastic model for infection and recovery. At each time step, we choose either an infection $(X \to X - 1,\ Y \to Y + 1)$, or a recovery $(Y \to Y - 1,\ Z \to Z + 1)$ with probabilities $\lambda_{\text{inf}}/(\lambda_{\text{inf}} + \lambda_{\text{rec}})$ and $\lambda_{\text{rec}}/(\lambda_{\text{inf}} + \lambda_{\text{rec}})$, respectively. The question now arises as to what values to use for the rates of infection and recovery λ_{inf} and λ_{rec}.

As argued in Subsection 3.2.1, the rate of infection should be proportional to the populations X and Y, whereas the rate of recovery should be simply proportional to Y. So

$$\lambda_{\text{inf}} = \beta XY, \quad \lambda_{\text{rec}} = \nu Y.$$

Note that we use the same name for the proportionality constants as in the deterministic rate equations. This is no coincidence, because if we use the

126

same values for the constants in both cases, then, just as in the population growth model of *Unit 1*, the stochastic model can be shown to give rise to the rate equations for average behaviour in large populations. We shall not prove this result here, but instead examine the behaviour of some specific models to demonstrate the relationship, later in this section.

Since the populations X and Y may change at any time step τ_i, clearly we need to calculate new rates with each time step. We do not, however, need to calculate new exponential distributions, since all exponential distributions are simply related. In fact, if we draw random numbers from an exponential distribution with rate 1, these will have mean 1, so multiplying the numbers by λ^{-1} will produce a set of random numbers with mean λ^{-1}, i.e. exponentially distributed with rate λ.

In Exercise 3.24, we demonstrate that this rescaling of random data will indeed produce random numbers distributed according to the exponential distribution with rate λ.

Exercise 3.24

Draw $100\,000$ random numbers distributed according to the exponential distribution with rate $\lambda = 1$. By plotting a histogram and the corresponding distribution functions $\rho(t)$, show that the data scaled by factors $1/2$ and 10 are exponentially distributed with rates 2 and $1/10$, respectively.

Remember to adjust the `plotrange` and the `binwidth` appropriately.

We now have all the tools required in order to simulate the stochastic model, and we end this subsection with a prescription of how we move from time τ_i to time τ_{i+1} in the model.

At time τ_i, we assume that we know $X(\tau_i)$, $Y(\tau_i)$, $Z(\tau_i)$, as well as β and ν.
1.   Calculate the total rate $\lambda = \lambda_{\mathrm{inf}} + \lambda_{\mathrm{rec}} = \beta XY + \nu Y$.
2.   Calculate the waiting time to the next event $\Delta\tau$, by drawing a random number from an exponential distribution with rate λ.
3.   Calculate the time of the next event $\tau_{i+1} = \tau_i + \Delta\tau$.
4.   Determine whether this is an infection or a recovery event, by drawing a random number from a Bernoulli trial, with probability $P_{\mathrm{inf}} = \lambda_{\mathrm{inf}}/\lambda$ for infection, and $P_{\mathrm{rec}} = \lambda_{\mathrm{rec}}/\lambda$ for recovery.
5.   Determine the populations $X(\tau_{i+1})$, $Y(\tau_{i+1})$ and $Z(\tau_{i+1})$ accordingly.

As indicated above, for step 2, we do not need to draw random numbers from an exponential distribution with rate λ, for each time step. Instead, it turns out to be much more efficient (see below for an explanation) to draw a sufficient number of random numbers from a fixed exponential distribution from the outset, and to scale these accordingly during each time step.

Maple time constraints

This small subsection is optional, and may be skipped on first reading. You may if you wish proceed directly to the next subsection 'Simulation of an epidemic outbreak'.

You may be asking yourself why we do not calculate the waiting time by drawing a single random number from an exponential distribution with rate λ, at each time step. The reason is that, as shown below, it takes Maple much longer to draw random numbers by repeated use of the `Sample` command than by a single call for a vector of random numbers.

Example 3.12

Using the `time` command, compare the time Maple needs to draw random numbers using a single `Sample` command for a list of 10 random numbers with the time needed to draw them one by one. Use `restart` to initialise Maple in both cases, and compare the random numbers you obtain.

Solution

The following Maple code produces two lists as required:

```
>  restart:  with(Statistics):
>  timeused := time():
>  rv1 := RandomVariable(Exponential(1)):
>  data1 := Sample(rv1,10):
>  timeused := time()-timeused;
>  data1;
>  restart:  with(Statistics):
>  timeused := time():
>  data2 := NULL:
>  for i to 10 do
>     rv2 := RandomVariable(Exponential(1)):
>     data2 := data2,Sample(rv2,1)[1]:
>  end do:
>  timeused := time()-timeused;
>  [data2];
```

$$timeused := 0.024$$

$[0.463715886461794902, 1.36947972503120807, 0.816679111629409204,$
$0.522755825019222242, 0.186153186274689325, 0.222210970186614509,$
$0.0329100178983721124, 1.61319287541386713, 1.88577949714177140,$
$0.444876172900739053]$

$$timeused := 0.036$$

$[0.463715886461794902, 1.36947972503120807, 0.816679111629409204,$
$0.522755825019222242, 0.186153186274689325, 0.222210970186614509,$
$0.0329100178983721124, 1.61319287541386713, 1.88577949714177140,$
$0.444876172900739053]$

Of course, the time taken on your computer could be quite different from that shown here.

The times that Maple needs to draw the 10 random numbers are similar, and the two sets of random numbers are identical. ◆

The fact that, after restarting, Maple produces identical sets of random numbers, has important consequences. On the one hand, it makes results reproducible – running the same program twice after restarting Maple will produce the same result, even if random numbers are involved. On the other hand, in actual simulations you often need to average a quantity over several realisations of the random process. In this case, you must *not* restart Maple between runs, in order to obtain different realisations.

The following exercise shows that for longer lists of random numbers the time difference becomes significant.

Exercise 3.25

Amend Example 3.12 (remembering to suppress the output of the random numbers!), to compare the time Maple needs to draw 10 000 random numbers.

Simulation of an epidemic outbreak

We now create a Maple program which implements our stochastic model of an epidemic, using only two processes: infection and recovery.

Example 3.13

Write a Maple procedure that simulates the infection and recovery processes, for given parameters β and ν, total population N, initial number of infected individuals Y, and a given number of time steps to be simulated.

Solution

We need to draw two lists of random numbers. The first, called rd1, is exponentially distributed with rate 1 to obtain the waiting times. The second list, rd2, is uniformly distributed on the interval $[0,1]$. We use this list to determine whether an event is an infection or a recovery. For our rates $\lambda_{\text{inf}} = \beta XY$ and $\lambda_{\text{rec}} = \nu Y$, this means that if the random number is in the interval $[0, \lambda_{\text{inf}}/\lambda]$, where $\lambda = \lambda_{\text{inf}} + \lambda_{\text{rec}}$ is the total rate, the event is an infection; if it falls into the complementary interval, it is a recovery event.

Note that it does not matter whether we include $\lambda_{\text{inf}}/\lambda$ in the interval or not, because the probability of hitting exactly this value is zero.

```
> simul1 := proc(beta,nu,totpop,infect,nsteps)              #1
>    local totrate,X,Y,Z,rd1,rd2,r2,Xdata,Ydata,Zdata,ct,i; #2
>    uses Statistics;                                        #3
>    rd1 := Sample(Exponential(1),nsteps);                   #4
>    rd2 := Sample(Uniform(0,1),nsteps);                     #5
>    X := totpop-infect;  Y := infect;  Z := 0;  ct := 0;    #6
>    Xdata := [ct,X];  Ydata := [ct,Y];  Zdata := [ct,Z];    #7
>    for i to nsteps while Y>0 do                            #8
>      totrate := beta*X*Y+nu*Y;               # Total rate  #9
>      ct := ct+rd1[i]/totrate;              # Current time #10
>                   # Random number between 0 and totrate
>      r2 := rd2[i]*totrate;                                #11
>      if r2<beta*X*Y then          # An infection event   #12
>        X := X-1;  Y := Y+1;                              #13
>        Xdata := Xdata,[ct,X];  Ydata := Ydata,[ct,Y];    #14
>      else                          # A recovery event    #15
>        Y := Y-1;  Z := Z+1;                              #16
>        Ydata := Ydata,[ct,Y];  Zdata := Zdata,[ct,Z];    #17
>      end if;                                             #18
>    end do;                                               #19
>    print("basic reproductive rate R0:",
>          evalf[6](beta*totpop/nu));                      #20
>    print("total number of steps:",i-1);                 #21
>    print("final populations:",X,Y,Z);                   #22
>    [Xdata],[Ydata],[Zdata];                             #23
> end proc:                                               #24
```

The inputs to this procedure are: beta and nu, corresponding to the parameters β and ν; totpop, the total population N; infect, the initial number of infected individuals $Y(0)$; nsteps, the number of time steps. The procedure outputs information using three print statements (lines #20,

#21 and #22), and returns the lists [Xdata], [Ydata], [Zdata] containing the X, Y and Z data in a suitable form for display. For example,

$$\texttt{Xdata} = [\tau_0, X(\tau_0)], [\tau_1, X(\tau_1)], \ldots, [\tau_{\texttt{nsteps}}, X(\tau_{\texttt{nsteps}})].$$

The values of X, Y and Z are initialised on line #6. This line also sets the time counter ct to zero. Line #7 initialises the data sequences.

The procedure contains a loop (line #8) over the number of required simulation steps, and in each step we do the following. (Compare with the model prescription on page 127.)

1. Calculate the total rate totrate (on line #9) for the step.

2 and 3. Calculate the waiting time to the next event, by scaling rd1 by the total rate, and then calculating the time of the next event (line #10).

4. Use rd2 to determine whether the event is an infection or a recovery (lines #12 and #15).

5. Update the populations X, Y and Z accordingly (lines #13 and #16), and store them in a suitable form for plotting Xdata, Ydata and Zdata (lines #14 and #17).

If the number of infected individuals ever becomes zero, both rates vanish. We need to stop the evaluation in this case, since otherwise we would divide by zero. This is done by the while option on line #8.   ◆

The procedure simul1 involves a number of Maple commands, and it is important that you understand exactly what is happening in each line.

Exercise 3.26

(a) Consider parameters $\beta = 1$, $\nu = 50$ in a total population $N = 100$ of which initially $Y = 1$ individual is infected. Using the procedure simul1, simulate and plot the populations for 1000 steps, for $0 \le t \le 0.25$. Observe how the result changes as you repeatedly perform the simulation.

(b) For the same parameter values, obtain the solution of the rate equations using procedure dsmodel2, and compare your solution with the results of part (a).

As Exercise 3.26 shows, simulations can lead to very different results. In some cases the disease disappears immediately; in others it resembles the solution of the deterministic rate equation model. In the stochastic model, there is a finite probability that the disease disappears before spreading.

Exercise 3.27

For the same parameters as in Exercise 3.26, calculate the probability that $Y = 0$ after the first step in the simulation.

Exercise 3.28

(a) By calling simul1 within a loop, perform 50 simulations for the parameter values of Exercise 3.26, and calculate the average value of the final number of susceptible individuals.

(b) Compare this with the fixed point value x_f (see Equation (3.16)) of the corresponding rate equation.

See also Exercise 3.11.

(c) Count how often the final number equals 99, and compare this with the expected result according to the previous exercise.

Exercise 3.29

Repeat parts (a) and (b) of Exercise 3.28, but for an initial infected population $Y = 20$.

The results of Exercises 3.28 and 3.29 show that while for very small populations such as $Y = 1$ the rate equations fail to describe the average behaviour of the stochastic model, the discrepancy becomes small for rather modest populations, such as $Y = 20$.

Simulations involving births and deaths

It is relatively straightforward to extend the simulation to include births and deaths. We again consider the case where birth and death rates agree, so there is no net growth or decline of the total population on average. However, within a stochastic simulation, the total population is no longer constant, but can fluctuate.

There are four additional processes that we need to consider. We again assume that all births are susceptible to the disease, so the corresponding process is $X \to X + 1$, which occurs with rate $\mu(X + Y + Z)$. Deaths can occur in all three populations, giving rise to processes $X \to X - 1$ with rate μX, $Y \to Y - 1$ with rate μY, and $Z \to Z - 1$ with rate μZ.

In the following exercise, you are asked to modify the procedure `simul1` to include these processes. Our approach makes this relatively easy to do. The only change in the calculation of the time interval to the next event is a change in the total rate, reflecting the additional four processes. Then, to decide which process happens at the next instant of time, the four additional processes have to be taken into account, which is achieved by adding `elif` statements to the conditional.

Exercise 3.30

Modify procedure `simul1` to obtain a procedure `simul2` that includes μ as an additional parameter, and simulates the infection, recovery, birth and death processes.

Exercise 3.31

For $\beta = 1/2$, $\nu = 50$, $\mu = 1$, and initial populations $N = 1000$ and $Y = 1$, run a simulation for $10\,000$ steps. Repeat the simulation a few times to see how much it varies, and compare a run where $Y > 0$ for nearly $10\,000$ steps with the result of the corresponding deterministic rate equation obtained with the procedure `dsmodel6`.

Simulations that include the process of external infections are deferred to Exercise 3.40 at the end of this unit.

3.2.5 Age distributions

In our rate equation model, we treated all individuals equally. However, populations can be subdivided in several ways, which may be very important, for instance if a disease affects men and women differently, or if it is primarily prevalent in children. Here, as an example, we discuss age dependence. Some of the parameters will depend strongly on age a, such as the mortality rate which becomes a function $\mu(a)$. In principle, we then have to treat the populations X, Y and Z as functions not only of time t, but also of the age a of the individuals. The corresponding rate equations lead to a system of partial differential equations, which we shall not consider in this course.

Instead, we shall consider the static case where X, Y and Z depend only on age a, not on time t. This corresponds to a situation where the disease is endemic in a stable population, so the populations X, Y and Z become independent of time t. For this to make sense, we have to assume that the deaths which appear with rates $\mu(a)$ are exactly balanced by births, in order to keep the total population $N(a) = X(a) + Y(a) + Z(a)$ constant in time t. The total number of deaths is given by integrating over all ages, which changes the total population by $-\int_0^\infty \mu(a)\, N(a)\, da$. To compensate, the net births B have to be given by

$$B = \int_0^\infty \mu(a)\, N(a)\, da. \tag{3.36}$$

This enters the calculation as a boundary condition at age $a = 0$, because the age of a newborn individual is set to zero. For X, Y and Z, we use initial conditions $X(0) = N(0) = B$ and $Y(0) = Z(0) = 0$, so all newborn individuals are assumed to be susceptible to the disease.

We consider the following rate equations, which describe infection, recovery and death, but do not describe birth:

$$X'(a) = -(\lambda + \mu(a))\, X(a), \tag{3.37}$$

$$Y'(a) = \lambda X(a) - (\mu(a) + \nu)\, Y(a), \tag{3.38}$$

$$Z'(a) = \nu Y(a) - \mu(a)\, Z(a), \tag{3.39}$$

where the force of infection λ is proportional to the total number of infected individuals,

$$\lambda = \beta \int_0^\infty Y(a)\, da,$$

and is a constant. The quantities on the left-hand sides of the rate equations are derivatives with respect to age a. To keep things simple, we have assumed that the recovery rate ν is independent of age. Equation (3.37) describes how, with increasing age, the number of susceptible individuals decreases through infection (rate λ) and death (rate $\mu(a)$). Equation (3.38) reflects the influx of infected individuals (rate λ), and the decrease of infected individuals by recovery (rate ν) or death (rate $\mu(a)$). Finally, in Equation (3.39) the number of recovered individuals increases through recovery (rate ν) and decreases through death (rate $\mu(a)$).

Adding Equations (3.37)–(3.39) yields

$$N'(a) = -\mu(a)\, N(a), \tag{3.40}$$

which has solution

$$N(a) = N(0) \exp\left(-\int_0^a \mu(b)\, db\right). \tag{3.41}$$

Note that, in treating the age a as a continuous variable, the functions $X(a)$, $Y(a)$ and $Z(a)$ in fact correspond to population densities, in the sense that the population of, for instance, susceptible individuals of ages between a_0 and a_1 is given by $\int_{a_0}^{a_1} X(a)\, da$.

Exercise 3.32

Verify that Equation (3.41) satisfies the differential equation (3.40).

Exercise 3.33

Setting $x(a) = X(a)/N(a)$, $y(a) = Y(a)/N(a)$ and $z(a) = Z(a)/N(a)$, rewrite the system of differential equations (3.37)–(3.39) in the form

$$x'(a) = -\lambda\, x(a), \qquad (3.42)$$
$$y'(a) = \lambda\, x(a) - \nu\, y(a), \qquad (3.43)$$
$$z'(a) = \nu\, y(a). \qquad (3.44)$$

The equations for x, y and z which have been derived in Exercise 3.33 are solved in the following example and exercises.

Example 3.14

Solve Equations (3.42) and (3.43) for $x(a)$ and $y(a)$.

Solution

Since $x(0) = X(0)/N(0) = 1$, Equation (3.42) has the solution

$$x(a) = e^{-\lambda a}. \qquad (3.45)$$

With Equation (3.45), the equation for $y(a)$ becomes $y'(a) = \lambda \exp(-\lambda a) - \nu\, y(a)$. The general solution of the homogeneous equation $y' = -\nu y$ is $y(a) = C \exp(-\nu a)$. For a particular solution, we try $y(a) = D \exp(-\lambda a)$, where D is constant. Inserting this function into the differential equation gives

Alternatively, you can solve the equation by using an integrating factor.

$$-D\lambda e^{-\lambda a} = \lambda e^{-\lambda a} - D\nu e^{-\lambda a},$$

which yields $D = \lambda/(\nu - \lambda)$. So the general solution of the inhomogeneous equation is

$$y(a) = C e^{-\nu a} + \frac{\lambda}{\nu - \lambda}\, e^{-\lambda a}.$$

Finally, C is determined by the initial condition $y(0) = Y(0)/N(0) = 0$, which gives $C = -\lambda/(\nu - \lambda)$, hence

$$y(a) = \frac{\lambda}{\nu - \lambda}\left(e^{-\lambda a} - e^{-\nu a}\right). \qquad (3.46)$$

$\blacklozenge$

Exercise 3.34

Check the solution (3.46) by solving the differential equation for $y(a)$ with the Maple `dsolve` command.

Exercise 3.35

(a) Solve Equation (3.44) for $z(a)$.

(b) Check your solution with Maple.

(c) Verify with Maple that $x(a) + y(a) + z(a) = 1$.

Interestingly, it turns out that the results for $x(a)$, $y(a)$ and $z(a)$ do not depend on the mortality rate $\mu(a)$ at all. All terms involving $\mu(a)$ cancelled when we derived Equations (3.42)–(3.44). You are asked to plot an example of the age distribution in the following exercise.

Exercise 3.36

We measure age in years, and consider parameter values $\lambda = 0.1$ and $\nu = 32$, which correspond to rubella infections.

(a) Plot the functions $x(a)$ and $z(a)$ for $0 \le a \le 70$.

(b) Plot the function $y(a)$ for $0 \le a \le 70$. If you obtain an unexpected result, can you explain what went wrong? How can you correct it?

Basic reproductive rate

Finally, we calculate the basic reproductive rate R_0 from the age distribution. This is useful, because R_0 was our main parameter governing the dynamics of an epidemic, and it usually cannot be measured directly. We consider a limiting case of a mortality rate $\mu(a)$ such that all individuals die at a certain age, which we denote by L (so $\mu(a) = 0$ for $a \le L$, and $\mu(a)$ is infinite for $a > L$). This means that $N(a) = N(0)$ for $a \le L$, and $N(a) = 0$ for $a > L$. For developed countries, this assumption is closer to reality than a constant rate which would yield an exponential decrease in $N(a)$.

From our previous discussion (see Equations (3.28)), we know that R_0 corresponds to the inverse of the proportion of susceptible individuals at equilibrium, so $R_0 = 1/x_f$. To calculate this in the static model, we need to integrate over all ages. The total number of susceptible individuals is $X = \int_0^\infty X(a)\,da$, while the total population is $N = \int_0^\infty N(a)\,da$. Due to our assumption on $N(a)$, we find that

$$N = \int_0^L N(a)\,da = \int_0^L N(0)\,da = L\,N(0)$$

and

$$X = \int_0^\infty e^{-\lambda a} N(a)\,da = N(0) \int_0^L e^{-\lambda a}\,da = N(0)\,\frac{1 - e^{-\lambda L}}{\lambda}.$$

So the result is

$$R_0 = \frac{1}{x_f} = \left(\frac{X}{N}\right)^{-1} = \frac{\lambda L}{1 - e^{-\lambda L}}.$$

In practice, the exponential term in the denominator is often small compared to 1, so we can approximate the result by $R_0 \simeq \lambda L$, so R_0 is given by the product of the force of infection and the lifetime of the individuals.

3.2.6   Concluding remarks

Modelling disease dynamics is an interesting and important application of mathematics. Stochastic models are important if the dynamics involves groups comprising a small number of individuals. In this case, stochastic effects may dominate the behaviour, and the description by rate equations breaks down. On the other hand, for large populations the rate equations reproduce the typical behaviour of the underlying stochastic model.

The models introduced here can serve as basic models for non-lethal infectious diseases such as measles, and would reproduce a behaviour that is similar to that which has been observed in human populations. One problem with the stochastic simulations is that our implementation in Maple takes quite a bit of computing time, and simulating a population of, say, a million individuals over a long period of time is not feasible.

In our models, we used a limited set of parameters, and neglected processes that may be important for particular diseases. First, we considered mixed populations, where infection rates do not depend on individuals. Clearly, that assumption is not true in reality, since rates will depend on the number of social contacts of the individual. We also neglected any dependency of rates on gender, the effect of maternal antibodies in young children, loss of immunity with time for some diseases, the effect of latent periods, and so on. All of these effects can in principle be included in generalised versions of our models.

Nevertheless, in the simple models we have studied, we observed interesting effects such as recurrent epidemics, an effect which is observed in human populations, for diseases such as measles.

3.3   End of unit exercises

Exercise 3.37

In this exercise, we explore the effect of a randomisation of the parameter K in the standard map; see Section 3.1. At the nth iteration step, we set $K_n = K(1 + \varepsilon_n)$, where the ε_n are drawn randomly from a normal distribution with a specified standard deviation.

(a) Write a procedure smrandiff which calculates the same quantity as smdiff (on page 103), but with K_n drawn randomly as discussed above. The average should be such that the *same* choices of K_n are considered for different orbits.

(b) Modify the procedure smfitplot (on page 104) appropriately to obtain an equivalent procedure smranfitplot for the randomised case. Plot the result for $K = 10$ with standard deviations 0.01, 0.1, 0.2 and 0.5 for ε_n, averaging over 500 orbits of length up to 50, and interpret the result.

Exercise 3.38

Modify the procedure dsmodel6 (on page 117) by adding grey horizontal lines to the plot which denote the equilibrium values of x_f, y_f and z_f; see Exercise 3.17. Also, add an additional variable that allows rescaling of the solution $y(t)$ and the asymptotic value y_f to make them more visible in the plot. Plot the solutions for $\nu = 12$, $\mu = 1/70$ and $y(0) = 10^{-4}$, for $R_0 = 25/3$ and $R_0 = 4$. Choose suitable values for the other parameters including the axis ranges.

Exercise 3.39

Consider the dynamical system defined by Equations (3.32)–(3.34).

(a) Using Equations (3.32)–(3.34), show that $\dot{x} + \dot{y} + \dot{z} = 0$ for $x + y + z = 1$, so the equations preserve the condition of Equation (3.7).

(b) Calculate the fixed points of the dynamical system by solving the equations by hand. Verify that for $\kappa = 0$ these agree with Equations (3.27) and (3.28).

(c) Calculate the Jacobian at the fixed points, expressed in terms of the parameters R_0, ν, μ and κ, and the fixed point value x_f.

(d) Using Maple, numerically calculate the fixed points for $R_0 = 4$, $\nu = 12$, $\mu = 1/70$ and $\kappa = 10^{-4}$, and classify the relevant fixed points.

Exercise 3.40

(a) Modify procedure `simul2` of Exercise 3.30 to obtain a procedure `simul3` which includes random infections by external contacts at a rate κ (see Subsection 3.2.3).

(b) Perform a simulation for parameter values $\beta = 1/2$, $\nu = 50$, $\mu = 1$, $\kappa = 1/10$, and initial populations $N = 1000$, $Y = 1$, for 20 000 steps.

(c) Compare the result with the corresponding deterministic model, using the procedure `dsmodel8` of Exercise 3.20.

Exercise 3.41

This exercise concerns exploratory simulations of random matrices, a topic which is not directly related to the content of this unit. Random matrices are matrices whose entries are random numbers. They have become of interest since the work of Eugene P. Wigner and Freeman J. Dyson in the 1950s in connection with the quantum mechanical description of atomic nuclei, for which a proper description turned out to be exceedingly complicated. It was demonstrated that the distribution of energies of different states of the nuclei is similar to the distribution of eigenvalues of suitable random matrices. Random matrix statistics are one of the footprints of the quantum mechanical analogue of chaotic systems, and they have also been linked with the distribution of zeros of the Riemann zeta function. In this exercise, we use Maple to produce real symmetric matrices with random entries, and investigate properties of their eigenvalues.

For more on random matrices, see M.L. Metha (1991) *Random matrices*, Academic Press, New York.

(a) In Maple, create a symmetric 3×3 matrix

$$\mathbf{A} = \begin{pmatrix} a & b & d \\ b & c & e \\ d & e & f \end{pmatrix},$$

using the option `shape=symmetric` of the `Matrix` command.

It will be useful to load the plots, `Statistics` and `LinearAlgebra` packages up front.

(b) Write Maple code which produces real symmetric 3×3 matrices with random entries, distributed according to a Gaussian distribution with mean 0 and standard deviation 1.

Use ?RandomVariable for Maple help on random distributions.

[*Hint*: The `Sample` command produces vectors. If you use `convert` to convert these into lists, they can be used in the `Matrix` command.]

(c) For random matrices of sizes 50×50 and 500×500, calculate the eigenvalues of the random matrix using the `Eigenvalues` command in the `LinearAlgebra` package. Sort the eigenvalues and divide by the maximum absolute value, such that all rescaled eigenvalues lie in the interval $[-1, 1]$, and use `Histogram` to plot the distribution of the eigenvalues. Compare this with the function $\rho(x) = 2\sqrt{1 - x^2}/\pi$.

(d) For matrices of the same sizes as in part (c), compile a list of the spacings between adjacent eigenvalues. Calculate the mean spacing between eigenvalues, and normalise such that the mean spacing becomes 1. Use `Histogram` to plot the distribution of the normalised spacings, and compare this with the function $P(s) = \pi s \exp(-\pi s^2/4)/2$ for $s \geq 0$.

This result is known as **Wigner's semicircle law**, because the distribution function, for suitably scaled quantities, is a semicircle.

This function is known as the **Wigner surmise**; it is a very good approximation for the spacing distribution of eigenvalues of certain random matrices.

Learning outcomes

After studying this unit, you should be able to:

- appreciate the connection between the standard map in the chaotic regime and a random walk;
- describe some simple models of disease spreading;
- understand the difference between rate equations and stochastic models;
- analyse the fixed point properties of rate equation models;
- appreciate that care is needed to interpret Maple output correctly;
- solve simple systems of coupled differential equations in Maple;
- perform simple simulations with random numbers in Maple;
- modify Maple procedures to solve or simulate related problems;
- write simple Maple procedures to solve or simulate a specified system.

Solutions to Exercises

Solution 3.1

(a) The numbers obtained by commands `smdiff(5,100,10)` and `smdiff(5,1000,10)` should be similar.

(b) A plot can be obtained as follows.

```
>  smdata := smdiff(5,1000,50):
>  plot(smdata,style=point,
        colour=black,symbol=circle);
```

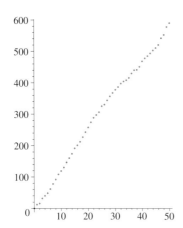

Solution 3.2

(a) The simplified procedure is

```
>  smfit := proc(K,norb,lorb)
>     local data,xd,yd,i;
>     uses Statistics;
>     data := smdiff(K,norb,lorb);
>     xd := <seq(i,i=0..lorb)>;
>     yd := <seq(data[i,2],i=1..lorb+1)>;
>     coeff(Fit(a+b*n,xd,yd,n),n);
>  end proc:
```

(b) Accumulating and plotting data can be done as follows:

```
>  dc := NULL:
>  for K from 5 to 30 by 0.25 do
>    dc := dc,[K,smfit(K,100,50)/(K^2/2)];
>  end do:
>  plot([[dc],[dc]],style=[line,point],
        colour=[red,black],symbol=circle);
```

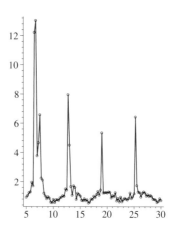

For clarity, we have plotted both the data points and a line connecting them. The result shows some periodic fluctuations: there are some values of K where the slope is enhanced. It appears to settle for larger K, in the sense that the amplitudes of the fluctuations decrease.

(c) Combining the plot of part (b) with that of the Bessel function, we obtain

```
>  plot([[dc],[dc],1-2*BesselJ(2,k)],k=5..30,
        style=[line,point,line],
        colour=[red,black,black],
        view=[5..30,0..3],symbol=circle);
```

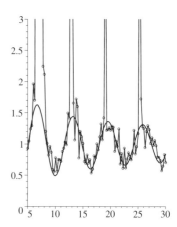

Apart from some values where the slope is enhanced, the function $1 - 2J_2(K)$ describes the ratios of the fitted slope with $K^2/2$ rather well.

Solution 3.3

Adding Equations (3.3)–(3.5) gives
$$\dot{X}(t) + \dot{Y}(t) + \dot{Z}(t)$$
$$= -\beta X(t)Y(t) + \beta X(t)Y(t) - \nu Y(t) + \nu Y(t)$$
$$= 0,$$

so $X(t) + Y(t) + Z(t)$ is constant, as required.

Solution 3.4

(a) The simplest solution consists of removing the equation and initial condition for the function $Z(t)$, and including the definitions of functions and plot command of Example 3.3.

```
>   dsmodel2 := proc(beta,nu,N,X0,Y0,plran,np)
>     local dseqs,dssol,X,Y,t;
>     uses plots;
>     dseqs := {diff(X(t),t)+beta*X(t)*Y(t)=0,
                diff(Y(t),t)
                  -(beta*X(t)-nu)*Y(t)=0,
                X(0)=X0, Y(0)=Y0};
>     dssol := dsolve(dseqs,{X(t),Y(t)},
                  numeric);
>     odeplot(dssol,[[t,X(t),colour=black],
                  [t,Y(t),colour=red],
                  [t,N-X(t)-Y(t),
                    colour=black]],
                plran,numpoints=np);
>   end proc:
```

Note that we no longer need the global and unassign statements, as we are only interested in returning the plot, rather than the functions $X(t)$ and $Y(t)$. For this reason we make X and Y local variables. We have also added a parameter np which is used in the plot option numpoints=np. This option tells Maple to calculate the function at a given number of points in preparing the plot.

(b) The command

```
>   dsmodel2(1e-3,12,10^5,10^5-10,
              10,0..1,200);
```

reproduces the figure of Example 3.3.

Solution 3.5

(a) With $\beta = 10^{-3}$, $\nu = 12$ and $N = 10^5$, we find
$$R_0 = \frac{\beta N}{\nu} = \frac{100}{12} = \frac{25}{3} \simeq 8.33.$$

(b) R_0 is proportional to N, so smaller values of N will result in smaller values of R_0. The required values for R_0 are $R_0 = 1/12 \simeq 0.08$ for $N = 10^3$, $R_0 = 5/6 \simeq 0.83$ for $N = 10^4$, and $R_0 = 5/3 \simeq 1.67$ for $N = 2 \times 10^4$.

The required plots are obtained as follows:

```
>   dsmodel2(1e-3,12,10^3,10^3-10,10,
              0..1,200);
```

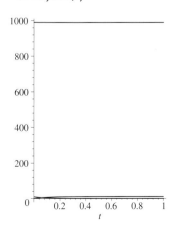

```
>   dsmodel2(1e-3,12,10^4,10^4-10,10,
              0..1,200);
```

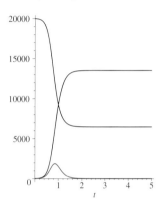

```
>   dsmodel2(1e-3,12,2*10^4,2*10^4-10,10,
              0..5,200);
```

For small $R_0 < 1$, the solutions show no epidemic, and the three functions are nearly constant. For $R_0 > 1$ there is an epidemic, but if R_0 is not too large you can see that it stops before the entire population is affected, so $X(t)$ and $Z(t)$ approach limiting values between 0 and N. Also, the timescale is different: the disease spreads slowly for values of R_0 just above 1 (and you may have to plot the solutions for larger t to observe this). For larger R_0, as in Example 3.3, the epidemic reaches almost the entire population.

Solution 3.6

(a) The following procedure finds the required solution.

```
>   dsmodel3 := proc(R0,nu,y0,plran,np)
>     local dseqs,dssol,x,y,t;
>     uses plots;
>     dseqs :=
          {diff(x(t),t)+nu*R0*x(t)*y(t)=0,
           diff(y(t),t)-nu*(R0*x(t)-1)*y(t)=0,
           x(0)=1-y0, y(0)=y0};
>     dssol := dsolve(dseqs,{x(t),y(t)},
                  numeric);
>     odeplot(dssol,[[t,x(t),colour=black],
                  [t,y(t),colour=red],
                  [t,1-x(t)-y(t),
                    colour=black]],
                plran,numpoints=np);
>   end proc:
```

(b) The following commands solve the system for the parameter values of Example 3.3:

```
>   N := 10^5:
>   dsmodel3(1e-3*N/12,12,10/N,0..1,200);
```

The graph produced by this command is consistent with the result of Example 3.3. The commands for other plots in Exercise 3.5 depend on the values of N, so you just need to change N in the command line above accordingly (and, if required, adjust the plot range).

Solution 3.7

(a) In our model, the condition for an epidemic to occur is $R_0 x(0) > 1$. So in order to prevent the disease from spreading, we would like to reduce $x(0)$ so that $x(0) \leq 1/R_0$. For a small fraction of infected individuals, $y(0) \simeq 0$, we have $x(0) + z(0) \simeq 1$, where $z(0)$ denotes the fraction of the population that is immune to the disease. In order to have $x(0) \leq 1/R_0$ and to prevent the disease from spreading, we need to immunise a fraction $z(0) \geq 1 - 1/R_0$ of the population.

(b) For $R_0 = 15$, the required fraction is

$$z(0) \geq 1 - \tfrac{1}{15} = \tfrac{14}{15} \simeq 0.933.$$

This means that in order to prevent measles from spreading, about 93.3% of the population needs to be immunised against the disease.

Solution 3.8

In Exercise 3.6, we considered two cases with $R_0 > 1/x(0)$, namely $R_0 = 25/3$ with $x(0) = (10^5 - 10)/10^5 = 9999/10\,000$ and $R_0 = 5/3$ with $x(0) = (2 \times 10^4 - 10)/(2 \times 10^4) = 1999/2000$. For these two cases, Equation (3.14) gives

$$y_{\text{max}} = 1 - \frac{1 + \ln(3333/400)}{25/3} \simeq 0.625\,58$$

and

$$y_{\text{max}} = 1 - \frac{1 + \ln(1999/1200)}{5/3} \simeq 0.093\,81,$$

respectively. The approximate result (3.15) gives

$$y_{\text{max}} = 1 - \frac{1 + \ln(25/3)}{25/3} \simeq 0.625\,57$$

and

$$y_{\text{max}} = 1 - \frac{1 + \ln(5/3)}{5/3} \simeq 0.093\,50,$$

respectively, which differ only slightly from the exact values. The results are in accordance with the maxima of $y(t)$ in the plots obtained in Exercise 3.6.

Solution 3.9

(a) For $R_0 \to 1/x(0)$, Equation (3.14) becomes

$$y_{\text{max}} \to 1 - \frac{1 + \ln(1)}{1/x(0)} = 1 - x(0) = y(0),$$

so the maximum value of $y(t)$ is the value at $t = 0$. For $R_0 \to \infty$ we find $y_{\text{max}} \to 1$, because the logarithm grows slower than linearly, so $\lim_{x \to \infty} \ln(x)/x = 0$. This can be proved by employing **l'Hospital's rule** which states that the limit of the ratio is the same as that of the ratio of the derivatives of the numerator and denominator, hence

$$\lim_{x \to \infty} \frac{\ln(x)}{x} = \lim_{x \to \infty} \frac{1/x}{1} = \lim_{x \to \infty} \frac{1}{x} = 0.$$

(b) The limits are obtained in Maple by

```
>   limit(1-(1+ln(R0*x(0)))/R0,R0=1/x(0));
```
$$1 - x(0)$$

```
>   limit(1-(1+ln(R0*x(0)))/R0,R0=infinity);
```
$$1$$

(c) Using Equation (3.15), the required graph is obtained by typing

```
>   plot(1-(1+ln(R0))/R0,R0=1..10,
        labels=["R0","ymax"]);
```

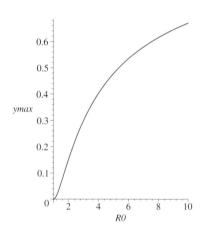

Note: The lower limit on the R_0 axis is $R_0 = 1/x(0) = 1$.

Solution 3.10

If $R_0 < 1/x(0)$, the coefficient $R_0 x(t) - 1$ in the differential equation (3.10) is negative for $t = 0$, and stays negative for any $t \geq 0$, so $y(t)$ decreases. This means that the expected value is $y_{\text{max}} = y(0)$.

In Example 3.4, we used the fact that $y'(x) = 0$ for $x = x(t_{\text{max}})$ with $\dot{y}(t_{\text{max}}) = 0$ to calculate the maximum. However, for $R_0 x(0) < 1$ there is no solution for this condition, and the maximum occurs at the boundary.

Solution 3.11

To see the relevant part of the curve where $y > 0$, we plot the curve for x between 0.9 and $x(0) = 0.99$. This is done by typing

```
>  x0 := 0.99:  R0 := 0.9:
>  plot(1-x-ln(x0/x)/R0,x=0.90..x0,
        labels=[x,y]);
```

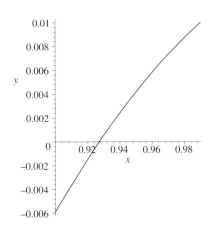

The plot shows that $x_f \simeq 0.928$.

Solution 3.12

We use commands

```
>  x0 := 0.99:  R0 := 4.0:
>  evalf[6](solve(1-xf-1/R0*ln(x0/xf)=0,xf));
                0.0196122, 1.00335
```

and

```
>  x0 := 0.99:  R0 := 0.9:
>  evalf[6](solve(1-xf-1/R0*ln(x0/xf)=0,xf));
                0.927287, 1.31776
```

In both cases, Maple finds two solutions. Since $x_f \in [0,1]$, the appropriate solutions are $x_f \simeq 0.0196$ and $x_f \simeq 0.9273$ for $R_0 = 4$ and $R_0 = 0.9$, respectively.

Solution 3.13

(a) The following Maple procedure contains the calculation of $y_{\max}$ and the asymptotic value x_f. For the latter, it uses the **select** command to extract the appropriate solution, and a conditional statement to produce an error message in the cases that either no solution or more than one solution is obtained.

```
>  dsmodel4 := proc(R0,nu,y0,plran,np)
>    local dseqs,dssol,asymp,x,y,t;
>    uses plots;
>  #
>  # Find solutions xf, such that 0<xf<1
>    asymp := evalf(solve(1-xf
                  -ln((1-y0)/xf)/R0=0,xf));
>    asymp := select(x->(x>=0 and x<=1),
                  asymp);
>    if nops([asymp])<>1 then
>      print("calculation failed");
>      return(asymp);
>    end if;
>    print("asymptotic susceptible pop.:",
          evalf[6](asymp));
>    print("asymptotic recovered pop.:",
          evalf[6](1-asymp));
>  #
>  # Determine the peak population
>  # For R0*x0<=1 this is y(0)
>    if R0*(1-y0)>1 then
>      print("peak infected pop.:",
          evalf[3](1-(1+ln(R0*(1-y0)))/R0)):
>    else print("peak infected pop.:",y0):
>    end if:
>  #
>  # Solve the DEs as in dsmodel3
>    dseqs :=
        {diff(x(t),t)+R0*nu*x(t)*y(t)=0,
         diff(y(t),t)-nu*(R0*x(t)-1)*y(t)=0,
         x(0)=1-y0, y(0)=y0};
>    dssol := dsolve(dseqs,{x(t),y(t)},
                  numeric);
>    odeplot(dssol,[[t,x(t),colour=black],
                  [t,y(t),colour=red],
                  [t,1-x(t)-y(t),
                   colour=black]],
              plran,numpoints=np);
>  end proc:
```

(b) You can, for instance, consider the case $R_0 = 25/3$, $\nu = 12$ and $y(0) = 10^{-4}$, by executing the command `dsmodel4(25/3,12,1e-4,0..1,200)`, comparing the plot with that of Example 3.3 or Exercise 3.6, and comparing the asymptotic results with those derived in Exercise 3.8.

You should try a few more examples to convince yourself that your procedure works appropriately.

Solution 3.14

Adding the three equations yields

$$\dot{X}(t) + \dot{Y}(t) + \dot{Z}(t)$$
$$= \mu N - \beta X(t) Y(t) - \mu X(t) + \beta X(t) Y(t)$$
$$\quad - \nu Y(t) - \mu Y(t) + \nu Y(t) - \mu Z(t)$$
$$= \mu (N - X(t) - Y(t) - Z(t))$$
$$= 0,$$

so the total population remains constant.

Solution 3.15

You will find that for some values of `eps`, you obtain a wrong solution like the one in Example 3.6(c), while for other values of `eps` you obtain an oscillating solution, like that shown here for $eps = 10^{-20}$, which we plotted over a period of 200 years.

```
> dsmodel6(4,12,1/70,1e-4,1e-20,
           0..200,1000);
```

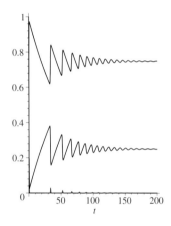

Solution 3.16

(a) The following procedure is similar to `dsmodel6`, but just plots $\log_{10}(|y(t)|)$:

```
> dsmodel7 := proc(R0,nu,mu,y0,eps,plran,np)
>    local dseqs,dssol,x,y,t;
>    uses plots;
>    dseqs := {diff(x(t),t)-mu*(1-x(t))
                +R0*(nu+mu)*x(t)*y(t)=0,
              diff(y(t),t)-(nu+mu)
                *(R0*x(t)-1)*y(t)=0,
              x(0)=1-y0, y(0)=y0};
>    dssol := dsolve(dseqs,{x(t),y(t)},
                   numeric,abserr=eps);
>    odeplot(dssol,[t,log10(abs(y(t)))],
            plran,numpoints=np);
>    end proc:
```

(b) The plots below indicate that the required accuracy is 10^{-50}.

```
> dsmodel7(4,12,1/70,1e-4,1e-10,
           0..200,1000);
```

Warning, cannot evaluate the solution further right of 30.375940, probably a singularity

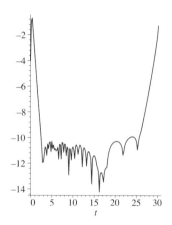

```
> dsmodel7(4,12,1/70,1e-4,1e-20,
           0..200,1000);
```

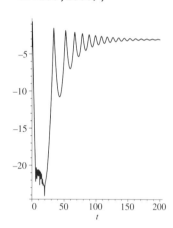

```
> dsmodel7(4,12,1/70,1e-4,1e-30,
           0..200,1000);
```

Warning, cannot evaluate the solution further right of 36.789741, probably a singularity

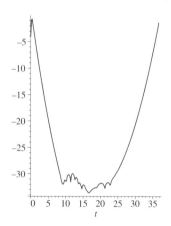

```
>   dsmodel7(4,12,1/70,1e-4,1e-40,
            0..200,1000);
```

Warning, cannot evaluate the solution further
right of 39.893439, probably a singularity

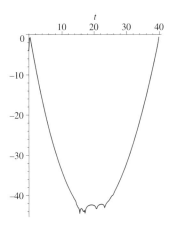

```
>   dsmodel7(4,12,1/70,1e-4,1e-50,
            0..200,1000);
```

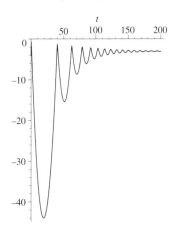

```
>   dsmodel7(4,12,1/70,1e-4,1e-60,
            0..200,1000);
```

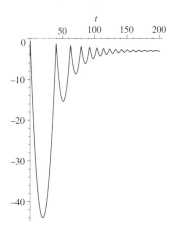

(c) The plot obtained from `dsmodel6` with
$\mathtt{eps} = 10^{-50}$ shows the expected oscillating behaviour:

```
>   dsmodel6(4,12,1/70,1e-4,1e-50,
            0..200,1000);
```

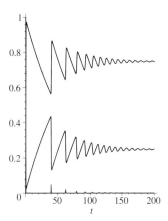

(d) In our example, $y(t)$ drops to about 10^{-46}
between epidemics. Such tiny values explain why `eps`
needs to be set so small for an accurate solution for y.
Remembering that $y(t) = Y(t)/N$, where $Y(t)$ denotes
the number of infected individuals, and N the total
population, this essentially means that the disease
would have disappeared from any reasonably sized
population – and within our model that would mean
that the disease is eradicated, so no further epidemics
can arise.

Solution 3.17

Using `solve` produces the two given solutions:

```
>   unassign('R0');
```

```
>   solve({mu*(1-xf)-(nu+mu)*R0*xf*yf=0,
            (nu+mu)*(R0*xf-1)*yf=0,
            nu*yf-mu*zf=0}, {xf,yf,zf});
```

$$\left\{ zf = \frac{\nu\,(R0-1)}{R0\,(\nu+\mu)}, \; yf = \frac{\mu\,(R0-1)}{R0\,(\nu+\mu)}, \; xf = \frac{1}{R0} \right\},$$
$$\{xf = 1, \; yf = 0, \; zf = 0\}$$

The `unassign` command was used because we had
previously assigned values to the variable `R0`.
(Alternatively, we could have issued a `restart`.)

For the solution by hand, we first realise that the
equation $\dot{y} = 0$ implies that one of the factors $\nu + \mu$,
$R_0\,x_\mathrm{f} - 1$ and y_f has to be zero. Since ν and μ are
both positive parameters, $\nu + \mu > 0$.

For $y_\mathrm{f} = 0$, it follows from $\dot{z} = 0$ that $z_\mathrm{f} = 0$ and hence
$x_\mathrm{f} = 1$, which gives the first fixed point solution.

For the second fixed point, we have $x_\mathrm{f} = 1/R_0$.
Inserting this in the equation $\dot{x} = 0$ yields

$$\mu\left(1 - \frac{1}{R_0}\right) - (\nu + \mu)\,y_\mathrm{f} = 0,$$

hence

$$y_\mathrm{f} = \frac{\mu}{\nu + \mu}\left(1 - \frac{1}{R_0}\right),$$

and finally

$$z_\mathrm{f} = \frac{\nu}{\mu}\,y_\mathrm{f} = \frac{\nu}{\nu + \mu}\left(1 - \frac{1}{R_0}\right).$$

As expected, this agrees with the Maple result.

143

Solution 3.18

For $\nu \gg \mu$, we can set $\nu + \mu \simeq \nu$ and $\mu/\nu \simeq 0$ in Equations (3.28). This gives

$$x_f = \frac{1}{R_0},$$

$$y_f = \frac{\mu(R_0 - 1)}{R_0(\nu + \mu)} \simeq \frac{\mu(R_0 - 1)}{R_0 \nu} \simeq 0,$$

$$z_f = \frac{\nu(R_0 - 1)}{R_0(\nu + \mu)} \simeq \frac{\nu(R_0 - 1)}{R_0 \nu} = 1 - \frac{1}{R_0}.$$

Solution 3.19

(a) Inserting the parameter values in Equations (3.28) gives

$$x_f = \tfrac{1}{4} = 0.250, \quad y_f \simeq 0.000\,892, \quad z_f \simeq 0.749.$$

The eigenvalues of Equation (3.31) become $\lambda_{1,2} \simeq -0.029 + 0.717i$, which gives a period $T = 2\pi/\omega \simeq 8.763$ years.

(b) In the figure below, we count ten periods between $t \simeq 204$ and $t \simeq 292$, giving an estimate of $T \simeq 8.80$, in good agreement with the asymptotic result $T \simeq 8.76$.

```
>   dsmodel7(4,12,1/70,1e-4,1e-50,200..300,
            1000);
```

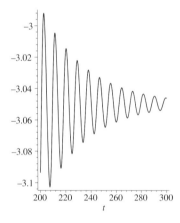

Note that the asymptotic value $y_f \simeq 10^{-3.05} \simeq 0.000\,89$ is in good agreement with the calculated result.

Solution 3.20

(a) The following procedure differs from `dsmodel6` only by the inclusion of an additional parameter `kappa`, representing κ, on lines #1, #2 and #3.

```
>   dsmodel8 := proc(R0,nu,mu,kappa,y0,eps,  #1
                     plran,np)
>     local dseqs,dssol,x,y,t;
>     uses plots;
>     dseqs := {diff(x(t),t)-mu*(1-x(t))
                  +kappa*x(t)                 #2
                  +R0*(nu+mu)*x(t)*y(t)=0,
               diff(y(t),t)-kappa*x(t)        #3
                  -(nu+mu)*(R0*x(t)-1)*y(t)=0,
               x(0)=1-y0, y(0)=y0};
>     dssol := dsolve(dseqs,{x(t),y(t)},
                     numeric,abserr=eps);
>     odeplot(dssol,
               [[t,x(t),colour=black],
                [t,y(t),colour=red],
                [t,1-x(t)-y(t),colour=black]],
               plran,numpoints=np);
>   end proc:
```

(b) The plots look as follows.

```
>   dsmodel8(4,12,1/70,0,1e-4,1e-50,
            0..200,1000);
```

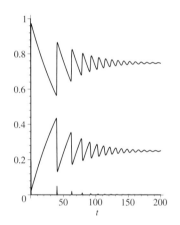

```
>   dsmodel8(4,12,1/70,1e-16,1e-4,1e-50,
            0..200,1000);
```

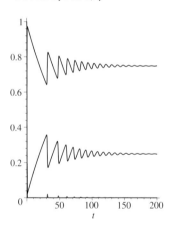

```
> dsmodel8(4,12,1/70,1e-8,1e-4,1e-50,
          0..200,1000);
```

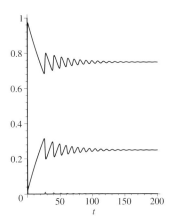

```
> dsmodel8(4,12,1/70,1e-4,1e-4,1e-50,
          0..200,1000);
```

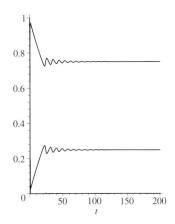

```
> dsmodel8(4,12,1/70,1e-2,1e-4,1e-50,
          0..200,1000);
```

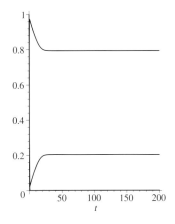

Apparently the constant infection rate smoothes the oscillations; their amplitudes decrease, and if κ (kappa) is sufficiently large, the oscillations completely disappear.

(c) The animated plot can be created by the commands

```
> with(plots):
> plotseq := NULL:
> for n from -20 to -1 do
>    plotseq := plotseq,
            dsmodel8(4,12,1/70,10^n,1e-4,
                     1e-50,0..200,1000);
> end do:
> display([plotseq],insequence=true);
```

To play the animation, right-click on the graph (which is not shown here) and choose 'Animation ▷ Play', or click the corresponding button (▷) in the menu bar. In the animation, you can see that the period between epidemics shortens with larger external infection rate, and that the amplitude decreases.

Solution 3.21

The modification to dsmodel7 is the same as in the previous exercise:

```
> dsmodel9 := proc(R0,nu,mu,kappa,y0,eps,
                   plran,np)
>    local dseqs,dssol,x,y,t;
>    uses plots;
>    dseqs := {diff(x(t),t)-mu*(1-x(t))
                +kappa*x(t)
                +R0*(nu+mu)*x(t)*y(t)=0,
              diff(y(t),t)-kappa*x(t)
                -(nu+mu)*(R0*x(t)-1)*y(t)=0,
              x(0)=1-y0, y(0)=y0};
>    dssol := dsolve(dseqs,{x(t),y(t)},
                   numeric,abserr=eps);
>    odeplot(dssol,[t,log10(abs(y(t)))],
                   plran,numpoints=np);
>    end proc:
```

The plots below show that the smallest values of $y(t)$ are approximately of the same order as κ.

```
> dsmodel9(4,12,1/70,0,1e-4,1e-50,
          0..200,1000);
```

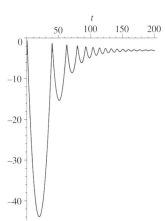

145

```
> dsmodel9(4,12,1/70,1e-16,1e-4,1e-50,
       0..200,1000);
```

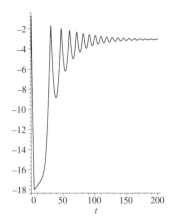

```
> dsmodel9(4,12,1/70,1e-2,1e-4,1e-50,
       0..200,1000);
```

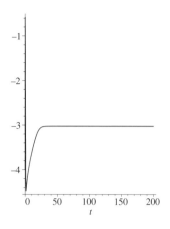

```
> dsmodel9(4,12,1/70,1e-8,1e-4,1e-50,
       0..200,1000);
```

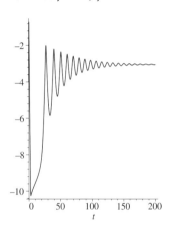

Solution 3.22

(a) Performing the integration gives

$$\int_0^\infty \rho(t)\,dt = \left[-e^{-\lambda t}\right]_0^\infty = e^0 = 1.$$

(b) The probability that you have to wait for longer than time T is

$$\int_T^\infty \rho(t)\,dt = \left[-e^{-\lambda t}\right]_T^\infty = e^{-\lambda T}.$$

This is the same as $1 - \int_0^T \rho(t)\,dt$.

Solution 3.23

(a) The following produces the required plot:

```
> with(Statistics):  with(plots):
> N := 100000:
> d1 := Sample(Exponential(1),N):
> d2 := Sample(Exponential(1/2),N):
> d3 := Sample(Exponential(1/3),N):
> d123 := [seq(min(d1[i],d2[i],d3[i]),
           i=1..N)]:
> display(plot(6*exp(-6*t),t=0..2,
               colour=black),
           Histogram(d123,binwidth=0.025,
               colour=red));
```

```
> dsmodel9(4,12,1/70,1e-4,1e-4,1e-50,
       0..200,1000);
```

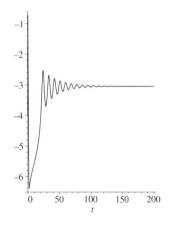

(b) The frequencies can be computed as follows.

```
> n1 := 0:  n2 := 0:  n3 := 0:
> for i to N do
>    if d1[i]<min(d2[i],d3[i]) then
>       n1 := n1+1;
>    elif d2[i]<min(d1[i],d3[i]) then
>       n2 := n2+1;
>    else
>       n3 := n3+1;
>    end if;
> end do:
> evalf[6]([n1,n2,n3]/N);
```

$$[0.166770, 0.334340, 0.498890]$$

The values agree well with the expected frequencies $1/6 \simeq 0.166\,667$, $2/6 \simeq 0.333\,333$ and $3/6 = 0.5$. The output values for the counts will depend on the realisation and fluctuate around the expected values.

Solution 3.24

The following Maple code generates the required plots.

```
> with(Statistics):  with(plots):
> data := Sample(Exponential(1),100000):
> display(plot(2*exp(-2*t),t=0..4,
            colour=black),
         Histogram(1/2*data,binwidth=0.1,
            colour=red));
```

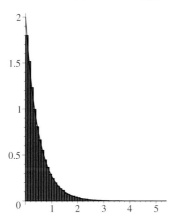

```
> display(plot(1/10*exp(-t/10),t=0..80,
            colour=black),
         Histogram(10*data,binwidth=2,
            colour=red));
```

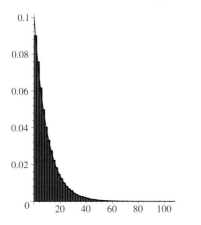

As expected, data scaled by factors $a = 1/2$ and $b = 10$ are again exponentially distributed, with $\lambda = 1/a = 2$ and $\lambda = 1/b = 1/10$, respectively.

Solution 3.25

Executing the following Maple code shows that drawing random numbers one by one takes considerably longer than drawing them with a single Sample command:

```
> restart:  with(Statistics):
> timeused := time():
> rv1 := RandomVariable(Exponential(1)):
> data1 := Sample(rv1,10000):
> timeused := time()-timeused;
> restart:  with(Statistics):
> timeused := time():
> data2 := NULL:
> for i to 10000 do
>    rv2 := RandomVariable(Exponential(1)):
>    data2 := data2,Sample(rv2,1)[1]:
> end do:
> timeused := time()-timeused;
```

$$timeused := 0.036$$
$$timeused := 10.117$$

Solution 3.26

(a) The following Maple code produces the required plot:

```
> data := simul1(1,50,100,1,1000):
> plot([data],colour=[black,red,black],
       view=[0..0.25,0..100]);
```

"basic reproductive rate R0:", 2.

"total number of steps:", 171

"final populations:", 14, 0, 86

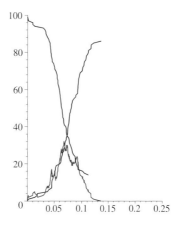

Repeating the calculation will result in rather different graphs. Note that the graphs end when the populations do not change any more. In this case the simulation terminated after 171 steps, because Y vanished.

(b) Remember that you first need to reload the `dsmodel2` procedure of Exercise 3.4. The plot below resembles the behaviour of the stochastic model in the case where the disease spreads.

```
>  dsmodel2(1,50,100,99,1,0..0.25);
```

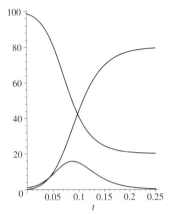

Solution 3.27

From the initial data, the rates for infection and recovery are $\lambda_{\text{inf}} = \lambda_1 = \beta XY = 99$ and $\lambda_{\text{rec}} = \lambda_2 = \nu Y = 50$. The probability that the first event is a recovery is $\lambda_2/(\lambda_1 + \lambda_2) = 50/149 \simeq 0.34$, so in just over a third of cases the disease will disappear before a second individual gets infected.

Solution 3.28

(a) The following `do` loop accumulates the final data of the population X. (Note that X is the first of the three sets returned by `simul1`, and the -1 selects the last element in that list, which contains the final population as its second entry.) The last command computes the average.

```
>  XF := NULL:

>  for i to 50 do

>    data := simul1(1,50,100,1,1000):

>    XF := XF,data[1,-1,2];

>  end do:

>  XF := [XF];

>  evalf(add(XF[i],i=1..nops(XF))/nops(XF));
```

$$XF := [21, 33, 29, 31, 29, 11, 99, 99, 99, 99, 99,$$
$$12, 99, 16, 99, 37, 99, 99, 26, 99, 24, 99, 99, 29,$$
$$99, 99, 17, 98, 13, 99, 99, 99, 98, 27, 14, 99, 26,$$
$$57, 23, 90, 98, 98, 22, 99, 99, 99, 98, 96, 99, 96]$$
$$68.94000000$$

The actual result depends on the realisation of the random process. Note that the outputs produced by the `print` commands in the procedure `simul1` are not shown.

(b) For our parameters, we find $R_0 = \beta N/\nu = 2$, and $x(0) = 99/100 = 0.99$. Solving Equation (3.16) in Maple gives

```
>  solve(1-xf-1/2*ln(0.99/xf)=0,xf);
```

$$0.1997960323, 1.010000660$$

so $x_{\text{f}} \simeq 0.2$, and $X_{\text{f}} = N x_{\text{f}} \simeq 20$, which is (with high probability) much lower than the value obtained in part (a).

(c) If the final susceptible population is 99, the disease disappears before a second individual is infected, which according to Exercise 3.27 happens with probability $50/149$. For our 50 realisations we therefore expect this to happen in about 17 cases. You can count the number by using the `select` command as follows:

```
>  nops(select(n->n=99,XF));
```
$$22$$

In this case, the disease disappeared in 22 out of 50 realisations before a second individual was infected.

Solution 3.29

Apart from the parameter values, the Maple code is the same as in Exercise 3.28. In this case, $x(0) = 80/100 = 0.8$ and $x_{\text{f}} \simeq 0.145$. You should find that the average value of the simulation now agrees rather well.

Solution 3.30

Performing the suggested changes gives the following procedure. The alterations are commented.

```
>  simul2 := proc(beta,nu,mu,totpop,infect,
                  nsteps)        # mu included

>    local totrate,X,Y,Z,rd1,rd2,r2,Xdata,
            Ydata,Zdata,ct,i;

>    uses Statistics;

>    rd1 := Sample(Exponential(1),nsteps);

>    rd2 := Sample(Uniform(0,1),nsteps);

>    X := totpop-infect;
     Y := infect;
     Z := 0;

>    ct := 0;

>    Xdata := [ct,X];
     Ydata := [ct,Y];
     Zdata := [ct,Z];

>    for i to nsteps do

>      if Y=0 then break end if;

>  # New rate defined on next line

>      totrate := 2*mu*(X+Y+Z)+beta*X*Y+nu*Y;

>      ct := ct+rd1[i]/totrate;

>      r2 := rd2[i]*totrate;

>      if r2<beta*X*Y then

>        X := X-1;   Y := Y+1;

>        Xdata := Xdata,[ct,X];

>        Ydata := Ydata,[ct,Y];

>      elif r2<beta*X*Y+nu*Y then

>        Y := Y-1;   Z := Z+1;

>        Ydata := Ydata,[ct,Y];

>        Zdata := Zdata,[ct,Z];

>  # Next line for birth

>      elif r2<beta*X*Y+nu*Y+mu*(X+Y+Z) then

>        X := X+1:

>        Xdata := Xdata,[ct,X];
```

```
>    # Next line for death in X
>        elif r2<beta*X*Y+nu*Y+mu*(2*X+Y+Z)
             then
>          X := X-1:
>          Xdata := Xdata,[ct,X];
>    # Next line for death in Y
>        elif r2<beta*X*Y+nu*Y+mu*(2*X+2*Y+Z)
             then
>          Y := Y-1:
>          Ydata := Ydata,[ct,Y];
>    # Next line for death in Z
>        else # r2<beta*X*Y+nu*Y+2*mu*(X+Y+Z)
>          Z := Z-1:
>          Zdata := Zdata,[ct,Z];
>        end if;
>    end do;
>    print("basic reproductive rate R0:",
             evalf[3](beta*totpop/(nu+mu)));
>    print("total number of steps;",i-1);
>    print("final populations:",X,Y,Z);
>    [Xdata],[Ydata],[Zdata];
>    end proc:
```

You can choose a different order for the various alternatives in the main `if – elif – else – end if` construction. The comparison is always between the *i*th random number in the list `rd2` and the sum of the rates of the processes divided by the total rate, which guarantees that each process occurs with the appropriate probability.

Solution 3.31

An example of the plot obtained is shown below:

```
>    data := simul2(1/2,50,1,1000,1,10000):
>    plot([data],colour=[black,red,black]);
```
   "basic reproductive rate R0:", 9.80
    "total number of steps;", 10000
   "final populations:", 109, 15, 927

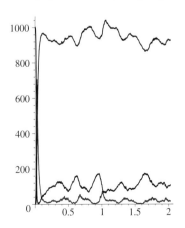

The corresponding deterministic result is (remember to load the definition of `dsmodel6` if you have restarted Maple)

```
>    dsmodel6(9.8,50,1,1e-3,1e-20,0..2,1000);
```

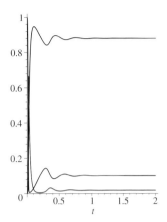

Overall, the rate equations describe the behaviour reasonably well. The stochastic simulation shows random fluctuations which do not decrease in amplitude, and will eventually lead to the eradication of the disease. This is due to the small population Y in the process.

Solution 3.32

The derivative is

$$N'(a) = -N(0)\,\frac{d}{da}\left(\int_0^a \mu(b)\,db\right)\exp\left(-\int_0^a \mu(b)\,db\right)$$
$$= -N(a)\,\frac{d}{da}\left(\int_0^a \mu(b)\,db\right)$$
$$= -\mu(a)\,N(a),$$

because the derivative of the integral with respect to a is $\mu(a)$.

Solution 3.33

Inserting $X(a) = x(a)\,N(a)$, $Y(a) = y(a)\,N(a)$ and $Z(a) = z(a)\,N(a)$ in Equations (3.37)–(3.39) gives

$$x'(a)\,N(a) + x(a)\,N'(a) = -(\lambda + \mu(a))\,x(a)\,N(a),$$
$$y'(a)\,N(a) + y(a)\,N'(a) = \lambda\,x(a)\,N(a)$$
$$- (\mu(a) + \nu)\,y(a)\,N(a),$$
$$z'(a)\,N(a) + z(a)\,N'(a) = \nu\,y(a)\,N(a)$$
$$- \mu(a)\,z(a)\,N(a).$$

Using $N'(a) = -\mu(a)\,N(a)$ and dividing by $N(a)$ yields

$$x'(a) - \mu(a)\,x(a) = -(\lambda + \mu(a))\,x(a),$$
$$y'(a) - \mu(a)\,y(a) = \lambda\,x(a) - (\mu(a) + \nu)\,y(a),$$
$$z'(a) - \mu(a)\,z(a) = \nu\,y(a) - \mu(a)\,z(a).$$

The desired form of the equations is obtained by cancelling terms that appear on both sides of the equations.

Solution 3.34

This solution is obtained by typing

```
> ysol := dsolve({diff(y(a),a)
                  -lambda*exp(-lambda*a)
                  +nu*y(a)=0,y(0)=0},y(a)):
> ysol := simplify(ysol);
```

$$ysol := \mathrm{y}(a) = -\frac{\lambda\left(e^{(-a(\lambda-\nu))}-1\right)e^{(-\nu a)}}{\lambda-\nu}$$

and agrees with the solution obtained in Example 3.14.

Solution 3.35

(a) The solution is given by direct integration:

$$
\begin{aligned}
z(a) &= \nu\int_0^a y(b)\,db\\
&= \frac{\nu\lambda}{\nu-\lambda}\left[-\frac{e^{-\lambda b}}{\lambda}+\frac{e^{-\nu b}}{\nu}\right]_0^a\\
&= \frac{-\nu e^{-\lambda a}+\nu+\lambda e^{-\nu a}-\lambda}{\nu-\lambda}\\
&= 1-\frac{\nu e^{-\lambda a}-\lambda e^{-\nu a}}{\nu-\lambda}.
\end{aligned}
$$

(b) We can check this with `dsolve`, making use of the result of the previous exercise:

```
> zsol := dsolve({diff(z(a),a)
          -eval(nu*y(a),ysol)=0,z(0)=0},z(a)):
> zsol := simplify(zsol);
```

$$zsol := \mathrm{z}(a) = -\frac{-\nu e^{(-\lambda a)}+\lambda e^{(-\nu a)}+\nu-\lambda}{\lambda-\nu}$$

(c) As expected, the sum of the solutions evaluates to 1:

```
> simplify(exp(-lambda*a)
           +eval(y(a),ysol)+eval(z(a),zsol));
```

$$1$$

Solution 3.36

Typing the following produces the required plots for parts (a) and (b):

```
> lambda := 0.1:  nu := 32:
> fx := a->exp(-lambda*a):
> fz := a->rhs(zsol):
> plot([fx(a),fz(a)],a=0..70,colour=black);
> fy := a->rhs(ysol):
> plot(fy(a),a=0..70,colour=red);
```

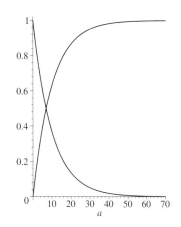

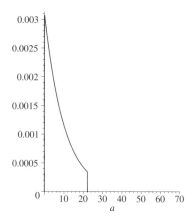

However, the second plot is odd – $y(a)$ just contains exponential functions so cannot have a singularity. What happens is that Maple had factorised the solution of the differential equation such that $y(a)$ contains the product of one term that grows exponentially and one that decays exponentially, and the apparent singularity arises from the loss of precision in the calculation.

This can be resolved by forcing Maple to expand the result before plotting:

```
> restart;
> ysol := dsolve({diff(y(a),a)
                  -lambda*exp(-lambda*a)
                  +nu*y(a)=0,y(0)=0},y(a)):
> ysol := expand(ysol);
> lambda := 0.1:  nu := 32:
> fy := a->rhs(ysol):
> plot(fy(a),a=0..70,colour=red);
```

$$ysol := \mathrm{y}(a) = -\frac{\lambda}{(\lambda-\nu)\,e^{(\lambda a)}}+\frac{\lambda}{e^{(\nu a)}\,(\lambda-\nu)}$$

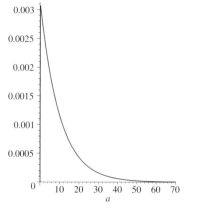

Solution 3.37

(a) `smrandiff` differs from `smdiff` on lines #1, #2, #3 and #4 (as numbered below):

```
> smrandiff := proc(K,KD,norb,lorb)        #1
>   local i,j,xi,dy,xc,yc,Ki;               #2
>   uses Statistics;
>   Ki := Sample(K*                         #3
         (1+RandomVariable(Normal(0,KD))),
         lorb);
>   xi := Sample(Uniform(0,2*Pi),norb);
>   dy := Array(1..lorb):
```

```
>     for j to norb do
>       xc := xi[j];
>       yc := 0;
>       for i to lorb do
>         yc := yc+Ki[i]*sin(xc);          #4
>         xc := xc+yc;
>         dy[i] := dy[i]+yc^2;
>       end do:
>     end do:
>     [[0,0],seq([i,dy[i]/norb],i=1..lorb)];
>   end proc:
```

The standard deviation is input as KD, and Ki (defined on line #3) is a vector containing the random coefficients K_n. These are used in the inner loop on line #4. The program thus performs an average of orbits for a fixed choice of parameters K_n.

(b) The modification of the other program is minimal, since we just need to pass on the additional parameter KD and call `smrandiff` rather than `smdiff`.

```
>   smranfitplot := proc(K,KD,norb,lorb)
>     local data,xd,yd,i,fitfun,
>           fitplot,dataplot;
>     uses plots,Statistics;
>     data := smrandiff(K,KD,norb,lorb);
>     xd := <seq(data[i,1],i=1..lorb+1)>;
>     yd := <seq(data[i,2],i=1..lorb+1)>;
>     fitfun := Fit(a+b*n,xd,yd,n);
>     print(evalf[6](fitfun));
>     fitplot := plot(fitfun(n),n=0..lorb);
>     dataplot := plot(data,style=point,
>              colour=black,symbol=circle);
>     display(dataplot,fitplot);
>   end proc:
```

The plots are

```
>   smranfitplot(10,0.01,500,50);
```
$$43.0367 + 28.0777\,n$$

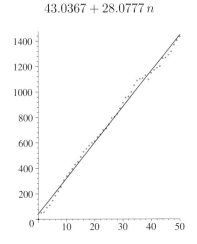

```
>   smranfitplot(10,0.1,500,50);
```
$$24.3986 + 31.7060\,n$$

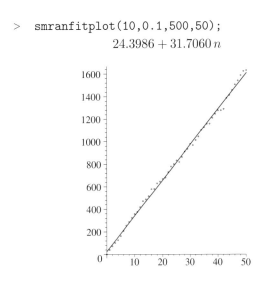

```
>   smranfitplot(10,0.2,500,50);
```
$$-83.2939 + 41.2753\,n$$

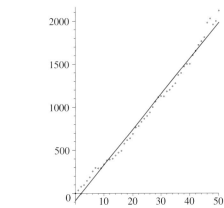

```
>   smranfitplot(10,0.5,500,50);
```
$$127.948 + 57.0146\,n$$

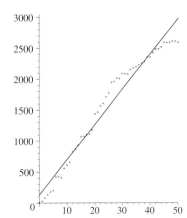

In this particular case, the presence of randomness increases the slope. However, to be sure that this effect is not an artifact, you need to average over many realisations of the distribution for the coefficient K.

Solution 3.38

The following procedure produces the required plot. It differs from `dsmodel6` on lines #1, #2, #3, #4, #5 and #6:

```
>   dsmodel6n := proc(R0,nu,mu,y0,eps,plran,
                      np,yscal)                  #1
>     local dseqs,dssol,xf,yf,pl1,pl2;           #2
>     uses plots;
>     xf := 1/R0;
      yf := mu/(nu+mu)*(R0-1)/R0;                #3
>     pl1 := plot([xf,yscal*yf,1-xf-yf],         #4
                  plran,colour=grey);
>     dseqs := {diff(x(t),t)-mu*(1-x(t))
                  +R0*(nu+mu)*x(t)*y(t)=0,
                diff(y(t),t)
                  -(nu+mu)*(R0*x(t)-1)*y(t)=0,
                x(0)=1-y0, y(0)=y0};
>     dssol := dsolve(dseqs,{x(t),y(t)},
                  numeric,abserr=eps);
>     pl2 := odeplot(dssol,
                [[t,x(t),colour=black],
                [t,yscal*y(t),colour=red],       #5
                [t,1-x(t)-y(t),colour=black]],
                plran,numpoints=np);
>     display(pl2,pl1,view=[plran,0..1]);        #6
>   end proc:
```

Here are the two plots, where we choose to enhance $y(t)$ by a factor of 20 and 4, respectively:

```
>   dsmodel6n(25/3,12,1/70,1e-4,1e-50,
              0..100,1000,20);
```

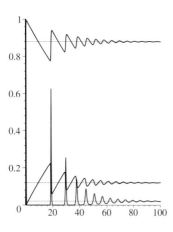

```
>   dsmodel6n(4,12,1/70,1e-4,1e-50,
              0..200,1000,4);
```

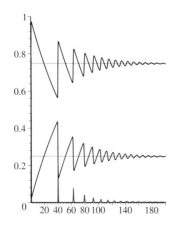

Solution 3.39

(a) Adding the right-hand sides of Equations (3.32)–(3.34) gives

$$
\begin{aligned}
\dot{x} + \dot{y} + \dot{z} &= \mu(1-x) - \kappa x - (\nu+\mu)R_0 x y \\
&\quad + \kappa x + (\nu+\mu)(R_0 x - 1)y \\
&\quad + \nu y - \mu z \\
&= \mu(1 - x - y - z),
\end{aligned}
$$

which vanishes for $x + y + z = 1$.

(b) The fixed points are obtained by setting $\dot{x} = \dot{y} = \dot{z} = 0$. The equations for x_f, y_f and z_f are

$$
\begin{aligned}
0 &= \mu(1 - x_f) - \kappa\, x_f - (\nu+\mu)R_0\, x_f\, y_f, \\
0 &= \kappa\, x_f + (\nu+\mu)(R_0\, x_f - 1)\, y_f, \\
0 &= \nu\, y_f - \mu\, z_f.
\end{aligned}
$$

Adding the first two equations gives

$$
0 = \mu(1 - x_f) - (\nu+\mu)\, y_f,
$$

which we can solve for y_f:

$$
y_f = \frac{\mu}{\nu+\mu}(1 - x_f).
$$

Inserting this in either of the first two equations yields a quadratic equation for x_f:

$$
\begin{aligned}
0 &= \mu(1 - x_f) - \kappa\, x_f - \mu R_0\, x_f\,(1 - x_f) \\
&= \mu R_0\, x_f^2 - (\mu R_0 + \mu + \kappa)\, x_f + \mu.
\end{aligned}
$$

The solutions of this equation are

$$
x_f = \frac{\mu R_0 + \mu + \kappa \pm \sqrt{(\mu R_0 + \mu + \kappa)^2 - 4\mu^2 R_0}}{2\mu R_0}.
$$

The corresponding values of y_f and z_f are

$$
y_f = \frac{\mu}{\nu+\mu}(1 - x_f), \quad z_f = \frac{\nu}{\mu}\, y_f = \frac{\nu}{\nu+\mu}(1 - x_f).
$$

For $\kappa = 0$ we find

$$
\begin{aligned}
x_f &= \frac{\mu R_0 + \mu \pm \sqrt{(\mu R_0 + \mu)^2 - 4\mu^2 R_0}}{2\mu R_0} \\
&= \frac{\mu R_0 + \mu \pm \sqrt{(\mu R_0 - \mu)^2}}{2\mu R_0},
\end{aligned}
$$

which gives either $x_f = 1$ or $x_f = 1/R_0$. The former yields $y_f = z_f = 0$, which is the fixed point of Equations (3.27), while the latter gives

$$
y_f = \frac{\mu}{\nu+\mu}\left(1 - \frac{1}{R_0}\right) = \frac{\mu(R_0 - 1)}{(\nu+\mu)R_0},
$$

$$
z_f = \frac{\nu}{\mu}\, y_f = \frac{\nu(R_0 - 1)}{(\nu+\mu)R_0},
$$

in agreement with Equations (3.28).

(c) Again, it suffices to consider the two-dimensional dynamical system involving x and y, since we have $x + y + z = 1$. The derivatives are

$$
\begin{aligned}
f_x(x_f, y_f) &= -\mu - \kappa - (\nu+\mu)R_0\, y_f \\
&= -\mu - \kappa - \mu R_0(1 - x_f), \\
f_y(x_f, y_f) &= -(\nu+\mu)R_0\, x_f, \\
g_x(x_f, y_f) &= \kappa + (\nu+\mu)R_0\, y_f = \kappa + \mu R_0(1 - x_f), \\
g_y(x_f, y_f) &= (\nu+\mu)(R_0\, x_f - 1),
\end{aligned}
$$

so the corresponding Jacobian is

$$
\mathbf{J}(x_f, y_f)
$$
$$
= \begin{pmatrix} -\mu - \kappa - \mu R_0(1 - x_f) & -(\nu+\mu)R_0\, x_f \\ \kappa + \mu R_0(1 - x_f) & (\nu+\mu)(R_0\, x_f - 1) \end{pmatrix}.
$$

(d) For the parameter values, we find $x_f \simeq 1.0023$ or $x_f \simeq 0.2494$. Since the former value is larger than 1, we only consider the latter. The Jacobian becomes

$$\mathbf{J}(x_f, y_f) \simeq \begin{pmatrix} -0.0573 & -11.9863 \\ 0.0430 & -0.0279 \end{pmatrix},$$

which has eigenvalues $\lambda_{1,2} \simeq -0.0426 \pm 0.7177i$, which shows that the fixed point is a stable spiral.

The corresponding Maple code is:

```
>  xf1 := ((mu*R0+mu+kappa)
              +sqrt((mu*R0+mu+kappa)^2
              -4*mu^2*R0))/(2*mu*R0):
>  xf2 := ((mu*R0+mu+kappa)
              -sqrt((mu*R0+mu+kappa)^2
              -4*mu^2*R0))/(2*mu*R0):
>  evalf[6](eval(xf1,{R0=4,mu=1/70,
              kappa=1e-4}));
>  evalf[6](eval(xf2,{R0=4,mu=1/70,
              kappa=1e-4}));
                  1.00233
                  0.249419
>  J := eval(Matrix([[-mu-kappa
              -mu*R0*(1-xf2),-(nu+mu)*R0*xf2],
              [kappa+mu*R0*(1-xf2),
              (nu+mu)*(R0*xf2-1)]]),
              {R0=4,nu=12,mu=1/70,kappa=1e-4}):
>  evalf[6](J);
```

$$J := \begin{bmatrix} -0.0572762 & -11.9864 \\ 0.0429905 & -0.0279 \end{bmatrix}$$

```
>  with(LinearAlgebra):
>  evalf[6](Eigenvalues(J));
```

$$\begin{bmatrix} -0.04259 + 0.717850\,I \\ -0.04259 - 0.717850\,I \end{bmatrix}$$

Solution 3.40

(a) We alter `simul2` by adding a parameter `kappa` for κ, altering the total rate `totrate` accordingly, and providing an additional `elif` to the conditional to simulate infection by external contact.

```
>  simul3 := proc(beta,nu,mu,kappa,
                  totpop,infect,nsteps)
>     local totrate,X,Y,Z,rd1,rd2,r2,Xdata,
              Ydata,Zdata,ct,i;
>     uses Statistics;
>     rd1 := Sample(Exponential(1),nsteps);
>     rd2 := Sample(Uniform(0,1),nsteps);
>     X := totpop-infect;
      Y := infect;
      Z := 0;
>     ct := 0;
>     Xdata := [ct,X];
      Ydata := [ct,Y];
      Zdata := [ct,Z];
>     for i to nsteps do
>        if Y=0 then break end if;
>        totrate := 2*mu*(X+Y+Z)+beta*X*Y+nu*Y
                  +kappa*X;
>        ct := ct+rd1[i]/totrate;
>        r2 := rd2[i]*totrate;
```

```
>        if r2<beta*X*Y then          # infection
>           X := X-1;   Y := Y+1;
>           Xdata := Xdata,[ct,X];
>           Ydata := Ydata,[ct,Y];
>        elif r2<beta*X*Y+nu*Y then   # recovery
>           Y := Y-1;   Z := Z+1;
>           Ydata := Ydata,[ct,Y];
>           Zdata := Zdata,[ct,Z];
>  # Next line for birth
>        elif r2<beta*X*Y+nu*Y+mu*(X+Y+Z) then
>           X := X+1:
>           Xdata := Xdata,[ct,X];
>  # Next line for death in X
>        elif r2<beta*X*Y+nu*Y+mu*(2*X+Y+Z)
              then
>           X := X-1:
>           Xdata := Xdata,[ct,X];
>  # Next line for death in Y
>        elif r2<beta*X*Y+nu*Y+mu*(2*X+2*Y+Z)
              then
>           Y := Y-1:
>           Ydata := Ydata,[ct,Y];
>  # Next line for death in Z
>        elif r2<beta*X*Y+nu*Y+2*mu*(X+Y+Z)
              then
>           Z := Z-1:
>           Zdata := Zdata,[ct,Z];
>        else               # external infection
>           X := X-1;   Y := Y+1;
>           Xdata := Xdata,[ct,X];
>           Ydata := Ydata,[ct,Y];
>        end if;
>     end do;
>     print("basic reproductive rate R0:",
              evalf[3](beta*totpop/(nu+mu)));
>     print("total number of steps;",i-1);
>     print("final populations:",X,Y,Z);
>     [Xdata],[Ydata],[Zdata];
>  end proc:
```

(b) A typical plot with a persistent disease is shown below.

```
>  data := simul3(1/2,50,1,1/10,1000,
                  1,20000):
>  plot([data],colour=[black,red,black]);
```
```
          "basic reproductive rate R0:", 9.80
               "total number of steps;", 6110
               "final populations:", 152, 0, 834
```

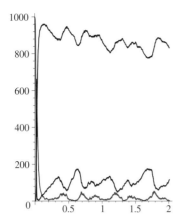

(c) The corresponding plot of the deterministic model is

```
>  dsmodel8(9.8,50,1,0,1e-3,1e-50,0..2,200);
```

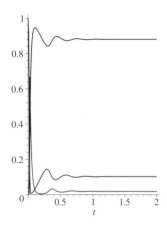

As observed before, the stochastic model shows a qualitatively similar behaviour to the deterministic model, but displays large fluctuations for small populations.

Solution 3.41

We load the plots, Statistics and LinearAlgebra packages by typing

```
>  with(plots):
```

```
>  with(Statistics):
```

```
>  with(LinearAlgebra):
```

(a) The matrix is obtained by typing

```
>  Matrix([[a],[b,c],[d,e,f]],
        shape=symmetric);
```

$$\begin{bmatrix} a & b & d \\ b & c & e \\ d & e & f \end{bmatrix}$$

(b) A symmetric matrix is obtained by a sequence of lists of random numbers of increasing length, as follows:

```
>  evalf[6](Matrix([seq(convert(Sample(
      Normal(0,1),i),list),i=1..3)],
      shape=symmetric));
```

$$\begin{bmatrix} 0.978197 & -0.712436 & -0.641276 \\ -0.712436 & 0.519839 & 0.172364 \\ -0.641276 & 0.172364 & 1.42459 \end{bmatrix}$$

Of course, you can also produce a 3×3 symmetric random matrix in a different way, but the advantage of this approach is that it can easily be adapted to produce large matrices.

(c) The following code produces the desired result:

```
>  N:=50:
```

```
>  rmat := Matrix([seq(convert(Sample(
      Normal(0,1),i),list),i=1..N)],
      shape=symmetric):
```

```
>  evlis := Eigenvalues(rmat):
```

```
>  evlis1 :=
      sort(evlis)/sort(abs(evlis))[-1]:
```

```
>  hist := Histogram(evlis1,binwidth=1/20,
                colour=red):
```

```
>  semi := plot(2*sqrt(1-x^2)/Pi,x=-1..1,
                colour=black):
```

```
>  display(hist,semi);
```

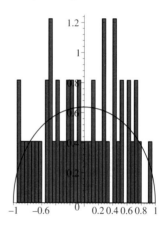

Here, evlis1 contains the eigenvalues of the matrix rmat. Since sort(abs(evlis)) sorts the moduli of the eigenvalues into increasing order, sort(abs(evlis))[-1] is the maximum absolute eigenvalue. Hence evlis1 contains the rescaled eigenvalues.

Repeating the same calculation with $N = 500$ gives a closer match to the distribution function, as shown below.

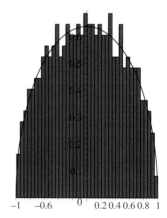

(d) The spacing distribution is obtained by typing

```
> N := 50:
> rmat := Matrix([seq(convert(Sample(
    Normal(0,1),i),list),i=1..N)],
    shape=symmetric):
> evmat := sort(convert(Eigenvalues(rmat),
                list)):
> spaclis := [seq(abs(evmat[i+1]-evmat[i]),
                i=1..N-1)]:
> meanspac := add(spaclis[i],
                i=1..N-1)/(N-1):
> spaclis1 := spaclis/meanspac:
> hist := Histogram(spaclis1,binwidth=1/10,
                colour=red):
> wigner := plot(Pi*s*exp(-Pi*s^2/4)/2,
                s=0..4,colour=black):
> display(hist,wigner);
```

Here `spaclis` is a list of the spacings between adjacent eigenvalues, and `meanspac` is their mean. Hence `spaclis1` is a list of the normalised spacings.

The same program with $N = 500$ produces a reasonable match with the function $P(s)$:

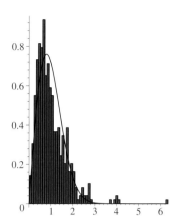

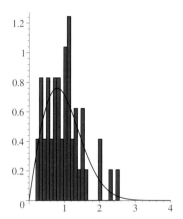

UNIT 4   Simulations: traffic flow and the trebuchet

Study guide

This unit is composed of two main topics, namely traffic flow and the trebuchet, and you will be required to use Maple throughout. The first section, on traffic flow, is relatively short, and you should attempt as many of the exercises as time allows. The remainder of this lengthy unit concerns the simulation and study of the trebuchet. If time is short we suggest that you study the non-optional parts of Sections 4.5–4.7, completing as many of the exercises as possible, then skim Section 4.8, noting the salient points discussed at the beginning of that section, then study Section 4.9. The end exercises on the trebuchet are quite lengthy and extend the work of the main text, so may be regarded as optional.

You should note that for those solutions depending on generated random numbers, you may obtain slightly different numerical results to those given in the text.

PART I: Modelling traffic flow

4.1   Introduction

This section is concerned with a simple traffic flow model which provides an explanation for why traffic jams form spontaneously in dense traffic, without any apparent reason. It is an example of a cellular automaton model; similar models are used in many practical applications (for instance in queuing theory).

We consider a simple traffic flow model for single-lane road traffic. The model was first investigated by Nagel and Schreckenberg in 1992. It uses a discrete description of space and time, and the speed of the cars is also taken to be discrete. Therefore this model belongs to a class of models called cellular automata, which can conveniently be investigated by computer. (Perhaps the best known example of cellular automata is Conway's *Game of life*.)

K. Nagel and M. Schreckenberg (1992) 'A cellular automaton model for freeway traffic', *Journal de Physique I France*, **2**, 2221–9.

4.2   Modelling traffic flow

Despite its simplicity, the model described below provides some insight into the formation of traffic jams. More elaborate models based on the same idea have been used for large-scale modelling of highway traffic in the Ruhr valley in Germany.

Since time is treated as a discrete variable, the model has to provide a set of rules that determine how a given traffic situation evolves from one time instant to the next. In a single time step, the model invokes four rules for each car, determining the changes in position of the cars and changes in speed due to acceleration or braking. In what follows, we introduce the ingredients of the model one by one.

4.2.1   Position and speed of cars

Space is discrete, so we think of the single-lane road as being partitioned into L cells of equal size. Each cell is either empty or occupied by a single car. In total, there are N cars, with $N \leq L$, and N/L measures the traffic density. An example configuration of $N = 3$ cars on $L = 10$ cells is shown in Figure 4.1.

In real-world applications, the cell size is usually taken as 7.5 metres.

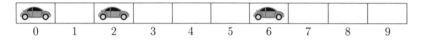

Figure 4.1   Example configuration of $N = 3$ cars on a road of length $L = 10$

The first task is to represent such a configuration in Maple, keeping it sufficiently general so we can use the setup later for our simulations. A convenient way to encode the positions p_n, $n = 1, 2, \ldots, N$, of the cars is in a list of length N (the number of cars). For reasons that will become clear later, it is preferable to denote the positions by $p_n \in \{0, 1, 2, \ldots, L - 1\}$, so we count from 0 rather than from 1. Because the model does not include the possibility of overtaking, it is reasonable to number cars sequentially, so that $0 \leq p_1 < p_2 < \cdots < p_N \leq L - 1$, which means that we know that the car labelled by $n - 1$ is following the car labelled by n (with cars moving from left to right).

For each car on the road, the speed v_n $(n = 1, \ldots, N)$ is an integer between 0 and $v_{\max}$, and we may assume that $v_{\max} < L$. In Maple, we collect these values in another list of length N, again with integer entries, this time in the range $v_n \in \{0, 1, \ldots, v_{\max}\}$.

Exercise 4.1

(a) Use Maple to prepare two lists, `pos` and `speed`, representing the initial configuration, with N cars at positions $p_n = (n - 1)L/N$, all having speed $v_n = 1$, $n = 1, \ldots, N$, for $N = 5$ and $L = 20$.

(b) Compute a list `dist` of distances $d_n = p_{n+1} - p_n$ between adjacent cars, and calculate the mean distance.

4.2.2   A circular road

Consider a finite section of road consisting of L cells, with all cars moving in the same direction according to the rules described in the next subsection. Eventually, all cars initially in this section will move out leaving an empty road.

There are two possible ways to prevent this. The first is to feed cars in at the leftmost cell 0 at a certain rate. The second is to make the road into a closed loop. Then the density of cars on the road will be constant, because no cars can enter or leave. As it is more straightforward to implement the boundary conditions for a circular road, we shall concentrate on this case.

On a circular road consisting of L cells, the cell numbered $L - 1$ is followed by cell 0. So a car in cell $L - 1$, after moving on one cell, will occupy cell 0. If it moves two cells in a single time step, it will end up in cell 1. In mathematical terms, this means that we consider positions modulo L, where $b = a \bmod L$ is an integer such that $a - b$ is divisible by L; we usually choose to take values $b \in \{0, 1, \ldots, L - 1\}$. Here, the position of a car initially in cell $L - 1$ that moves s cells forward is given by $(L - 1 + s) \bmod L$, which is an integer between 0 and $L - 1$. In Maple, this is implemented by using `mod`.

Exercise 4.2

(a) Calculate 3 mod 5, 7 mod 5, 10 mod 5 and -2 mod 5 in Maple.

(b) Enter 4 + 7 mod 5 and 4 + (7 mod 5) in Maple, and compare the output.

(c) Use `mod` to create the list $[1, 1, 3, 2, 5, 3, 7, 4, \ldots, 19, 10]$ obtained by dividing the even numbers in $[1, 2, 3, \ldots, 20]$ by 2.

Note that on the circular road we need to relax the condition that the positions are ordered as $0 \leq p_1 < p_2 < \cdots < p_N \leq L - 1$, since we do not wish to re-label cars as they circle around. However, we still want them to be ordered sequentially, so that neighbouring entries correspond to neighbouring cars. Initially, we can start from an arrangement where $0 \leq p_1 < p_2 < \cdots < p_N \leq L - 1$.

The distance between two cars at positions p_n and p_{n+1} is now given as follows. If $p_{n+1} > p_n$, we are in the situation as before, and the distance is simply $d_n = p_{n+1} - p_n$. However, if $p_{n+1} - p_n < 0$, which means that car $n + 1$ has passed cell $L - 1$ and moved around the circular track, the distance is $p_{n+1} - p_n + L$. This can be conveniently expressed as

$$d_n = (p_{n+1} - p_n) \bmod L,$$

so calculating the differences between the positions, modulo the road length, will automatically yield the correct car distances. So d_n is always the distance between the car with position p_n and the car in front.

Note the example -2 mod 5 in Exercise 4.2(a).

Exercise 4.3

(a) For the same initial positions as in Exercise 4.1, calculate the distances `circdist` between adjacent cars on a circular road, and calculate the corresponding mean distance. (Remember to include the distance between the first and last cars, which are now adjacent.)

(b) Now consider the general case of N cars on a circular road consisting of L cells, and calculate the mean distance between cars (without using Maple). Is the mean distance a good quantity for analysing the traffic situation?

4.2.3 Modelling the motion of cars

The main variables in the model are the position p_n and the speed v_n of each car. As mentioned above, we treat time as a discrete variable. In each time step, the position and speed of each car is updated, describing the motion of the car due to its present speed, and a possible change in speed, for example to prevent collision with the car ahead.

Forward motion of cars

In each time step, each car moves ahead a number of cells, according to its current speed v_n. This is an integer between 0 and v_{max}, so a car at speed 0 stays put, a car at speed 1 moves one cell ahead, a car at speed 2 moves two cells, and so on. The maximum distance a car can travel in a single time step is thus v_{max} cells. An example is shown in Figure 4.2.

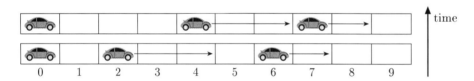

Figure 4.2 One time step of the motion of $N = 3$ cars on a road of length $L = 10$. The bottom row shows cars at their initial positions $p_1 = 0$, $p_2 = 2$ and $p_3 = 6$, with arrows indicating speeds $v_1 = 0$ (no arrow), $v_2 = 2$ and $v_3 = 1$, respectively. Cars two and three move ahead retaining their speed, resulting in the configuration shown in the top row.

Exercise 4.4

Consider the case $L = 20$ with a single car at speed 3. If the car is initially at position $p = 7$, to where does it move in the next time step? If the road is circular, and the car is at position $p = 19$, to where does it move?

So the rule is that a car with speed v at position p with $0 \leq p \leq L - 1$ moves to position $p' = p + v$, as long as $p' \leq L - 1$. Otherwise, the car either leaves the system or, for a circular road, moves to position $p' = p + v - L$ (assuming that $v < L$). For a circular road, we can neatly express this rule as $p' = (p + v) \bmod L$. The boundary conditions for a circular road amount to using addition modulo L, which always results in an integer between 0 and $L - 1$.

This is the reason why we prefer to count the position from 0.

Example 4.1

Write a Maple function `drive` which implements the driving step for a circular road.

Solution

The following function implements the driving step for car position list `pl`, speed list `sl` and road length `len`.

```
>  drive := (pl,sl,len) -> (pl+sl) mod len:
```

Note that we can add two lists together and apply the `mod` function to the entire list, with the same effect as performing these operations element by element. ♦

Exercise 4.5

With `pos` and `speed` as given in Exercise 4.1, apply ten driving steps with the function `drive` and observe the changes in positions.

Accelerating

So far, cars are moving at constant speed. However, most drivers tend to try to move as quickly as allowed, so whenever possible they will try to accelerate towards the maximum permitted speed. This is modelled by increasing the speed of cars which are not yet travelling at maximum speed v_{max} by one in each time step. This means that a car travelling at speed v accelerates to speed $v' = \min(v + 1, v_{\mathrm{max}})$ in the time step.

$\min(x, y)$ gives the minimum of x and y.

Exercise 4.6

Write a Maple procedure `accelerate` which accelerates the speed according to the rule explained above.

Braking to keep a safe distance

Driving at constant or increasing speed is not always possible – indeed, with the rules above, cars may end up in the same cell or even overtake each other, which we do not want to happen on our single-lane road. We therefore assume that all drivers are sensible and adjust their speed to keep a safe distance from the car in front. This means that in each time step, we must ensure that the speed of each car is at most equal to the number of empty cells in front of the car.

In other words, speeds are adjusted according to the rule

$$v'_n = \min(v_n, (p_{n+1} - p_n - 1) \bmod L), \quad \text{for } n = 1, 2, \dots, N - 1,$$
$$v'_N = \min(v_N, (p_1 - p_N - 1) \bmod L).$$

Therefore a car for which the cell ahead is occupied must wait for the car ahead to move out of the way. An example is shown in Figure 4.3.

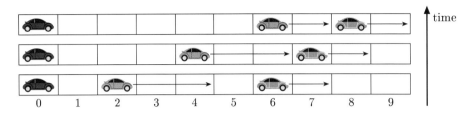

Figure 4.3 This figure shows the effect of braking alone (no acceleration). In the second time step, the car $n = 2$ needs to brake to speed $v_2 = 1$ (top row).

Example 4.2

Write a Maple procedure `brake` that adjusts the speeds according to the distances between cars.

Solution

The procedure inputs are the list of positions `pl`, the list of current speeds `sl` and the length `len` of the circular road.

```
>   brake := proc(pl,sl,len)
>       local n;
>       [seq(min(sl[n],(pl[n+1]-pl[n]-1) mod len),
        n=1..nops(sl)-1), min(sl[-1],(pl[1]-pl[-1]-1) mod len)]
>   end proc:
```

Recall that if X is a list or expression sequence, then X[-1] is its last element.

Here, `min` is used to select the minimum between the current speed and the number of free cells ahead, given by $(p_{n+1} - p_n - 1)$ mod L. The `mod` function takes care of the circular boundary conditions. ♦

Exercise 4.7

Consider the example of Figure 4.3 and show that the function `drive` and procedure `brake` reproduce the expected behaviour.

More generally, we need to introduce the effect of both acceleration and braking into our model. The procedures `accelerate` and `brake` both affect the speeds of the cars. In order to simulate traffic flow, we have to perform the two in the correct order – first accelerate, then brake (if necessary) to ensure a safe distance. An example is shown in Figure 4.4.

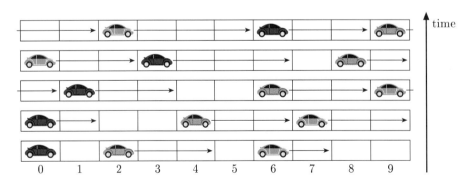

Figure 4.4 This figure shows the effect of acceleration and braking over four time steps, assuming that $v_{\max} = 3$

Since the two steps are always performed together, it is preferable to combine them into a single procedure in Maple. It turns out that this can be done by slightly modifying the `brake` procedure, where instead of comparing the number of free cells $(p_{n+1} - p_n - 1) \bmod L$ with the current speed v_n, we compare it with the accelerated speed $v_n + 1$, provided that this does not exceed v_{max}. This is done in the following example.

Example 4.3

Combine the two procedures `accelerate` and `brake` into a single procedure `adjust`.

Solution

The code of the procedure `accelerate` is modified so that the speed is limited by v_{max}, using `min` as in the procedure `brake`.

```
>   adjust := proc(pl,sl,len,vmax)
>      local n;
>      [seq(min(sl[n]+1,(pl[n+1]-pl[n]-1) mod len,vmax),
         n=1..nops(sl)-1), min(sl[-1]+1,(pl[1]-pl[-1]-1) mod len,
         vmax)]
>   end proc:
```

♦

Exercise 4.8

Consider the example of Figure 4.4 and show that the function `drive` and procedure `adjust` reproduce the expected behaviour. (You may assume that $v_{max} = 3$.)

4.2.4 A first simulation

We now have the necessary ingredients to simulate car movement. For the time being, we stick with a small example of $N = 5$ cars on a circular road of $L = 20$ cells. In the following example we go through 50 time steps.

Example 4.4

Starting from initial positions $p_n = (n-1)L/N$ and speeds $v_n = 0$ for $n = 1, \ldots, N$, with $N = 5$ cars on a circular road of length $L = 20$, write a Maple program that performs 50 driving steps, using the procedure `adjust` and function `drive`, with $v_{max} = 5$.

Solution

A `for` loop is used to perform the 50 steps.

```
>   L := 20:  N := 5:  vmax := 5:  nstep := 50:
>   speed := [0$N]; pos := [seq((n-1)*L/N,n=1..N)];
>   for i to nstep do
>      speed := adjust(pos,speed,L,vmax);
>      pos := drive(pos,speed,L);
>   end do;
```

The output is not shown here (see the Maple worksheet). If you execute this program, you receive (apart from the initial data) 50 successive results for each of the lists `speed` and `pos`.   ◆

Example 4.4 shows that the program works as expected – you can see this by looking at how the positions and speeds change. If you look closely, you may notice that the speed settles to $v_n = 3$ for all $n = 1, \ldots, 5$, and that all cars, after an initial acceleration, move at constant distances from each other with the same speed. So this case appears a little boring, and there seems to be no traffic jam on the horizon. However, we shall soon see how adding a little randomness to the rules alters this situation.

Before we do this we need to find a useful way of representing the motion of our cars. It is not particularly useful to receive the complete output of all the positions and speeds, as we did above, particularly for larger simulations with many cars on a road consisting of hundreds or thousands of cells. Instead, it is much more convenient to visualise the motion using a graphical representation, allowing us to actually 'see' how the cars move around the circular road. To do this, we modify our program so that the information about the positions is collected during the simulation.

Example 4.5

(a) Modify the program of Example 4.4 to accumulate the positions of $N = 5$ cars (maximum speed $v_{\max} = 5$) on a circular road of length $L = 150$ for 100 steps, by making `pos` a list of lists whose first element is the list of initial positions.

(b) Produce a plot of the positions of cars, highlighting the motion of one specific car.

Solution

(a) This can be done in the following way.

```
>   L := 150:  N := 5:  vmax := 5:  nstep := 100:
>   speed := [0$N]:  pos := [[seq((n-1)*L/N,n=1..N)]]:
>   for i to nstep do
>      speed := adjust(pos[-1],speed,L,vmax);
>      pos := [op(pos),drive(pos[-1],speed,L)];
>   end do:
>   pos;
```

Again the output is not shown here (see the Maple worksheet); as required, it consists of a list containing the positions of cars throughout the simulation.

If you compare this with the code of Example 4.4, you will find that `pos` is now a list of lists, initialised as required. The two lines in the main loop have been modified accordingly, with `pos[-1]` referring to the last element in the list `pos`, which corresponds to the current positions. At the end of each step, the new positions are appended to the end of the list `pos`.

(b) Now we want to plot the position of the cars as they move along. To do this, we define two functions `carplot` and `carline` which produce plots of the motion of a single car, as a set of points and as a line, respectively.

```
> carplot := n -> plot([seq([pos[t,n],t],t=1..nops(pos))],
            style=point,symbolsize=10):
> carline := n -> plot([seq([pos[t,n],t],t=1..nops(pos))],
            style=line,colour=black,thickness=1):
```

The reason for choosing both presentations is that, in this particular example, it turns out that representing cars by points does not show the motion very clearly, because cars are moving at speed 3 and distance 4, so it is not visually obvious which points correspond to the same car. Highlighting the motion of a single car by a line improves the presentation.

Figures 4.5–4.7 show the plots obtained using `carplot(1)`, `carline(1)`, and

```
> with(plots):
> display(seq(carplot(n),n=1..N),carline(1));
```

which depicts the motion of all cars and highlights the motion of car number 1 by a continuous line. The positions of the cars are along the horizontal direction, while time increases along the vertical axis – so this is like a 'condensed' view of the presentation used in Figures 4.1–4.4. ♦

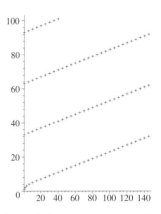

Figure 4.5   Visualisation of the motion of one car (car 1) in Example 4.5, as a set of points

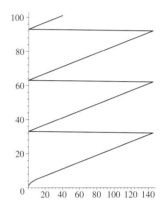

Figure 4.6   Visualisation of the motion of one car (car 1) in Example 4.5, as a line

Exercise 4.9

Modify the parameters of Example 4.5 to simulate $N = 5$ cars moving on a circular road consisting of $L = 150$ cells with maximum speed $v_{max} = 5$. The cars are initially at rest (i.e. speed $v_n = 0$) at positions $p_1 = 0$, $p_2 = 10$, $p_3 = 20$, $p_4 = 30$, $p_5 = 40$. Display the data corresponding to 100 time steps.

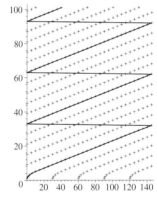

Figure 4.7   Visualisation of the motion of all cars in Example 4.5, with car 1 highlighted by a continuous line

4.2.5   Traffic jams in a stochastic model

The model so far does not include any randomness. Once the initial configuration is given, the rules determine the motion. From the examples considered so far, it seems plausible that the system settles in a regular, 'laminar' motion where cars move as quickly as possible.

To obtain a more realistic picture, we add a random element to the rules. This is done by slowing down a car randomly, by reducing its speed v_n by one (provided that $v_n > 0$). In reality, this might correspond to a driver who is overreacting when braking in order to keep a safe distance from the car in front, or a driver who is taking longer to accelerate, or a driver who just dropped his speed because of a distraction. It does not matter to us why a driver does not stay at the optimum speed; all we consider is what happens as a consequence of this behaviour.

To implement this in our Maple code, we use binary random numbers provided by the `Bernoulli` distribution in the `Statistics` package. Here `Bernoulli(x)` corresponds to a distribution where 1 occurs with probability x and 0 occurs with probability $1 - x$. For the remainder of this section, we assume that the `Statistics` package has been loaded by executing `with(Statistics)`.

Exercise 4.10

Use the `Sample` command in the `Statistics` package to draw 10 random numbers from a Bernoulli distribution on $\{0, 1\}$, where 1 occurs with probability 0.3. Calculate the number of 1s in the sample, and compare with the expected number. Repeat the calculation five times, without restarting Maple.

Given a list of random numbers `rs`, the following Maple procedure `dawdle` reduces the speed of the cars `sl` accordingly.

```
>   dawdle := proc(sl,rs)
>     local n;
>     [seq(max(sl[n]-round(rs[n]),0),n=1..nops(sl))];
>   end proc:
```

Exercise 4.11

Create a list `speed` of length 10 with all entries 3. Apply the procedure `dawdle` ten times, each time drawing a new sample of random numbers `rs`, to repeatedly slow down cars with a probability 0.3. Observe how the speeds change.

Now we are in a position to put everything together and simulate traffic flow with the full model of Nagel and Schreckenberg. In the following example, we develop a Maple procedure `circtraffic1` which performs the simulation.

Example 4.6

(a) Write a Maple procedure `circtraffic1` which performs a number of steps for a given number of cars on a circular road, starting from a configuration where cars are at rest with maximal distances between them.

(b) Simulate traffic of $N = 5$ cars on a circular road consisting of $L = 200$ cells, for a maximum speed $v_{\max} = 5$ and probability 0.1 of slowing down. Consider 100 time steps and visualise the result.

(c) Simulate traffic of $N = 40$ cars on a circular road consisting of $L = 200$ cells, for a maximum speed $v_{\max} = 5$ and probability 0.1 of slowing down. Consider 100 time steps and visualise the result.

Solution

(a) The following procedure has as inputs the length of the road `len`, the number of cars `cars`, the maximum speed `vmax`, the probability of a random reduction in speed `dawprob`, and the number of steps `nstep`. It returns the accumulated list of positions.

```
>   circtraffic1 := proc(len,cars,vmax,dawprob,nstep)
>     local pl,sl,i,n,rs;
>     uses Statistics;                                        #1
>     if cars>len then                                        #2
>       return("error - too many cars");                      #3
>     end if;                                                 #4
>     pl := [[seq(trunc(n*len/cars),n=0..cars-1)]];           #5
>     sl := [0$cars];                                         #6
>     for i to nstep do                                       #7
>       rs := Sample(Bernoulli(dawprob),cars);                #8
>       sl := dawdle(adjust(pl[-1],sl,len,vmax),rs);          #9
>       pl := [op(pl),drive(pl[-1],sl,len)];                  #10
>     end do;                                                 #11
>     pl;                                                     #12
>   end proc:
```

On line **#1** we employ the command `uses`, introduced in *Unit C3*, which tells Maple that commands from a package are used in the procedure, and loaded when necessary. The subsequent `if` statement, on lines **#2** to **#4**, checks that the number of cars does not exceed the length of the road. The lists for the positions and speeds are initialised on lines **#5** and **#6**, where we distribute cars so that they are equally spaced on the road, using the `trunc` function to make sure that the positions are integers. The main loop, on lines **#7** to **#11**, contains calls to the procedures `dawdle`, `adjust` and `drive`. Line **#8** calculates the random speed reductions, line **#9** updates the speeds by performing the required accelerations followed by the random speed reductions, and line **#10** determines the new car positions.

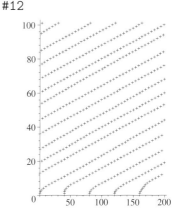

Figure 4.8   Visualisation of motion of the 5 cars in Example 4.6(b)

(b) We use the procedure `circtraffic1` with the given input parameters.

```
>   pos := circtraffic1(200,5,5,0.1,100):
>   display(seq(carplot(n),n=1..5));
```

An example graph is shown in Figure 4.8. You can see that the five cars stay well separated, and most of the time move at maximum speed.

(c) Using the same code as in part (b), replacing the number of cars by 40, yields a graph as shown in Figure 4.9. In this case, notice that in certain areas of the plot the cars are denser, and that these areas appear to move to the left (so backwards) as time progresses. These are small traffic jams which were created spontaneously, and they move backwards because cars get trapped at their ends, while cars speed off at the front of the traffic jam. Note that traffic jams can both arise and disappear spontaneously. ♦

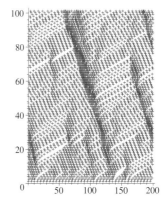

Figure 4.9   Visualisation of motion of the 40 cars in Example 4.6(c)

Exercise 4.12

(a) In the procedure `circtraffic1`, the `Sample` command is used within the main loop. As discussed in *Unit C3*, this causes Maple to slow down considerably. Write a modified procedure `circtraffic2` which draws all required random numbers once outside the loop.

(b) Compare the performance of `circtraffic1` and `circtraffic2` by simulating 200 time steps for $N = 100$ cars on a road of length $L = 500$, for maximum speed 5 and probability 0.1 of slowing down.

Exercise 4.13

Repeat the simulation of `circtraffic2` in Exercise 4.12(b), but for a smaller value, 0.01, for the probability of slowing down. What do you notice?

Further explorations of the properties of this model will be performed in the longer Exercises 4.14 and 4.15 below. In particular, Exercise 4.15 considers how the mean speed varies in relation to traffic density.

4.3   End of part exercises

Exercise 4.14

In this exercise, we look at the speed of cars during a simulation of the model introduced in Section 4.2.

(a) Modify procedure `circtraffic2` of Exercise 4.12 to obtain a procedure `circtraffic3` which returns two lists containing the values of positions and speeds of cars accumulated throughout the simulation.

(b) Use your procedure `circtraffic3` to simulate 250 time steps for $N = 150$ cars on a road of length $L = 500$, with maximum speed $v_{max} = 5$ and a probability of slowing down of 0.1. Use `carplot` and `carline` to plot the positions of cars, highlighting the path of the first car.

[*Hint*: To see the path of the first car clearly, you may have to adjust the values of `symbolsize` in `carplot` and `thickness` in `carline`. We use `symbolsize=3`, and `thickness=3` in the solution.]

(c) Create functions `posline` and `speedline` (similar to the function `carline` introduced in Example 4.5) which, for an individual car, plot its position and speed (vertically) as a function of the number of time steps (horizontally), respectively. For the simulation of part (b), plot the position and speed of the first car, and interpret the result.

(d) Calculate the average speed of the first car in the simulation of part (b), and the average speed of all cars. Compare the result with the maximum speed of cars, and the maximum achievable average speed of 150 cars on a road of length 500.

Exercise 4.15

In this exercise, we calculate the mean speed of cars during simulations of the model introduced in Section 4.2, and investigate how the mean speed depends on the traffic density.

(a) Modify procedure `circtraffic2` of Exercise 4.12 to obtain a procedure `circtraffic4` which calculates and returns the mean speed of the cars. In order to avoid the influence of initial conditions in the first few time steps, the procedure should first perform a number `ninit` initial time steps (which is another input variable) before calculating the average over `nstep` time steps.

(b) Calculate the mean speed for $N = 10k$ cars on a road of length 500, for $k = 1, 2, \ldots, 50$, with maximum speed $v_{\max} = 5$, using 100 initial steps and averaging over 500 time steps, and collect the data in a list. Produce three such lists for probabilities of slowing down of 0, 0.1 and 0.2.

(c) Plot the average speed as a function of car density N/L for the three cases, and interpret the result.

(d) Can you understand the graph for the case without randomness? Plot the mean speed for the three cases as function of the inverse density L/N, and discuss the graphs.

Note that the calculation in part (b) may take a long time, depending on your computer. If this happens, adapt the question by reducing the number of calculations or the size of the individual simulations.

PART II: The trebuchet

4.4   Introduction

The simulation discussed in this part is different from previous examples partly because it deals with a deterministic system and partly because our goals are different. We aim to understand how the system behaves and how this changes with the various system parameters; this cannot be achieved only by examining numerical solutions of the appropriate equations.

We study the motion of a trebuchet, which is a medieval siege engine. No prior knowledge of this is assumed, so it is described in some detail in Section 4.5, to accompany which we provide short video clips of two real trebuchets and a Maple animation. If you want more information on trebuchets, type 'trebuchet' into Google, or into Google Images for a variety of pictures; but do not spend too long perusing the thousands of sites unearthed, and remember that information on the internet is not always reliable.

A trebuchet may seem like an odd choice for a course written in the twenty-first century, but it provides a good example of a mechanical system that is simple to describe, yet sufficiently complicated for its workings to be quite subtle. Indeed, a trebuchet engineer in the middle ages was highly paid, being the equivalent of an IT expert today, because getting the details right could be the difference between a successful and an unsuccessful siege. Essentially a trebuchet can be viewed as a pivoted beam with a heavy pendulum attached to one end which drives a sling attached to the other end; in French a trebuchet is a small balance. In *Unit B1* we saw that the motion of two coupled pendulums can be chaotic, so we expect this possibility for this more complicated arrangement, but here we are concerned with short times during which the motion is complicated but the ideas of instability and chaos are not relevant.

169

We study a simplified version of the trebuchet in which there are six free parameters, four lengths and two masses, and three independent variables coupled together by three second-order nonlinear equations. These equations are complicated, though easily solved numerically. Our task, however, is not only to solve these equations but to understand why the solutions behave as they do, which is harder but more important. Consequently, this is a long, quite demanding part; if time is in short supply we suggest that you study Sections 4.5–4.7, then briefly skim Section 4.8, taking note of the salient points discussed at the beginning of that section, then study Section 4.9. The end of part exercises are quite lengthy and extend the work of the main text, so may be regarded as optional.

The derivation of these equations of motion is not part of the course, but it is provided on the course website; this derivation requires methods taught in Block III of MS324.

Section 4.5 contains a short historical introduction and a qualitative description of trebuchet mechanics. In Section 4.6 we consider a simple version of the system having fewer free parameters; in this section we use conventional mathematics to determine some properties of the motion, and in Section 4.7 we test these ideas numerically.

The three coupled equations for the complete trebuchet are given in Section 4.8, and there we discuss the two phases of the motion and derive approximate equations that determine the time when the motion changes phase. In Section 4.9 we apply these equations to particular types of trebuchet.

4.5   *The trebuchet*

The trebuchet is a siege weapon used mainly for throwing great weights large distances to breach castle walls: typically they could throw 100 kg about 200 m, though some estimate a distance in excess of 400 m; see Exercise 4.17.

Siege warfare is one of the oldest forms of conflict, and the respected military historian John Keegan[1] takes the view that before the advent of gunpowder, all siege techniques had been devised between 2400 and 400 BC. These techniques include surprise attacks, exploitation of the defender's complacency, treachery, battering rams, scaling ladders, siege towers, mine shafts and siege engines.

The trebuchet is a particular example of the collection of devices known as siege engines, and was the final development of stone-throwing engines before the use of gunpowder: a good account of the development of this technology is given by Bradbury[2]. An authoritative account of the history of catapults, the precursor of trebuchets, is provided by Rihll[3]. Nossov's book[4] is well illustrated, as are the booklets by Nicolle[5]. An enthusiastic view of the importance of the trebuchet is promoted in an article by Chevedden[6]; some of the claims in this paper are examined in Exercise 4.17.

[1] J. Keegan (1992) *A history of warfare*, Pimlico.

[2] J. Bradbury (1992) *The medieval siege*, The Boydell Press.

[3] T. Rihll (2007) *The catapult: a history*, Westholme Publishing.

[4] K. Nossov (2005) *Ancient and medieval siege weapons*, The Lyons Press.

[5] D. Nicolle (2002) *Medieval siege weapons (1), Western Europe AD 585–1385* and (2003) *Medieval siege weapons (2), Byzantium, the Islamic world and India AD 476–1526*, Osprey Publishing.

[6] P.E. Chevedden (2000) 'The invention of the counterweight trebuchet: a study in cultural diffusion', available online at `www.doaks.org/etexts.html`, under Dumbarton Oaks Papers No. 54.

There seems to be no agreed date for the first use of a trebuchet, partly because the texts describing sieges were rather casual with terminology and there are no clear descriptions; neither is it clear who first used a trebuchet as we now understand the term. But they seem to have been first used in the early twelfth century, roughly coinciding with the construction of stone castles. Any particular siege generally progressed though many stages (see, for instance, Bradbury's book) and was often concluded by the use of methods mentioned above. As a consequence, Keegan suggests that the significance of large siege engines has been exaggerated by the requirement of art and propaganda to emphasise the spectacular over the mundane – a common phenomenon.

From written texts and illustrations there is, however, no doubt that trebuchets were used frequently in the thirteenth century: Bradbury suggests that they were used during the first Crusade at the siege and capture of Nicaea (present day Iznik, near Constantinople) in 1097 and at Jerusalem in 1099.

Evidence that trebuchets were new in England in the twelfth century comes from the siege of Wark, in Northumberland, by William the Lion, king of Scots, during his rebellion against Henry II. In 1174 King William ordered an engine whose maker claimed would demolish the gate and win the bailey 'in no time at all'. The machine failed, with the first stone tumbling from the sling onto one of William's men; the siege failed.

By 1350 trebuchets were found at most major sieges; because trebuchets were relatively expensive and required skilled carpenters with specialised knowledge, this was a sign of economic growth. The range of these trebuchets was considerable: it is said (Bradbury, page 267) that Napoleon III constructed trebuchets to throw stones weighing 25 lb about 200 yards, which suggests speeds of at least 90 miles per hour. Similar results have been produced by modern experiments in Denmark.

The sieges where trebuchets played a significant role in their success are too numerous to list here, but Edward I, a master of castle warfare, used them to good effect at Caerlaverock (near Carlisle) in 1300 – a siege recorded for prosperity in *The song of Caerlaverock* – and at the siege of Stirling in 1304 where he used 13 engines, some with names, which itself demonstrates their significance. Further, Edward's castles were built to withstand such attacks.

Towards the end of the fifteenth century, cannons were beginning to supersede trebuchets. The latter were useful at Burgos in 1476 and at Rhodes in 1480, where 22 stone-throwing engines and 10 large guns were used; by then, however, the trebuchets were considered outmoded and skilled operators were difficult to find.

A photograph of the trebuchet at Warwick in the process of firing is shown in Figure 4.10; here the projectile is just about to be lifted into the air.

Figure 4.10   Photograph of the Warwick trebuchet in operation (August 2007)

The trebuchet is a fairly complicated machine, so it is unlikely to have been built *ab initio*; rather, it would have evolved from simpler machines. Here we very briefly describe some of the weapons that may have played a role in its development, though we should add that no causal chain has been established.

The trebuchet is essentially a large mechanical sling: the first evidence of elementary slings, of the sort David used to slay Goliath, is from 10 000 BC. These were used, in various forms, up to Roman times; indeed, Roman legionaries were trained in their use. They were used in the siege of Jerusalem, AD 69, to throw stones weighing about 1 lb, and contributed to the defeat of the defenders. A variant, the *staff-sling*, used a pole about 4 ft in length to add leverage which increased projectile speeds: modern tests of staff-slings show that a stone can be projected with speeds of about 70 mph, giving a maximum range of about 300 ft. There was also the two-handed sling for throwing larger missiles, and this is probably the origin of the modern sport of hammer throwing. Slings, however, require much training and the exit direction can be unreliable: it is said that of those in the vicinity, only the slinger is really safe. On the other hand, ammunition is plentiful, being easy to find or manufacture.

Weapons based on torsional energy, obtained from twisted hair or tendons, first appeared about 350 BC. Rihll (page 76) suggests that the first such weapon was the *monagkon*, a one-armed catapult which is simply a mechanised staff-sling; it is also named a *mangonel*. This machine is described and discussed in Exercise 4.51 (page 220). The Roman version is named the *onager*, after the name for an Asian wild donkey. A simpler version of this machine, also often named the *mangonel*, has the sling replaced by cups; this is discussed in Exercise 4.50 (page 218). Apparently this type of machine was first described in the fifteenth century, but there is no evidence that it actually existed. The calculations in Exercise 4.50 suggest why, for by adding a sling the range can be increased by a factor of up to four.

The staff-sling also evolved into the more powerful beam-sling catapult, otherwise known as the one-armed traction stone-thrower, or traction-trebuchet, for which the earliest illustration dates from the late seventh or early eighth century. The only difference between this and the trebuchet, as discussed here, is that the counterweight is replaced by human power, whereby a large number of men pull down on ropes to rotate the beam. The machine has various names, for example, the *cheiromangana* (sometimes spelt *kheiromangana*), the *hand-mangonel*, the *perrière*, the *petroboloi* or the *helepolis*; this plethora of names reflects the diverse origins of these weapons. The paucity of clear definitions illustrates the difficulty we have in understanding past cultures.

You should now view the short videos, provided on the course CD, of the Warwick Castle and Rocktec trebuchets in action. Towards the end of the Warwick video, after the projectile has landed, notice in the top right-hand corner the fairly violent oscillations of the counterweight. In the Rocktec trebuchet the ratio of projectile mass to counterweight mass is far larger than in the Warwick trebuchet, and this affects the motion: in particular, at times 1:23 and 2:22 of the longer video, a slight hesitation in the beam motion is seen and this is about the time when the sling is released. Such a hesitation is also seen in the Maple animations to be viewed later in this section.

The Warwick video is referred to as the BBC Trebuchet Clip or the BBC Birmingham Midlands Today – Trebuchet Clip depending on how you access it.

Schematic diagrams of two types of trebuchet are shown in Figure 4.11, with the fixed counterweight trebuchet on the left and the swinging counterweight trebuchet on the right: the Warwick and Rocktec trebuchets are examples of the latter.

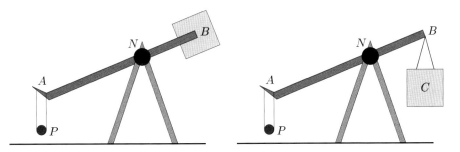

Figure 4.11 Sketches of the two basic types of trebuchet: fixed counterweight (left) and swinging counterweight (right). In both, the beam AB rotates on a horizontal axis at N, with $AN \gg NB$. The projectile P is attached to the beam end A by a sling; the heavy counterweight is attached to B. On the left the counterweight is fixed to the beam at B; on the right it swings freely from B in a cradle. The latter system is more effective in converting the potential energy of the counterweight to the kinetic energy of the projectile; reasons for this are discussed in Section 4.6.

These machines comprise three essential parts, together with a substantial frame for support.

P1: The driving force is supplied by a very heavy counterweight which can weigh in excess of 15 tons.

P2: A long beam, AB, that can rotate about the horizontal axis at N, supported by a strong frame. Typically the beam is over 10 m long and the axis is much closer to B than to A.

P3: The sling AP holding the projectile P; the projectile can weigh more than 100 kg, and the length AP is usually less than AN.

The two types of trebuchet sketched in Figure 4.11 differ in the way the counterweight is attached to the beam AB. On the left it is firmly fixed to the beam, so rotates on a circle of radius NB. On the right it is allowed to swing from the end B in a cradle; this means that a sufficiently heavy counterweight falls almost vertically and consequently the time taken to launch the projectile is smaller – which is essentially why the second type of trebuchet is more powerful and, despite being more complicated, was preferred. We explain later why this is so.

The firing sequence of a trebuchet with a fixed counterweight is shown in Figure 4.12.

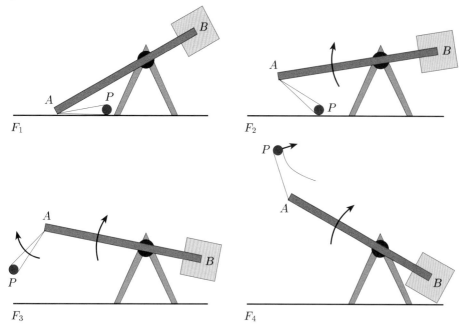

Figure 4.12   The firing sequence of a fixed counterweight trebuchet, from the start, F1, to the launch of the projectile, F4

F1: Initially, the counterweight is raised as high as possible, with the sling horizontal on a trough (not shown). The system is held in place by a trigger mechanism, which can be seen at the beginning of the Warwick video.

F2: On release of the trigger, the counterweight falls, the end A rises and the projectile is pulled horizontally along the trough, gathering speed with time. Phase I of the motion is defined to be when the projectile is moving horizontally.

   The sling is initially horizontal, and the angle between AP and the horizontal increases as the counterweight falls. Eventually, the tension in the sling is sufficient to lift the projectile off the trough. At this point the phase I motion is finished.

F3: After the projectile lifts off the trough, phase II of the motion begins. Now the sling swings clockwise about the moving beam end A, until . . .

F4: . . . a mechanism, described below, releases one end of the sling from A and allows the projectile to move freely away from the sling at a velocity, perpendicular to the direction of the sling immediately prior to release, and with a magnitude determined by the angle and angular speed of the beam and the sling.

The release mechanism for the projectile is simple and elegant. It comprises a spigot attached to the beam at A, at an angle $\beta > 0$ to the beam, such that when the beam is horizontal the spigot points upwards; see Figure 4.13.

One arm of the sling is fixed to the beam; the other, free arm loops round the spigot and can slide off when pulled in an appropriate direction. Thus in the second phase of the motion, if the sling rotates clockwise about the beam through a sufficiently large angle, it will slip off the spigot and release the projectile, as shown on the extreme right of Figure 4.13.

The spigot angle, β, is usually fixed during the trebuchet's construction. An example is shown in Figure 4.14, a photograph of the Warwick trebuchet spigot taken when the arm is vertical; the rope hanging down the right-hand side is the attached part of the sling.

In practice, the actual point of release will depend upon the shape of the spigot, and the friction between the sling and the spigot. It is therefore very difficult to predict the release point, but there are two extreme possibilities. First, we could assume that the projectile is released when the free arm of the sling is parallel to the spigot, as shown in Figure 4.13. Second, if there is very little friction between the spigot and the sling, it will slide off very soon after the sling becomes perpendicular to the spigot; this occurs before it is parallel to the spigot, and in practice is the most likely case, particularly if the spigot is greased.

Without a quantitative understanding of how the sling slides on the spigot, an accurate estimate of the release point is impossible. Consequently, we consider the release point as a variable parameter.

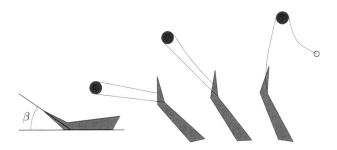

Figure 4.13   Sketch showing how a release mechanism works when the sling is released when parallel to the spigot

Figure 4.14   Spigot of the Warwick trebuchet

You should now study the Maple animation `rocktec-anim.mws` which shows the motion of a trebuchet either up to the time at which the projectile is launched or, if the sling does not reach the correct angle, up to the time when AB is vertical. Here we assume that the projectile is launched when the sling is perpendicular to the spigot. In this animation the lengths AN, NB and BC (see Figure 4.11) are chosen to approximately represent the Rocktec trebuchet, by taking $AN = 9.3$ m, $NB = 2.9$ m and $BC = 1.4$ m, so we set the ratios $BC/NB = 0.5$ and $AN/NB = 3.2$. The sling length AP can vary between 1.5 m and 6 m, so $l_4 = AP/AN \in (0.16, 0.7)$. The weight of the counterweight is $M = 19\,200$ kg, and the projectiles weigh between $m = 600$ kg and $m = 1450$ kg, giving the mass ratio $\mu = m/M \in (0.03, 0.075)$.

In the Maple worksheets we set $\mathtt{m} = \mu$ and $\mathtt{l4} = l_4$.

In this animation we have set $\beta = 90°$ and assumed that the projectile is released when the sling is perpendicular to the spigot. All parameter values may be changed, but we suggest that you first keep $\mu = 0.05$ and vary l_4 in the interval $(0.2, 1.3)$. You should see that for small values of l_4 the projectile is launched backwards; it is launched forwards for $0.4 \leq l_4 \leq 1.3$, with the largest range occurring at $l_4 \simeq 0.67$.

Keeping all parameters fixed and decreasing μ to 0.01, that is, increasing the counterweight mass, increases the rate of rotation of the beam, and the sling takes longer to reach the launch angle. A further decrease to

$\mu = 0.001$ means that the sling never reaches the launch angle: for this value of μ we need to decrease β to about $30°$ and use values of $l_4 \in (0.60, 0.88)$.

A primary purpose of a trebuchet was to breach castle or town walls by a constant bombardment of heavy missiles. But other uses included the spread of diseases, by delivering decaying animal carcasses, or terror, by launching earthenware pots of poisonous snakes, prisoners or just their heads. In order to breach walls the kinetic energy of the projectile needs to be as large as possible and the projectile needs to hit the wall close to a right angle; this requires some skill from the operators, and heavy missiles. Also, moats and the need to be sufficiently far from outgoing missiles suggest that a long range is beneficial. These factors lead to working trebuchets being very large and heavy, weighing in excess of 20 tons.

In recent years an interest has developed in building and operating trebuchets. The emphasis now appears to be mainly on throwing relatively light projectiles, with weights of about 10 kg, as far as possible; but the tossing of large objects, such as cars, as far as possible is inspiration for a benign global arms race. Internet sites, too numerous to list, describe the exploits of dedicated fanatics and their home-made trebuchets. Further, it is now possible to purchase toy trebuchets, typically about one foot high, that can throw a light missile about 10 m. Some typical sizes are given in Table 4.1.

Table 4.1   Approximate numerical values for various trebuchets. The symbols in the first heading row are defined in Figures 4.16 (page 180) and 4.26 (page 199). The Rocktec beam weighs about 2 tonnes.

Trebuchet	H	L_1 AN	L_2 NB	L_3 BC	L_4 AP	m	M
Warwick	4 m	6 m	1 m	1.5 m	4 m	13 kg	5–6 tonnes
Rocktec	5.4 m	9.3 m	2.9 m	1.4 m	1.5–6 m	600–1850 kg	19.2 tonnes
Toy	22 cm	30 cm	9 cm	9 cm	20 cm	negligible	1 kg

It is clear from this brief description that a trebuchet is essentially a sling fired by two coupled pendulums. It was seen in Block B that two coupled pendulums can behave chaotically, so it is possible that the motion of a trebuchet, without friction, can be chaotic.

The approximations used

The simplest description of a trebuchet with a swinging counterweight requires four lengths and two masses. Referring to Figure 4.11, the four lengths and the symbols used to denote their lengths are as follows.

BC: the distance of the centre of mass of the counterweight from B, L_3.

AP: the length of the sling, L_4, and usually $L_4 < L_1$.

AN and NB: the lengths of each section of the beam, with $AN \gg NB$, L_1 and L_2, respectively.

The two masses are those of the projectile and the counterweight; these are denoted by m and M, respectively, always with $m \ll M$; in the analysis presented here, only the ratio $\mu = m/M$ is important.

In practice most of the parameters listed in this table are fixed when the trebuchet is constructed. But the projectile mass is clearly variable; the sling length, L_4, can also be changed, and this is used to adjust the range.

There are clearly other effects that should be taken into account. We have already discussed the launch condition (Figure 4.13). Two other important factors are the mass of the beam and frictional effects, which are not included in this simple approximation because their addition would add several extra parameters that are difficult to estimate and which would complicate the discussion too much.

The beam is normally quite heavy: the Warwick beam weighs about one ton, and the Rocktec beam is also very heavy – see Table 4.1. Usually the beam is not uniform, so we would require its mass, the position of its centre of mass and its moment of inertia about the pivot N. The addition of these factors simply changes two coefficients in one of the equations of motion, and generally decreases the range, because energy is needed to rotate the beam. This effect is discussed in Exercise 4.56.

Frictional effects are more difficult to estimate, but are not expected to significantly affect the motion over the short times required to launch the projectile.

In the simple example considered here, four lengths and two masses are needed to define the system, so there are three length ratios and one mass ratio, that is, four independent parameters. In addition there are the initial angle of the beam and the angle at which the sling is released from the spigot. All six of these parameters will, to a greater or lesser extent, affect the motion, so it is difficult to obtain a complete understanding of the trebuchet motion.

The pivot height H is assumed large enough not to disrupt the trebuchet mechanism.

In any simulation we need to be clear about which questions are to be addressed. But for any complicated system, such as the trebuchet, it is necessary to understand many details before attempting to answer these questions, if only because it is necessary to be sure that the derived equations are correct and that they have been programmed and solved correctly. Here most of these difficulties have been overcome and the sample programs on the CD have been checked, though errors may still exist.

For simplicity we assume that the range of the projectile is the variable of interest and that this needs to be maximised with a suitable choice of the various parameters. The range is determined, if we ignore air resistance, by the initial velocity $\mathbf{v}$ and the launch height h of the projectile, that is, its velocity and height at the time when the sling slides off the spigot. Using elementary mechanics, the range R is given by

$$R = \frac{v^2}{g}\left(\tfrac{1}{2}\sin 2\alpha + \cos\alpha\sqrt{\sin^2\alpha + \gamma}\right), \quad \gamma = \frac{2gh}{v^2}, \quad 0 < \alpha < \frac{\pi}{2}, \quad (4.1)$$

where $v = |\mathbf{v}|$ and α is the angle between $\mathbf{v}$ and the horizontal. Both $\mathbf{v}$ and h depend upon the trebuchet dynamics, so the maximum range is not necessarily given by the usual maximum derived in Exercise 4.16.

The overall size of the trebuchet can be varied without changing the three length ratios mentioned above. It will be shown later that v^2/g varies directly as this size, so the range of a trebuchet is proportional to the size of the trebuchet. The variation of R with the mass ratio is, however, not easy to estimate.

A trebuchet is simply a machine for converting the potential energy of the counterweight into the kinetic energy of the projectile. The masses of the counterweight and the projectile are M and m, respectively, and we assume $M \gg m$. The counterweight falls a distance of approximately $2\,NB$ (see Figure 4.11), so the available potential energy is about $2Mg\,NB$; and the kinetic energy of the projectile at launch is $mv^2/2$. A measure of the efficiency of the machine is the ratio of these two energies, given approximately by

$$E_{\text{eff}} = \frac{1}{4}\frac{m}{M}\frac{v^2}{g\,NB}.\tag{4.2}$$

But the time taken for a body to fall a given distance is independent of its mass, so if $M \gg m$, the time taken to launch the projectile, and hence the value of v, will be independent of M. Thus we expect the efficiency to decrease as the ratio m/M decreases.

Exercise 4.16

(a) If $h = 0$ and α is independent of v, show that for a fixed v, the range R given in Equation (4.1) has a maximum value $R_{\text{max}} = v^2/g$, attained when $\alpha = \pi/4$.

(b) If $h > 0$ and both h and v are independent of α, show that

$$R_{\text{max}} = \frac{v^2}{g}\sqrt{1+\gamma}, \quad \text{which is attained when } \cos 2\alpha = \frac{\gamma}{2+\gamma}.$$

Exercise 4.17

In the historical paper by Chevedden referenced on page 170, estimates for the range R of a particular trebuchet built between AD 1220 and AD 1240 are quoted. For various counterweight and projectile masses these are as follows.

M /kg	m /kg	R /m
30×10^3	100	400
30×10^3	250	160
15×10^3	100	217
15×10^3	60	365

A naive view of trebuchet dynamics is obtained by equating the projectile energy with that given up by the counterweight during its fall, which is proportional to M. The projectile energy is proportional to mv^2 and the range $R \propto v^2$; see Equation (4.1). Assuming the proportionalities to be true, show that Rm/M should be a constant and that the data quoted in the above table approximately satisfy this relation.

Later we shall see that the elementary dynamics of a falling body, as studied by Galileo, drastically limits the energy transfer, so the above simple relation is generally approximately true only if the ratio $\mu = m/M$ is not too small.

4.6   The trebuchet without a projectile: theory

A trebuchet is a machine for converting the potential energy of a falling counterweight into the kinetic energy of a projectile. Our objective is to understand how the various parameters of the system affect the efficiency of this conversion. To this end we first consider a simplified system, for which the equations of motion are simpler and have solutions that can be understood more easily. Without this stage it is more difficult to understand how the complete system behaves.

The equations of motion of this simple system remain quite complicated and even an experienced scientist would find it very hard to predict its behaviour by only studying the equations. The purpose of this section is to use physical intuition to obtain a qualitative description of the motion. Before making this analysis the author had the benefit of seeing trebuchets in action; we cannot provide the reader with this experience, but the video clips and the Maple animation should be an adequate alternative. In the next section we use Maple to numerically solve the equations of motion in order to check the ideas developed here.

We consider the two types of trebuchet described in Section 4.5, shown schematically in Figure 4.15, where the counterweight is either fixed or allowed to swing freely. A fixed counterweight is simpler, so has practical advantages but, as we see later in this section, the extra complication of a swinging counterweight improves the efficiency of the energy transfer sufficiently to compensate for the increased complexity. Essentially, the swinging counterweight falls faster, so the beam AB rotates faster. This study also suggests that the distance between the hinge B and the centre of mass of the counterweight must not be too much smaller than NB.

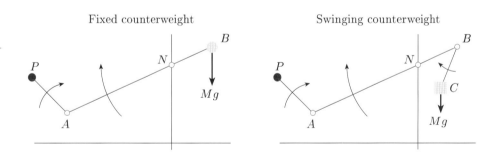

Figure 4.15   Schematic diagram of the two types of trebuchet. On the left is a trebuchet with a fixed counterweight, which rotates the beam AB clockwise about the pivot N. This propels the projectile, P, by rotating the sling, AP, about A, also clockwise. On the right is a trebuchet with a swinging counterweight suspended from B.

In the simplified system we assume that the mass of the projectile, m, is small by comparison to the counterweight mass, M, so the motion of the projectile and its sling during launch does not affect the counterweight motion. This assumption is made by fixing the projectile at A, the end of the beam furthest from the pivot at N, as shown in Figure 4.16, which also defines some necessary parameters.

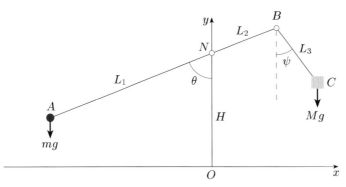

Figure 4.16   Diagram defining the parameters needed to describe the simplified system. All distances are measured with respect to the Oxy coordinate system, where the y-axis is vertically upwards and the beam hinge is on this axis, a distance H from the origin.

In this simplified system there are three lengths, L_1, L_2 and L_3, and two masses, m and M, and in real systems these satisfy the relations

$$L_1 > L_2 \simeq L_3 \quad \text{and} \quad M \gg m.$$

Some typical values of these parameters are given in Table 4.1 (page 176).

The equations of motion of this simplified system can be shown to be

$$\left(mL_1^2 + ML_2^2\right)\ddot{\theta} - \left(ML_2 - mL_1\right)g\sin\theta$$
$$+ ML_2L_3\left(\ddot{\psi}\cos(\theta+\psi) - \dot{\psi}^2\sin(\theta+\psi)\right) = 0 \qquad (4.3)$$

and

$$L_3\ddot{\psi} + g\sin\psi + L_2\left(\ddot{\theta}\cos(\theta+\psi) - \dot{\theta}^2\sin(\theta+\psi)\right) = 0. \qquad (4.4)$$

Notice that the second equation is independent of the masses and L_1, and that the two angles θ and ψ appear on their own but also in the combination $\theta + \psi$, which is the angle between the beam and the counterweight support, that is, AB and BC.

At this juncture an important point needs to be made. We do not know that these equations correctly represent the system being studied, because many approximations have been made and, in addition, there may be algebraic errors: much of the analysis in this section, and the exercises, is performed to check that these equations and their solutions behave appropriately in certain limiting cases, where we know what happens. This type of analysis is an essential prerequisite to numerical studies; it also provides a check that the equations are correctly programmed and that the numerical methods employed are reliable. This is not the same as checking the assumptions used to derive these equations; this is also necessary, but generally much harder.

Equations (4.3) and (4.4) for θ and ψ are second-order, coupled, nonlinear equations, and for a unique solution they require four initial conditions:

$$\theta(0) = \theta_0 = \cos^{-1}(H/L_1), \quad \text{the mass } m \text{ is resting on the } x\text{-axis,}$$
$$\psi(0) = 0, \qquad\qquad\qquad\quad \text{the counterweight is hanging vertically,}$$
$$\dot{\psi}(0) = \dot{\theta}(0) = 0, \qquad\qquad \text{the system is initially at rest.}$$
$$(4.5)$$

We shall assume that $0 < \theta_0 < \pi/2$, so initially B is higher than A: for both the Warwick and Rocktec trebuchets, $\theta_0 \simeq 0.8$. In subsequent analysis H is defined by the relation $H = L_1\cos\theta_0$.

The equation for a fixed counterweight system is derived from Equation (4.3) simply by setting $L_3 = 0$. In this limit the angle ψ has no meaning, so Equation (4.4) can be ignored, and the required equation is

$$\left(mL_1^2 + ML_2^2\right)\ddot{\theta} - (ML_2 - mL_1)\,g\sin\theta = 0. \tag{4.6}$$

Equation (4.6) can be derived separately, and this derivation yields the same equation, thus providing some confidence that Equation (4.3) is not completely wrong.

Exercise 4.18

Notice that in Equation (4.6) the coefficient of $\sin\theta$ is negative if $ML_2 > mL_1$, and positive otherwise. By considering the fixed points of this system, or otherwise, explain the physical significance of this sign change.

Deduce that we must have $ML_2 > mL_1$ for the trebuchet to work.

Accurate solutions of Equations (4.3)–(4.6) can only be found numerically, and whilst this is a relatively easy task it is not satisfactory if the aim of our studies is to understand how the system depends upon the various system parameters. For this type of study numerical solutions are just one of the necessary tools, but we also need to develop an intuitive understanding of the system, which is important when deciding if the numerical solutions are plausible.

Equations (4.3) and (4.4) may be simplified by noting that the five parameters may be reduced to three dimensionless ratios:

$$l = \frac{L_1}{L_2} > 1, \quad L = \frac{L_3}{L_2} \simeq 1 \quad \text{and} \quad \mu = \frac{m}{M} \ll 1. \tag{4.7}$$

Table 4.2   The approximate values of l, L and μ corresponding to the data given in Table 4.1. Note that we need $\mu l < 1$ for the trebuchet to work (see Exercise 4.18).

Trebuchet	$l = L_1/L_2$	$L = L_3/L_2$	$\mu = m/M$
Warwick	6	1.5	0.0025
Rocktec	3.2	0.5	0.03–0.1
Toy	3.3	1.0	< 0.001

Exercise 4.19

By dividing Equations (4.3) and (4.4) by ML_2^2 and L_2, respectively, show that they can be written in the form

$$(1 + \mu l^2)\ddot{\theta} - (1 - \mu l)\frac{g}{L_2}\sin\theta + L\left(\ddot{\psi}\cos(\theta + \psi) - \dot{\psi}^2\sin(\theta + \psi)\right) = 0$$

and

$$L\ddot{\psi} + \frac{g}{L_2}\sin\psi + \ddot{\theta}\cos(\theta + \psi) - \dot{\theta}^2\sin(\theta + \psi) = 0.$$

Now observe that g and L_2 occur only in the ratio g/L_2, which has the dimensions of $(\text{Time})^{-2}$. This suggests defining a new, dimensionless, independent variable τ given by

$$\tau = \omega t, \quad \text{where } \omega^2 = \frac{g}{L_2}. \tag{4.8}$$

181

The parameter ω is the angular frequency of small oscillations of a simple pendulum of length L_2. For the Warwick trebuchet shown in Figure 4.10, $\omega \simeq 3.1 \text{ s}^{-1}$.

Exercise 4.20

What is the value of ω for the Rocktec trebuchet?

The chain rule gives $\dot{\theta} = \omega \, d\theta/d\tau$ and $\ddot{\theta} = \omega^2 \, d^2\theta/d\tau^2$, so using the dimensionless 'time' τ, the equations of motion become

$$
\left(1 + \mu l^2\right) \frac{d^2\theta}{d\tau^2} - (1 - \mu l) \sin\theta
$$
$$
+ L \left(\frac{d^2\psi}{d\tau^2} \cos(\theta + \psi) - \left(\frac{d\psi}{d\tau}\right)^2 \sin(\theta + \psi) \right) = 0 \tag{4.9}
$$

and

$$
L \frac{d^2\psi}{d\tau^2} + \sin\psi + \frac{d^2\theta}{d\tau^2} \cos(\theta + \psi) - \left(\frac{d\theta}{d\tau}\right)^2 \sin(\theta + \psi) = 0. \tag{4.10}
$$

Useful alternative forms for these equations, derived in Exercise 4.21, are

$$
(1 + \mu l^2)\theta'' - (1 - \mu l)\sin\theta + L\left(\cos\theta(\sin\psi)'' + \sin\theta(\cos\psi)''\right) = 0, \tag{4.11}
$$
$$
L\psi'' + \sin\psi + \cos\psi(\sin\theta)'' + \sin\psi(\cos\theta)'' = 0. \tag{4.12}
$$

These are the basic equations used in this section, and our aim is to understand how their solutions behave. The technique of reducing the number of free parameters by introducing dimensionless ratios is important.

Exercise 4.21

Using the addition formulae for $\cos(\theta + \psi)$ and $\sin(\theta + \psi)$, show that Equations (4.9) and (4.10) contain the factors

$$
z'' \sin z + z'^2 \cos z \quad \text{and} \quad z'' \cos z - z'^2 \sin z,
$$

where $z = \theta$ or ψ. Further, show that

$$
-z'' \sin z - z'^2 \cos z = \frac{d^2}{d\tau^2} \cos z = (\cos z)'',
$$
$$
z'' \cos z - z'^2 \sin z = \frac{d^2}{d\tau^2} \sin z = (\sin z)''.
$$

Hence derive Equations (4.11) and (4.12) from Equations (4.9) and (4.10).

Equations (4.9) and (4.10) depend upon three independent parameters, l, L and μ. They are versions of the equations describing the motion of a double pendulum (see Block B) and, except when the beam and counterweight are both nearly vertical, so that $\sin\theta \simeq 0$ and $\sin\psi \simeq 0$, their solution cannot be expressed in terms of known functions; the only interesting limit is when $\theta \simeq \pi$ and $\psi \simeq 0$, and this is considered in Exercise 4.49. Accurate solutions can be obtained numerically, but for the reasons discussed above we first need to give some thought to how we expect the system to behave.

Before reading further you are advised to study the animations given in the worksheet `trebuchet-anim.mws`, which solves Equations (4.9) and (4.10) and displays these solutions as a moving trebuchet. In this animation we have fixed $l = 3$, $L = 1$ and $\theta_0 = 0.8$, but you are free to change $\mu = m/M$.

This worksheet contains instructions for its use (and also for changing the parameters l, L and θ_0, but only sensible values should be used). In addition to producing an animation, this worksheet also computes and displays the values of some variables for reasons that are discussed in the next few pages. We suggest that you look at the animation for the cases $\mu = 0.1$, 0.01, 0.001 and 0.0001, and you should look for the following two features of the motion.

F1:   For the initial stage, $\theta_0 < \theta < \pi$, notice that the counterweight falls almost vertically, particularly for small μ.

F2:   As the beam AB and counterweight BC become parallel, when $\theta + \psi \simeq \pi$, notice how the angular speed of the beam changes, particularly for small μ, and that the counterweight motion suddenly changes direction.

After studying the motion of a real trebuchet, a little thought leads to the following four observations.

O1:   We are primarily interested in the solution for $\theta_0 \leq \theta \leq \pi$, because the projectile leaves the sling at some $\theta < \pi$, though the motion after this time is important, for the reason discussed in Subsection 4.7.5.

O2:   The counterweight is relatively heavy, so we expect it to fall almost vertically as a free body and we expect that during the first part of the motion $|\psi| \ll 1$ and $\psi(\tau) < 0$, for $0 < \tau \ll 1$, as seen in the animation.

Initially, BC (see Figure 4.16, page 180) is vertical and stationary, $\psi(0) = \dot{\psi}(0) = 0$, so the only force on the counterweight is vertical. As it begins to fall, NB rotates clockwise and (because $\theta_0 < \pi/2$) the point B moves away from the y-axis; thus for small times $\psi(\tau) < 0$. If T is the tension in BC, then the horizontal force on the counterweight is $T \sin \psi \simeq T\psi$ (because initially ψ must be small): this relatively small force has little effect on the counterweight, so its x-component of velocity remains small, and we expect it to fall almost vertically. That is, we expect the horizontal distance of the counterweight, x_C, from the y-axis to remain almost constant. In Exercise 4.23 it is shown, using the equations of motion, that x_C'' is proportional to ψ, if $|\psi|$ is small.

Further, when $\theta \simeq \pi - \theta_0$, NB and BC are nearly parallel, but now the beam AB is rotating rapidly clockwise, $\dot{\theta} \gg 1$ (this is the sole purpose of the counterweight), so at about this time the support of the counterweight, B, is pulled rapidly to the left and then ψ starts relatively large oscillations, as seen in the animations.

These oscillations are not relevant to the projectile, which should have been released before this point, but because the counterweight is very heavy they do impose large stresses on the trebuchet structure.

O3:   If the mass M of the counterweight far exceeds all other masses, it is essentially in free fall through the distance BB' as the beam rotates from $\theta = \theta_0$ to $\pi - \theta_0$, as shown in Figure 4.17. The end B of the beam traces out an arc of a circle of radius L_2, so traverses a distance $L_2(\pi - 2\theta_0)$, while the counterweight falls a distance equal to the length of the chord BB', which elementary geometry shows to be $2L_2 \cos \theta_0$.

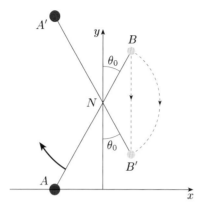

Figure 4.17   Diagram showing the lines followed by the counterweight when fixed and when swinging

Assuming that the swinging counterweight falls almost vertically, while θ increases to $\pi - \theta_0$ we expect $\psi(\tau)$ to be negative, and when $\theta \simeq \pi - \theta_0$ we expect $\psi(\tau) \simeq 0$.

As θ increases past $\pi - \theta_0$ the beam is rotating relatively rapidly and hence jerks the counterweight support towards the y-axis. This is seen in the animations and in graphs shown later, for instance Figure 4.20 (page 194).

It is therefore useful to consider the time taken for θ to increase from θ_0 to $\pi - \theta_0$. The shortest possible time is when the counterweight falls freely from B to B', that is, vertically through the distance $2L_2 \cos \theta_0$, starting from rest: we denote this time by T_{free}, and the scaled free-fall time by $\tau_{\text{free}} = \omega T_{\text{free}}$. Elementary mechanics gives

$$T_{\text{free}} = 2\sqrt{\frac{L_2}{g} \cos \theta_0}, \quad \text{hence} \quad \tau_{\text{free}} = \omega T_{\text{free}} = 2\sqrt{\cos \theta_0}. \quad (4.13)$$

Here we have used the formula for the distance s travelled by a particle under constant acceleration g, in a time t, when starting from rest, that is, $s = gt^2/2$.

The beam of a trebuchet rotates from θ_0 to $\pi - \theta_0$ in a time that exceeds T_{free}, and we denote this time by T_{swg} and T_{fxd} for a swinging and a fixed counterweight: the associated scaled times are $\tau_{\text{swg}} = \omega T_{\text{swg}}$ and $\tau_{\text{fxd}} = \omega T_{\text{fxd}}$, with $\omega = \sqrt{g/L_2}$. These times are important because they provide a measure of the angular speed of the beam and hence the speed of the projectile: for instance, the smaller τ_{swg}, the faster the beam must be rotating when the projectile is launched. Usually, if $\mu \ll 1$ then $\tau_{\text{swg}} \simeq \tau_{\text{free}}$ and $\tau_{\text{fxd}} > \tau_{\text{swg}}$. Moreover, $\tau_{\text{swg}} > \tau_{\text{free}}$ and this imposes an upper limit on the range of a given trebuchet as the mass ratio changes.

An advantage of using the scaled time τ rather than the actual time t is that the relevant dynamics lasts similar scaled times, regardless of the size of the trebuchet. For the Warwick and Rocktec trebuchets, $\theta_0 \simeq 0.8$ hence $\tau_{\text{free}} = 1.67$, but $T_{\text{free}} \simeq 0.53\,\text{s}$ and $0.91\,\text{s}$, respectively.

O4:   The mass ratio $\mu = m/M$ is usually small, so it is tempting to set $\mu = 0$ in order to simplify Equation (4.9). This approximation, however, has interesting consequences, because when $\mu = 0$, Equations (4.9) and (4.10) are singular at $\theta + \psi = \pi$, that is, when the beam AB and counterweight support BC are parallel. This means that if $\mu = 0$, the equations have no solution at $\theta + \psi = \pi$; the reason for this is discussed in Exercise 4.22. Thus if $\mu = 0$, the numerical integration fails when $\theta + \psi \simeq \pi$: you can set $\mu = 0$ in the animation to see the error message that occurs.

The procedure in `trebuchet-anim.mws` also outputs the values of the angular speeds θ' and ψ' when $\theta + \psi = \pi$. Some typical values of these angular speeds are given in Table 4.3.

Table 4.3   The values of (θ', ψ') when $\theta + \psi = \pi$, for the case $\theta_0 = 0.5$, $L = 1$, $l = 3$ and various values of μ

μ	0.1	0.01	0.001
(θ', ψ')	$(1.5, 1.4)$	$(6.2, 6.0)$	$(20, 19)$
$(\sqrt{\mu}\theta', \sqrt{\mu}\psi')$	$(0.47, 0.44)$	$(0.62, 0.60)$	$(0.63, 0.60)$

From these values we see that for small μ, $\theta' \simeq \psi' \gg 1$, and that the magnitude of these angular speeds increases as μ decreases. In fact, $\theta' \simeq \psi' = O(\mu^{-1/2})$, and this means that it is desirable for the projectile to be launched before $\theta + \psi = \pi$.

Physically, the limit $\mu \ll 1$ corresponds to a heavy pendulum BC (see Figure 4.16, page 180), freely suspended from a very light pendulum AB, hinged at N, and this system when executing small oscillations close to the downward vertical has two frequencies, one of which is proportional to $\mu^{-1/2}$; see Exercise 4.49.

We expect these observations to remain true when the mass m, at A, is replaced by the sling and the projectile, provided that the counterweight is sufficiently massive.

We noted above that initially the counterweight falls almost vertically, so $|\psi|$ is small. Therefore it is worth approximating Equations (4.9) and (4.10) by assuming that both $|\psi|$ and $|\dot{\psi}|$ are small; this analysis is part of Exercise 4.23.

Exercise 4.22

Show that if $\mu = 0$ when $\theta + \psi = 0$ or π, both Equations (4.9) and (4.10) become the same.

This result shows that at this time there is only one equation for the two independent variables, so the equations do not have a unique solution at this point. The numerical integration used in `trebuchet-anim.mws` fails at or near this time, as may be confirmed by setting `m=0` in this worksheet.

Exercise 4.23

(a) The x-coordinate of the counterweight, x_C, is given by $x_C/L_2 = \sin\theta + L\sin\psi$. Use a Taylor expansion to show that, to first-order in ψ,

$$\cos(\theta + \psi) = \cos\theta - \psi\sin\theta, \quad \sin(\theta + \psi) = \sin\theta + \psi\cos\theta$$

and

$$\frac{x_C}{L_2} = \sin\theta + L\psi.$$

(b) Use Equations (4.11) and (4.12) to show that if both $|\psi|$ and $|\psi'|$ are small, then Equations (4.9) and (4.10) can be written in the form

$$(1 + \mu l^2)\theta'' - (1 - \mu l)\sin\theta + L\psi''\cos\theta = 0, \tag{4.14}$$
$$L\psi'' + \left(1 + (\cos\theta)''\right)\psi + (\sin\theta)'' = 0. \tag{4.15}$$

(c) Using Equation (4.15), show that

$$\frac{d^2}{d\tau^2}\left(\frac{x_C}{L_2}\right) = -\left(1 + (\cos\theta)''\right)\psi.$$

Later, in Subsection 4.7.2, we shall see that when $\theta_0 < \theta < \pi - \theta_0$, $(\cos\theta)'' \simeq -1$ and hence $x_C'' \simeq 0$, giving $x_C \simeq$ constant, since $x_C'(0) = 0$.

4.7   The trebuchet without a projectile: numerical investigation

Here we test the ideas developed in Section 4.6 by solving Equations (4.9) and (4.10) numerically and examining various features of these solutions.

The first two subsections are most important; the remaining three make interesting observations that may be treated as optional, or read quickly. In the first subsection we compare the timescales of the important part of the motion for fixed and swinging counterweight trebuchets, and show that the predictions made in Section 4.6 are accurate if μ is small enough. The second and third sections examine the free-fall approximation, finding it reliable only if θ_0 is not too small and μ is very small.

4.7.1   The fixed and swinging counterweight timescales

Before becoming embroiled in the mathematical details, recall that during the initial stage of the motion (see Figure 4.17), a fixed counterweight travels on an arc of a circle with length $L_2(\pi - 2\theta_0)$, while in the free-fall approximation, a swinging counterweight travels a distance $2L_2\cos\theta_0$ in a straight line which is the chord of this arc, and hence a shorter distance. This suggests that the swinging counterweight will fall in a shorter time, that is, $\tau_{fxd} > \tau_{swg} > \tau_{free}$, and will hence launch the projectile with a higher speed.

For a fixed counterweight, the equation of motion is derived from Equation (4.9) by setting $L = L_3/L_2 = 0$, giving the simpler equation, involving only one dependent variable,

$$(1 + \mu l^2)\frac{d^2\theta}{d\tau^2} - (1 - \mu l)\sin\theta = 0, \quad \theta(0) = \theta_0, \quad \theta'(0) = 0 \quad (\mu l < 1). \tag{4.16}$$

This is a version of the equation for the simple pendulum; see Equation (1.5) in *Unit B1*. Its solution with the given initial conditions behaves quite simply: $\theta(t)$ oscillates periodically between θ_0 and $2\pi - \theta_0$. The period of these oscillations increases without bound as $\theta_0 \to 0$, as you will see in the following exercise: this should be expected because if $\theta(0) = \theta'(0) = 0$, then $\theta(\tau) = 0$ for all τ.

Exercise 4.24

Use the following procedure to plot representative graphs of the solution $\theta(\tau)$ of Equation (4.16), with $\mu = 0$, for the initial conditions $\theta_0 = 0.5$, 0.2, 0.1, 0.01 and 0.001. The arguments of this procedure are `th0` and `T`, where `th0` $= \theta_0$ and the graph is plotted on the interval $0 \leq \tau \leq T$; you will find that $T = 40$ suffices.

```
>   restart:  with(plots):
>   G := proc(th0,T)
>     local eq,s;
>     eq := diff(y(t),t,t)-sin(y(t))=0, y(0)=th0, D(y)(0)=0;
>     s := dsolve({eq},numeric,relerr=10^(-6));
>     odeplot(s,[t,y(t)],t=0..T);
>   end proc:
```

Is the graph you obtain with $\theta_0 = 0.001$ correct?

Equation (4.16) may be integrated once (as shown in *Unit B1*, Exercise 1.6) to give

$$\frac{d\theta}{d\tau} = \sqrt{\frac{2(1 - \mu l)}{1 + \mu l^2}} \sqrt{\cos \theta_0 - \cos \theta}, \tag{4.17}$$

where we have assumed that θ is increasing. Now integrate this equation to give the time τ_{fxd} for θ to increase from θ_0 to $\pi - \theta_0$ in terms of the integral:

$$\tau_{\mathrm{fxd}} = \sqrt{\frac{1 + \mu l^2}{2(1 - \mu l)}} \int_{\theta_0}^{\pi - \theta_0} d\theta \, \frac{1}{\sqrt{\cos \theta_0 - \cos \theta}}. \tag{4.18}$$

Exercise 4.25

Derive Equations (4.17) and (4.18).

Exercise 4.26

Write a Maple procedure to evaluate τ_{fxd}, defined in Equation (4.18), as a function of θ_0 for $\mu = 0$, and plot the graph of the ratio $\tau_{\mathrm{fxd}}/\tau_{\mathrm{free}}$, where $\tau_{\mathrm{free}} = 2\sqrt{\cos \theta_0}$, for $0.1 \leq \theta_0 \leq 1.0$.

Note that this ratio varies between 2.2 and 1.1, which confirms the qualitative argument presented at the beginning of this subsection and is part of the reason why a swinging counterweight can give the projectile a higher speed.

[*Hint*: You should evaluate this integral numerically using the commands `evalf(Int(..))`. Also, the term $\cos \theta_0 - \cos \theta$ should be replaced by $|\cos \theta_0 - \cos \theta|$ in order to avoid possible numerical difficulties that occur if $\cos \theta$ is too close to $\cos \theta_0$.]

Now we compute the ratio $\tau_{\mathrm{swg}}/\tau_{\mathrm{free}}$ by solving Equations (4.9) and (4.10) numerically. The Maple commands for this task are best written as a procedure, with μ, l, L and θ_0 as input variables. However, we first present and execute these commands individually because then they are easier to understand: the equivalent procedure, `Tswg(th0,L,l,m)`, is given in the solution to Exercise 4.27.

First define suitable values of L, l and μ, which will eventually be arguments of the procedure

```
>   L := 1:   m := 0.005:   l := 6:
```

Henceforth we normally associate the Maple and mathematical variables as follows: `th0` $= \theta_0$, `m` $= \mu$, `l` $= l$, `L` $= L$ and `t` $= \tau$.

and then define the parameters $1 + \mu l^2$ and $1 - \mu l$

```
>   par1 := 1+m*l^2:   par2 := 1-m*l:
```

and the initial value of θ, which will also be one of the procedure arguments

```
>   th0 := 0.6:
```

It is also convenient to define $\mathtt{c} = \cos(\theta + \psi)$ and $\mathtt{s} = \sin(\theta + \psi)$

```
>   s := sin(th(t)+ps(t)):   c := cos(th(t)+ps(t)):
```

where we have denoted τ by `t` (to save typing), and also θ by `th(t)` and ψ by `ps(t)`. Then Equation (4.9) (page 182) is

```
>   eq1 := par1*diff(th(t),t,t)-par2*sin(th(t))
            +L*(c*diff(ps(t),t,t)-s*diff(ps(t),t)^2)=0:
```

and Equation (4.10) is

```
>   eq2 := L*diff(ps(t),t,t)+sin(ps(t))
            +c*diff(th(t),t,t)-s*diff(th(t),t)^2 =0:
```

The initial conditions are

```
>   ic := th(0)=th0, D(th)(0)=0, ps(0)=0, D(ps)(0)=0:
```

The integration of these equations is to stop when $\theta(\tau) = \pi - \theta_0$, so we define a stop condition, `stc`:

```
>   stc := [th(t)-Pi+th0]:
```

The procedure that solves these equations for $\theta_0 \leq \theta(\tau) \leq \pi - \theta_0$ is then produced with the command

```
>   p := dsolve({eq1,eq2,ic},numeric,stop_cond=stc):
```

The free-fall time, $\tau_{\text{free}} = 2\sqrt{\cos\theta_0}$, is 1.82 for these parameters, so we can find τ_{swg} by evaluating `p` at a suitably larger value of τ, chosen by guessing:

```
>   z := p(3);
```

```
Warning, cannot evaluate the solution further right of 2.1305675, stop
condition #1 violated
```

$$z := [t = 2.13056758762856857, \, \text{ps}(t) = 0.0790390082617902778,$$
$$\tfrac{d}{dt}\,\text{ps}(t) = 2.35601766812840418, \, \text{th}(t) = 2.54159265358978903,$$
$$\tfrac{d}{dt}\,\text{th}(t) = 2.73346174573719436]$$

Notice that this command produces a warning, to say that integration cannot proceed beyond $\tau \simeq 2.131$, and also a list of the variable values at this value of τ. Notice also that $\psi(\tau_{\text{swg}}) \simeq 0.08$, which is close to zero as suggested by the free-fall approximation. If μ is decreased to $\mu = 0.001$, then $\tau_{\text{swg}} = 1.88$, which is closer to τ_{free}, and $\psi(\tau_{\text{swg}}) = 0.02$.

Evaluating `p(t)` at a value of `t` that is too small, say 1, does not give the warning message because the stop condition is not reached. This warning message is useful, but can be a nuisance; it is suppressed by the assignment

```
>   _Env_dsolve_nowarnstop := true:
```

The number of significant figures delivered by `dsolve` far exceeds the accuracy of the quoted results, so the same code run on different computers may yield values differing in the last few digits. The accuracy can be judged by setting the optional arguments `abserr` and `relerr` of `dsolve` to small values, say 10^{-10} and 10^{-15}.

and we use this in the procedure. The value of τ_{swg} can be extracted from the list z computed above using the eval command as follows:

```
>   tswg := eval(t,z);
```
$$tswg := 2.13056758762856857$$

With these commands we can construct a procedure Tswg(th0,L,l,m) to compute τ_{swg} and compare these values with τ_{fxd}, given by the integral (4.18). This procedure is given in the solution to the next exercise. For $L = 1$, $l = 6$, $\theta_0 = 0.6$ and various values of μ, the values of τ_{swg}, τ_{fxd} and $\psi(\tau_{swg})$ are given in Table 4.4. The scaled free-fall time τ_{free} is independent of μ, and for $\theta_0 = 0.6$ is 1.82, and we see that as $\mu = m/M$ decreases, $\tau_{swg} \to \tau_{free}$.

In this case z[1] also gives t=2.13..., but there is no guarantee that t will always be the first element of this list, so this method should not be used.

Table 4.4   The values of the times for the beam to rotate from $\theta = \theta_0$ to $\pi - \theta_0$, when $L = 1$, $l = 6$ and $\theta_0 = 0.6$, for various values of μ. Here τ_{swg} is the time for the swinging counterweight, computed using the above commands, and τ_{fxd} is the time for a fixed counterweight, calculated from the integral (4.18) (page 187). Notice that as $\mu \to 0$, $\tau_{fxd} > \tau_{swg} \to \tau_{free} = 1.82$. Also given is the value of $\psi(\tau_{swg})$, and we see that this tends to zero as $\mu \to 0$; this is discussed in Subsection 4.7.2.

μ	0.1	0.01	0.001	0.0001
τ_{fxd}	7.88	2.79	2.37	2.33
τ_{swg}	7.90	2.41	1.88	1.82
$\psi(\tau_{swg})$	0.33	0.16	0.02	0.00

Exercise 4.27

(a) Write a Maple procedure Tswg that computes the values of τ_{swg} and $\psi(\tau_{swg})$, and a procedure Tfixed that computes τ_{fxd}, defined by the integral (4.18). Use these to reproduce Table 4.4.

(b) For $0.0001 \le \mu \le 0.1$, plot the graphs of the ratio τ_{swg}/τ_{fxd} against $\log \mu$, for $L = 1$, $l = 6$ and $\theta_0 = 0.2$, 0.4 and 0.6, on the same plot.

(c) Also consider the cases $L = 0.5$ and $L = 2.0$, for the same range of μ and $\theta_0 = 0.6$.

The calculations performed in this subsection have shown that for small μ, a swinging counterweight falls faster than one that is fixed. A fixed counterweight can be made to fall faster by putting the whole trebuchet on wheels in order to allow it to move horizontally: this mechanism is examined in Exercise 4.55. Another mechanism that allows the counterweight to fall vertically is considered in Exercise 4.54.

4.7.2 The free-fall approximation

In this subsection we use the numerical solutions of Equations (4.9) and (4.10) to check the validity of the free-fall approximation for $\theta_0 < \theta < \pi - \theta_0$, and to check that $\psi(\tau) \simeq 0$ when $\theta = \pi - \theta_0$. Recall that as θ increases through $\pi - \theta_0$, the beam and counterweight support are almost parallel, and the subsequent motion becomes more complicated. Thus we expect this early part of the motion to be the most important for the projectile launch.

The approximate motion for $\theta_0 < \theta(\tau) < \pi - \theta_0$

In the free-fall limit we can obtain simple functions for $\theta(\tau)$ and $\psi(\tau)$ as follows. Denote the height of B above N (see Figure 4.16, page 180) by y_B, so $y_B = L_2 \cos\theta$. Newton's equation of motion gives $\ddot{y}_B = -g$, and since $y_B(0) = L_2 \cos\theta_0$ and $\dot{y}_B(0) = 0$, integration gives $y_B(t) = L_2 \cos\theta_0 - gt^2/2$. Since $t = \tau\sqrt{L_2/g}$, dividing by L_2 gives

$$\cos\theta = \cos\theta_0 - \tfrac{1}{2}\tau^2, \quad \tau < 2\sqrt{\cos\theta_0}. \tag{4.19}$$

This is an approximate solution of Equation (4.9), valid when both ψ and μl are small. With this approximation we see that $(\cos\theta)'' = -1$ and then Equation (4.15) (page 186) for ψ becomes

$$L\psi'' = -(\sin\theta)''.$$

This may be integrated directly to give $L\psi' = \text{constant} - (\sin\theta)'$. Initially, $\psi' = 0$ and also $(\sin\theta)' = \theta'\cos\theta = 0$, so the constant of integration is zero. A further integration gives $L\psi = \text{constant} - \sin\theta$. Initially, $\psi = 0$ and $\theta = \theta_0$, and hence the free-fall approximation to $\psi(\tau)$ is

$$\psi(\tau) = \frac{1}{L}\left(\sin\theta_0 - \sin\theta\right). \tag{4.20}$$

This approximation shows that $\psi(\tau) = 0$ when $\sin\theta = \sin\theta_0$, that is, when $\theta = \theta_0$ and $\theta = \pi - \theta_0$, which ends the free-fall period. Also, because $(\cos\theta)'' = -1$, the result found in Exercise 4.23 (page 185) shows that $x_C'' \simeq 0$, which confirms that the counterweight falls almost vertically. The following exercise derives similar results directly from the equations of motion in the limit $\mu l = 0$.

Exercise 4.28

Show that if $\mu l = 0$, then Equations (4.11) and (4.12) can be written in the form

$$\theta'' - \sin\theta + L\cos\theta(\sin\psi)'' + L\sin\theta(\cos\psi)'' = 0,$$
$$L\psi'' + \sin\psi + \cos\psi(\sin\theta)'' + \sin\psi(\cos\theta)'' = 0.$$

Show that

$$\theta'' = \cos\theta(\sin\theta)'' - \sin\theta(\cos\theta)'',$$

and hence deduce that if $x = \sin\theta + L\sin\psi$ and $y = \cos\theta - L\cos\psi$, then

$$x''\sin(\theta + \psi) = 0 \quad \text{and} \quad (y'' + 1)\sin(\theta + \psi) = 0. \tag{4.21}$$

From these equations, deduce that provided $\sin(\theta + \psi) \neq 0$, $x'' = 0$ and $y'' = -1$, and that during the free-fall period,

$$\sin\theta + L\sin\psi = \sin\theta_0 \quad \text{and} \quad \cos\theta - L\cos\psi = \cos\theta_0 - L - \tfrac{1}{2}\tau^2.$$

Note that x is the x-coordinate of the counterweight and y is, to within an additive constant, its y-coordinate, so these relations represent a free-falling counterweight.

Note also that, unlike the approximation used in Exercise 4.23, in the above exercise it was not assumed that $|\psi|$ is small. Equations (4.21) explain more than just the free-fall approximation; they show that provided $\sin(\theta + \psi) \neq 0$, the counterweight moves like a particle falling freely under gravity, that is, $x'' = 0$, so $x = \alpha + \beta t$, in between the times when $\sin(\theta + \psi) = 0$, when the beam and counterweight support are parallel. When $\sin(\theta + \psi) = 0$, the equations with $\mu = 0$ are singular, but the long-time numerical solutions confirm that for small μ, $x(t)$ is almost piecewise-linear, as seen in Figures 4.24 and 4.25 (page 197).

The graph of a piecewise-linear function is made up of straight-line segments, with sharp angles at their intersections.

Exercise 4.29

(a) Use the free-fall approximations, Equation (4.19) and (4.20), to show that when $\theta = \pi - \theta_0$,

$$\theta' \simeq \frac{2\sqrt{\cos \theta_0}}{\sin \theta_0} \quad \text{and} \quad \psi' \simeq \frac{2(\cos \theta_0)^{3/2}}{L \sin \theta_0}.$$

(b) Write a Maple procedure to solve the equations of motion from $\tau = 0$ to $\tau = \tau_{\text{swg}}$, where $\theta(\tau_{\text{swg}}) = \pi - \theta_0$, and to print out the values $(\theta'(\tau_{\text{swg}}), \psi'(\tau_{\text{swg}}))$, together with the free-fall approximation of these quantities.

For $L = 1$, $l = 7$, $\theta_0 = 0.6$ and $\mu = 10^{-p}$, $p = 1, 2, \ldots, 5$, tabulate the exact and free-fall approximations of $(\theta'(\tau_{\text{swg}}), \psi'(\tau_{\text{swg}}))$.

In Exercise 4.29 it was seen that for μ sufficiently small, the free-fall aproximation is accurate, though it fails for larger μ, as expected. Another way of seeing this is to plot the graphs of $(\theta(\tau), \psi(\tau))$ and compare these with the free-fall approximation. These graphs also highlight another important feature of the dynamics that occurs when the beam and counterweight support are almost parallel, that is, after the free-fall period has ended.

The procedure `Graph01(th0,L,l,mu)` uses `odeplot` (line #3 below) to plot graphs of $(\theta(\tau), \theta'(\tau), \psi(\tau))$ for $\theta_0 \le \theta \le \pi$, and superimposes on these the free-fall approximation. The procedure listed below is quite long, but up to line #1 it is practically identical to the Maple procedure `Tswg` written in Exercise 4.27.

```
>   restart:  with(plots):  with(plottools):
>   Graph01 := proc(th0,L,l,m)
>      local eq1,eq2,s,c,p,ic,st,par1,par2,cl1,cl2,cl3,z,
         tmax,tswg,tt,g1,g2,ln1,thfree,psfree,tfreea,ptha,ppsa;
>      _Env_dsolve_nowarnstop := true:
>      par1 := 1+m*l^2;  par2 := 1-m*l;
>      s := sin(th(t)+ps(t)):  c := cos(th(t)+ps(t)):
>      eq1 := par1*diff(th(t),t,t)+L*c*diff(ps(t),t,t)
             -L*s*diff(ps(t),t)^2-par2*sin(th(t))=0;
>      eq2 := L*diff(ps(t),t,t)+c*diff(th(t),t,t)
             -s*diff(th(t),t)^2+sin(ps(t))=0;
>      ic := th(0)=th0, D(th)(0)=0, ps(0)=0, D(ps)(0)=0;
>      # First find the time when theta=pi-theta0
>      st := [th(t)-Pi+th0]:
>      p := dsolve({eq1,eq2,ic},numeric,stop_cond=st);
>      z := p(10);
>      tswg := eval(t,z);                                #1
>      print('Stop time theta=Pi-th0',evalf[4](tswg));
```

The next statement uses the command `line` to create a vertical line on the plot created in line #6, at the time when $\theta = \pi - \theta_0$.

```
>     ln1 := line([tswg,0],[tswg,evalf(Pi)]);
```

Define the stop condition to compute the time `tmax` (line #2) when the beam is vertical, $\theta = \pi$, and then use `odeplot` (line #3) to plot the graphs of $\theta(\tau)$, $\theta'(\tau)$ and $5\psi(\tau)$: we plot 5ψ because $|\psi|$ is small and this magnification helps visualise it.

```
>     st := [th(t)-Pi]:
>     p := dsolve({eq1,eq2,ic},numeric,stop_cond=st);
>     z := p(20):
>     tmax := eval(t,z);                            #2
>     print('Stop time theta=Pi ',evalf[4](tmax));
>     cl1 := colour=black;
>     cl2 := colour=black:
>     cl3 := colour=red;
>     tt := cat("theta=Pi when t=",
            convert(evalf[3](tmax),string)):
>     tt := title=cat(tt,":  theta=Pi-th0 when t=",
            convert(evalf[3](tswg),string)):
>     g1 := odeplot(p,[[t,5*ps(t),cl1],[t,th(t),cl2],
            [t,diff(th(t),t),cl3]],t=0..tmax,
            numpoints=300,tt);                      #3
```

The procedure `line([a,b],[c,d])`, defined in the package `plottools`, draws a straight line between the points $[a,b]$ and $[c,d]$; this package contains many other useful procedures, several of which were used in the animations of the trebuchet.

Define the functions `thfree` and `psfree`, given in Equations (4.19) and (4.20), respectively, use these to compute 10 equally spaced points with $0 < \tau < 2\sqrt{\cos\theta_0}$, `ptha` and `ppsa`, and superimpose these on the numerical solutions of the differential equations using the `display` procedure.

```
>     thfree := unapply(arccos(cos(th0)-t^2/2),t);   #4
>     psfree := unapply((sin(th0)-sin(thfree(t)))/L,t);  #5
>     tfreea := evalf(2*sqrt(cos(th0))):
>     ptha := [seq([ta,thfree(ta)],ta=0..tfreea,tfreea/10)];
>     ppsa := [seq([ta,5*psfree(ta)],ta=0..tfreea,tfreea/10)];
>     g2 := plot([ptha,ppsa],style=point,
            symbol=[cross,circle],colour=black);
>     display(g1,g2,ln1);                            #6
>   end proc:
```

Two graphs produced by this command are shown in Figures 4.18 and 4.19; in each case $\theta_0 = 0.6$, $L = 1$ and $l = 6$, so that $2\sqrt{\cos\theta_0} = 1.82$.

In Figure 4.18, produced with the command `Graph01(0.6,1,6,0.01)`, $\mu = 0.01$. In this case the mass ratio μ is too large for the free-fall approximation to be very accurate; however, we see that for most of the time when $\theta_0 < \theta < \pi - \theta_0$, $\psi(\tau) < 0$, and when $\theta = \pi - \theta_0$, $|\psi|$ is small. Also, we note that $\theta'(\tau)$ has a local maximum between $\theta = \pi - \theta_0$, marked by the vertical line, and $\theta = \pi$.

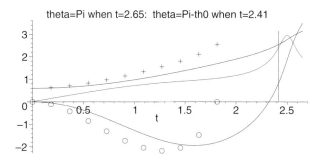

theta=Pi when t=2.65: theta=Pi-th0 when t=2.41

Figure 4.18   Swinging counterweight, $L = 1$, $l = 6$, $\theta_0 = 0.6$ and $\mu = 0.01$. The black lines depict θ and 5ψ, the red line depicts θ'; the crosses and circles are, respectively, the approximations given in Equations (4.19) and (4.20). The vertical line indicates the time when $\theta = \pi - \theta_0$.

In Figure 4.19, produced by the command `Graph01(0.6,1,6,0.001)`, $\mu = 0.001$ and now we see that the mass ratio is sufficiently small for the free-fall approximation to be quite accurate, and also that the maximum in $\theta'(\tau)$ is larger and sharper.

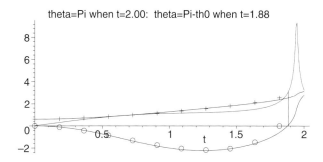

theta=Pi when t=2.00: theta=Pi-th0 when t=1.88

Figure 4.19   Swinging counterweight, $L = 1$, $l = 6$, $\theta_0 = 0.6$ and $\mu = 0.001$. The black lines depict θ and 5ψ, the red line depicts θ'; the crosses and circles are, respectively, the approximations given in Equations (4.19) and (4.20). The vertical line indicates the time when $\theta = \pi - \theta_0$.

In the next exercise other parameter values are considered.

Exercise 4.30

(a) Use the procedure `Graph01(th0,L,l,m)` to reproduce the graphs shown in Figures 4.18 and 4.19.

(b) Consider the nine cases $\mu = 0.01$, 0.001, 0.0001 with $\theta_0 = 0.8$, $l = 7.0$, each with $L = 1$, 2 and 3, and comment on the accuracy of the free-fall approximation.

The comparisons made in Exercise 4.30 show that the free-fall approximation is accurate if μ is sufficiently small; we also require that θ_0 is not too small. In Subsection 4.9.1 we derive an approximation which, for short times, is better for a wider range of μ and θ_0, and which will be used to compute the time when the projectile ceases its horizontal motion and starts phase II.

Figures 4.18 and 4.19 also show that $\theta'(\tau)$ has a local maximum, which seems to increase in height and become sharper as μ decreases. It can be shown empirically that this occurs when $\theta + \psi = \pi$, that is, when the beam and counterweight are parallel. In the next (optional) exercise we examine this maximum, which also occurs in $\psi'(\tau)$, and show that $l\sqrt{\mu}\max(\theta') \simeq 2$, $L\max(\psi') \simeq \max(\theta')$.

Exercise 4.31

Create a modified version of `Graph01(th0,L,l,m)` that stops the integration when $\theta + \psi = \pi$ and prints out the values of τ_s, $\theta(\tau_s)$, $\theta'(\tau_s)$, $\psi(\tau_s)$ and $\psi'(\tau_s)$ at this time.

This exercise is optional.

In the cases $L = 1$, 2 and 3, $l = 7$, $\theta_0 = 0.8$, show that for $\mu < 0.01$, $l\sqrt{\mu}\theta'(\tau_s) \simeq 2$ and $L\psi'(\tau_s) \simeq \theta'(\tau_s)$.

4.7.3   The variation of $x_C(\tau)$ (optional)

In the free-fall approximation, the distance of the counterweight from the vertical axis, $x_C(\tau)/L_2 = \sin\theta + L\sin\psi$, is constant. It is a simple matter to modify `Graph01(th0,L,l,m)` to plot this function until the first time that $x_C = 0$. Define the variable `xc` to be the required scaled distance

```
>   xc := sin(th(t))+L*sin(ps(t)):
```

then replace the stop condition defined on page 188 with

```
>   stc := [xc]:
```

which stops the integration when $x_C(\tau) = 0$. Then use the command

```
>   odeplot(p,[t,xc],t=0..10,numpoints=400);
```

to plot the graph of $x_C(\tau)$. In Figure 4.20 we show some graphs of $x_C(\tau)$ up to this time. Here $\theta_0 = 0.5$, $L = 1$ and $l = 6$, and the mass ratio $\mu = m/M$ varies from 0.05 down to 0.0001, the latter being depicted with the red line. We see that if μ is small, $x_C(\tau)$ is almost constant up to a certain time, and then decreases approximately linearly. By doing Exercise 4.32 you will see that the first maximum in $x_C(\tau)$ occurs when $\theta + \psi \simeq \pi$, that is, when the beam AB and counterweight support BC are almost parallel, for the first time: this behaviour is consistent with the result derived in Exercise 4.28 (page 190), and the subsequent discussion.

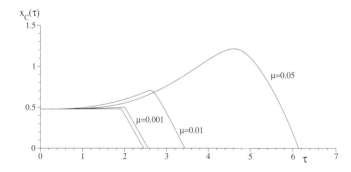

Figure 4.20   Graph of $x_C(\tau)$ up to the time when it is first zero. Here $\theta_0 = 0.5$, $L = 1$, $l = 6$ for various values of μ; the red line is the graph for $\mu = 0.0001$.

If L is small, we shall see in Figure 4.23 (page 196) that both $\theta'(\tau)$ and $\psi(\tau)$ oscillate rapidly. These oscillations are not present in x_C, although in this case the counterweight cannot fall vertically. The following optional exercise demonstrates this behaviour.

Exercise 4.32

Write a Maple procedure to plot the graphs of $x_C(\tau)$ and $(\theta(t) + \psi(t))/\pi$, for $0 \leq \tau \leq \tau_d$, where $x_C'(\tau_d) = \varepsilon$, for ε a small negative number; note that we really wish to use the condition $x_C'(\tau_d) = 0$, but because $x_C'(0) = 0$ we need to improvise.

Use your procedure to plot the graphs of $x_C(\tau)$ and $(\theta(\tau) + \psi(\tau))/\pi$ for a few example cases. The following sets of parameters are representative:

L	1	2	1	0.25	0.1
l	7	7	4	7	6

with $\theta_0 = 0.5$, and consider both $\mu = 0.01$ and $\mu = 0.001$. Observe that $x_C'(\tau) = 0$ when $\theta + \psi \simeq \pi$, except when L is small.

4.7.4   The case $L < 1$ and the limit $L = 0$ *(optional)*

In this subsection we consider the effect of changing the ratio $L = BC/NB$ (see Figure 4.16, page 180), and show that this must not be too small. There are two reasons for this. First, if $0 < L \ll 1$, then the trebuchet cannot work properly. The second consequence is due to an important mathematical property of the equations of motion that occurs frequently in applied mathematics, especially quantum mechanics and fluid dynamics: namely, if $L = 0$, then the coefficient of the highest derivative of ψ, that is, ψ'', in Equation (4.10) (page 182) vanishes and the nature of the equation changes – it is no longer a differential equation for ψ, but an algebraic equation giving ψ directly in terms of θ, θ' and θ''. Thus we might expect interesting behaviour when L is small, and we demonstrate that this is the case numerically. Nevertheless, in the fixed counterweight limit, that is, $L = 0$, the equation of motion for θ simplifies to Equation (4.16) (page 186), and the counterweight moves on a circular arc.

First, consider the practical consequences: if L is small, the ψ-motion can be complicated because the horizontal motion of the counterweight is more affected by the rotation of the beam, so the smaller L, the more rapidly ψ decreases. The geometry of this effect is shown in Figure 4.21, where it is assumed that the counterweight falls vertically. This figure alone suggests that L must not be too small. In addition, because the counterweight is usually physically large (see Figure 4.10), the angle between NB and BC, $\theta + \psi$, must remain large enough for the counterweight not to hit the beam.

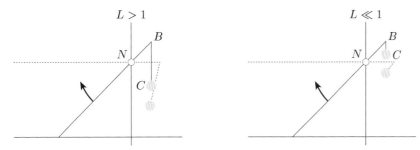

Figure 4.21   Diagram showing how decreasing the value of L affects the value of ψ. Here we see that as the beam rotates clockwise about N, provided the counterweight falls vertically, ψ decreases faster the smaller L.

Now consider the effect of making L small. In Figure 4.22 we show solutions for $\mu = 0.001$, $l = 6$ and $\theta_0 = 0.6$, with $L = 0.5$ on the left and $L = 0.1$ on the right. These graphs show that both $\theta'(\tau)$ and $\psi(\tau)$ oscillate with a period that decreases as L decreases, and also that when $L = 0.1$, the value of $\theta + \psi$ becomes negative. The oscillations in $\theta'(\tau)$ may affect the projectile motion and are therefore undesirable.

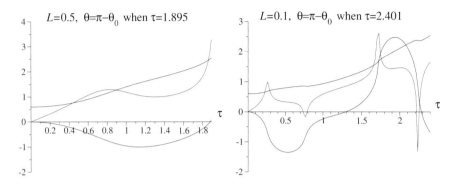

Figure 4.22   Swinging counterweight with parameters $l = 6$, $\theta_0 = 0.6$ and $\mu = 0.001$; on the right $L = 0.1$ and on the left $L = 0.5$. The black lines depict θ and ψ, the red line depicts θ'; integration stops when $\theta = \pi - \theta_0$.

The equation for the fixed counterweight trebuchet can be derived from Equation (4.9) by setting $L = 0$, so it is interesting to examine an example where L is very small. In Figure 4.23 we show the solutions for $L = 0.01$, and here we see that the oscillations in $\theta(\tau)$ and $\psi(\tau)$ are now very rapid, and that the value of ψ exceeds π at $\tau \simeq 1.6$ and subsequently $\psi(\tau)$ executes large oscillations.

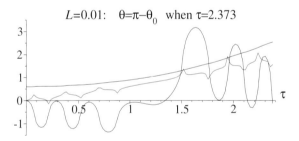

Figure 4.23   Swinging counterweight, $L = 0.01$, $l = 6$, $\theta_0 = 0.6$ and $\mu = 0.001$. The black lines depict θ and ψ, the red line depicts θ'; integration stops when $\theta = \pi - \theta_0$.

Exercise 4.33

Here we explore how the solutions for the swinging counterweight trebuchet, Equations (4.9) and (4.10), and the fixed counterweight trebuchet, Equation (4.16), approach each other as $L \to 0$.

(a) Write a procedure that numerically solves the equations for both the swinging and the fixed counterweight trebuchet and for $l = 6$, $\theta_0 = 0.5$ and $\mu = 0.001$, plot the graphs of $(\theta(\tau), \psi(\tau), \theta'(\tau))$ for the former and $(\theta(\tau), \theta'(\tau))$ for the latter, in the cases $L = 1, 0.5, 0.1, 0.01$ and 0.001, on the interval $0 \le \tau \le \tau_m$, where for the swinging counterweight $\theta(\tau_m) = \pi$.

(b) Modify the procedure from part (a) to plot the graphs of the distance of the counterweight from the y-axis, $x_C/L_2 = \sin\theta + L\sin\psi$, up to the time when $x_C(\tau) = 0$, for each type of trebuchet, and compare these functions using the same parameters.

4.7.5   The motion for long times (optional)

You will recall from the video clips and the animations that after the projectile has been launched, after the beam first becomes vertical, the beam and the counterweight execute fairly violent oscillations. Here we consider, graphically, two cases which demonstrate this motion.

In particular we look at the time-dependence of $x_C(\tau)$, the distance of the counterweight from the y-axis, and the beam angle $\theta(\tau)$. Previously we saw that provided $L > 1$, usually $|\psi|$ remains small when θ increases from θ_0 to $\pi - \theta_0$, and in Figure 4.20 we saw $x_C(\tau) \simeq$ constant. This changes when $\theta(\tau)$ exceeds $\pi - \theta_0$.

For larger times, both $\theta(\tau)$ and $x_C(\tau)$ execute quite large oscillations, as seen in the animations presented earlier. Since the counterweight is heavy, these oscillations impose large forces on the trebuchet structure, though in practice friction will damp these oscillations; in the present approximation they persist forever. For the example we set $L = 1$, $l = 3$ and $\mu = 0.01$, starting at $\theta_0 = 0.5$; the graphs of θ shown in Figures 4.24 and 4.25 suggest that $\theta(\tau)$ does not vary periodically.

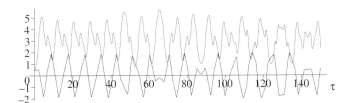

Figure 4.24   The black line depicts $x_C(\tau)$ and the red line $\theta(\tau)$, for $\mu = 0.01$, $L = 1$, $l = 3$, with initial condition $\theta_0 = 0.5$

Notice that the changes in $x_C(\tau)$ are almost piecewise-linear; that is, the x-motion of the counterweight is, for most of the time, uniform, but with frequent, sudden changes in x'_C. For a heavier counterweight, $\mu = 0.0001$ (see Figure 4.25), this type of motion is more exaggerated.

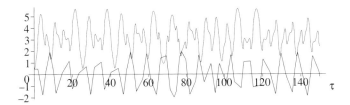

Figure 4.25   The black line depicts $x_C(\tau)$ and the red line $\theta(\tau)$, for $\mu = 0.0001$, $L = 1$, $l = 3$, with initial condition $\theta_0 = 0.5$

The physical reason for the observed behaviour of $x_C(\tau)$ is simple. The counterweight is very heavy, so it can accelerate in the x-direction only if the horizontal force acting upon it is large. Most of the time this force is too weak to affect the counterweight, so $x_C''(\tau) \simeq 0$; but the trebuchet geometry forces frequent, sudden changes in $x_C'(\tau) \simeq 0$. In Exercise 4.28 (page 190) we saw that when $\mu = 0$, $x_C'' = 0$ if $\sin(\theta + \psi) \neq 0$, which suggests that the changes in x_C' occur when $\sin(\theta + \psi) = 0$: this is confirmed by the calculation suggested in Exercise 4.34.

This type of behaviour is not the sort expected from the solution of a second-order differential equation with benign coefficients. However, the equations of motion are for θ and ψ, and these angles change more smoothly.

By comparison, the beam of the fixed counterweight trebuchet simply oscillates periodically, as seen in Exercise 4.24 (page 187).

Exercise 4.34

(a) Write a Maple procedure to plot the graphs of $x_C(\tau)$ and $\sin(\theta + \psi)$ to show that in the cases illustrated in Figures 4.24 and 4.25, the times when $\sin(\theta + \psi) = 0$ coincide with the changes in $x_C'(\tau)$.

(b) Modify your procedure to draw the graphs of $x_C(\tau)$ and $x_C'(\tau)$, on the same plot.

4.8 The equations for trebuchets

In this section we define all relations needed to simulate the trebuchet. Recall that there are two phases of the motion, as illustrated in Figure 4.12 (page 174) and described in the associated text. These two phases are described by different equations, but we also require an equation that defines the time when transition between these two phases occurs, and the geometric relation that governs the launch of the projectile; finally, we need an expression that gives the range of the projectile. Thus this section is fairly long, but little effort is required to grasp the salient points, because the derivations of all the equations are not part of the course: for the interested reader these are provided on the course website.

You should not require much time to grasp the significant points of this section, and to help we provide a brief summary of each subsection which highlights the most important results.

Subsection 4.8.1: Phase I motion

Initially, the trebuchet beam is pointing downwards with the projectile resting on its slide. When released, the counterweight falls and the projectile is pulled horizontally by the sling along the slide (see Figure 4.12, page 174); this motion requires one new variable, the angle ϕ between the sling and the horizontal, and another parameter, the sling length L_4 or its associated scaled variable $l_4 = L_4/L_1$ (see Figure 4.26).

The value of ϕ during phase I is determined solely by the beam and counterweight angles, θ and ψ, respectively; that is, ϕ is not an independent variable. The next important pair of results is Equations (4.25) and (4.26), which give $\theta(\tau)$ and $\psi(\tau)$, and hence the progress of the projectile along the slide. There is also the related Equation (4.28) for the fixed counterweight trebuchet, and you should be able to relate this to the first two equations.

As the counterweight falls, the angle of the sling to the horizontal increases, and at some time τ_L the vertical component of the tension in it is sufficient to lift the projectile off the slide; after this, the sling and projectile rotate freely about the end of the beam, that is, ϕ becomes an independent variable. The lift-off time is given by the solution of Equation (4.27), and this is the last important result in this subsection.

Subsection 4.8.2: Calculation of the lift-off time

In this subsection we approximate the solution of the equations for θ and ψ for small times with a truncated Taylor series, which allows us to find the lift-off time τ_L by solving an algebraic equation rather than a pair of differential equations. You should try to understand this simple analysis. You should also understand the Maple procedure `Tlift`, given on page 202, which computes τ_L and the initial conditions required to start the phase II motion, needed to simulate a trebuchet.

Subsection 4.8.3: Phase II motion

This subsection gives the three equations that describe the phase II motion, which are Equations (4.37) to (4.39); for a fixed counterweight these reduce to Equations (4.40) and (4.41). You should be acquainted with these equations and understand how the latter two follow from the first three.

Phase II of the motion ends, for all practical purposes, when the projectile is launched. The geometric condition for this is given in Equation (4.42); this condition involves a new, free parameter with which you need to be familiar.

Finally, the range of the projectile is given in Equation (4.44). This expression is just a complicated version of Equation (4.1) (page 177), because the position and velocity of the projectile at launch depend on two angles, θ and ϕ.

4.8.1   Phase I motion

The basic geometry of the trebuchet during phase I of the motion and the definitions of all angles are given in Figure 4.26.

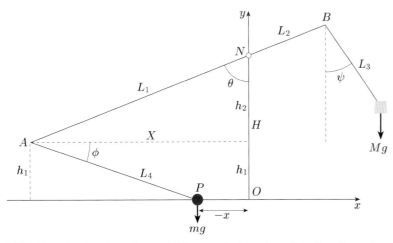

Figure 4.26   Sketch showing the variables needed to describe the phase I motion

In Figure 4.26 the angles θ, ψ and lengths L_1, L_2, L_3 are the same as introduced in Figure 4.16 (page 180). The new angle ϕ defines the orientation of the sling, and L_4 is the length of the sling. Usually $L_4 < L_1$, and initially $\phi(0) = 0$. Elementary trigonometry gives

$$\frac{h_2}{L_1} = \cos\theta, \quad \frac{h_1}{L_4} = \sin\phi, \quad H = h_1 + h_2 = L_1\cos\theta + L_4\sin\phi. \quad (4.22)$$

Since H is fixed, the latter equation gives the relation between ϕ and θ. Also,

$$\frac{X}{L_1} = \sin\theta, \quad x = -X + L_4\cos\phi = L_4\cos\phi - L_1\sin\theta. \quad (4.23)$$

This geometry is used only if $0 \le \phi < \pi/2$. Initially, $\phi(0) = 0$ and $\cos\theta_0 = H/L_1$.

Exercise 4.35

Show that in terms of the scaled variables and the initial value of θ, the relation between ϕ and θ can be written in the form

$$\sin\phi = \frac{1}{l_4}(\cos\theta_0 - \cos\theta), \quad l_4 = \frac{L_4}{L_1} < 1. \quad (4.24)$$

Using the scaled variables, the two equations for ψ and θ can be shown to be

$$L\psi'' + \sin\psi + \theta''\cos(\theta+\psi) - \theta'^2\sin(\theta+\psi) = 0, \quad L = \frac{L_3}{L_2}, \quad (4.25)$$

which is the same as Equation (4.10) (page 182), and

$$\left(1 + \mu l^2 f(\theta)^2\right)\theta'' + \mu l^2 f(\theta) f'(\theta)\theta'^2 - \sin\theta$$
$$+ L\left(\psi''\cos(\theta+\psi) - \psi'^2\sin(\theta+\psi)\right) = 0, \quad (4.26)$$

which is the equivalent of Equation (4.9) (page 182). In this equation

Note that $\theta' = \dfrac{d\theta}{d\tau}$ and

$$f(\theta) = -\frac{\cos(\theta-\phi)}{\cos\phi}, \quad f'(\theta) = \frac{\sin(\theta-\phi)}{\cos\phi} - \frac{\sin\theta}{\cos^2\phi}\frac{d\phi}{d\theta}, \quad \frac{d\phi}{d\theta} = \frac{\sin\theta}{l_4\cos\phi}, \quad f'(\theta) = \dfrac{df}{d\theta}.$$

and $\sin\phi = (\cos\theta_0 - \cos\theta)/l_4$.

Equations (4.25) and (4.26) are valid only if the vertical component of the tension in the sling is less than the weight of the projectile. The projectile lifts off the x-axis when the vertical component of the tension exceeds the weight of the projectile, and it can be shown that this occurs when

$$l\sin\phi\left(\theta''\cos(\phi-\theta) + \theta'^2\sin(\phi-\theta) + \theta'^2\frac{\sin^2\theta}{l_4\cos^2\phi}\right) = \cos^2\phi. \quad (4.27)$$

Initially, $\phi = 0$ and the left-hand side of this equation is zero, and it is infinite when $\phi = \pi/2$. The right-hand side is initially 1, and is zero when $\phi = \pi/2$. Hence for some $0 < \phi < \pi/2$ the equation has a root, that is, lift-off occurs before $\phi = \pi/2$ provided that the counterweight is heavy enough to sufficiently increase ϕ. We define $\tau = \tau_L$ to be this lift-off time. At this time the integration of Equations (4.25) and (4.26) will give the values of

$$\theta(\tau_L), \quad \theta'(\tau_L), \quad \psi(\tau_L) \quad \text{and} \quad \psi'(\tau_L).$$

Equation (4.24) will give $\phi(\tau_L)$, and by differentiation of this equation, $l_4\phi'\cos\phi = \theta'\sin\theta$, we obtain $\phi'(\tau_L)$. These are initial conditions for the phase II motion.

For a fixed counterweight the condition (4.27) is the same, but now θ is given by Equation (4.26) with $L = 0$, that is,

$$\left(1 + \mu l^2 f(\theta)^2\right) \theta'' + \mu l^2 \theta'^2 f(\theta) f'(\theta) - \sin\theta = 0, \quad \theta(0) = \theta_0, \quad \theta'(0) = 0.$$
$$(4.28)$$

Exercise 4.36

Show that Equation (4.27) can be written in the alternative form

$$l \sin\phi \left((\sin\theta)'' - l_4(\cos\phi)''\right) = \cos\phi.$$

Exercise 4.37

Show that Equation (4.28) can be integrated once to give

$$\tfrac{1}{2}\left(1 + \mu l^2 f(\theta)^2\right) \theta'^2 = \cos\theta_0 - \cos\theta.$$

4.8.2 Calculation of the lift-off time

The lift-off condition (4.28) is complicated and requires the solution of the differential Equations (4.25) and (4.26) with a complicated stop condition. We expect, however, the change from phase I to phase II to occur early during the motion, so we now find an approximation to the motion, valid for short times, so that the lift-off condition Equation (4.27) becomes an algebraic function and the value of τ_L can be found using `fsolve`, without the need to solve any differential equations.

An approximation to the initial motion

The free-fall approximation given in Equations (4.19) and (4.20) has been shown, in Exercise 4.30, to be quite accurate in some cases, particularly for small μ. But when $\theta_0 = 0$, the exact solution is $\theta = \psi = 0$ for all τ, so we expect this approximation to fail for small θ_0. Here we derive another approximation to $\theta(\tau)$, which is the same as the free-fall approximation when $\mu = 0$, but a better approximation for small θ_0 and larger values of μ.

A second-order Taylor approximation for θ is trivially obtained by computing the second derivative directly from Equations (4.25) and (4.26), by substituting for the initial values of θ, θ', ψ and ψ', that is, $\theta(0) = \theta_0$, $\psi(0) = \theta'(0) = \psi'(0) = 0$. This gives the following equations for $\theta''(0)$ and $\psi''(0)$:

$$(1 + \mu l^2 \cos^2\theta_0)\theta''(0) - \sin\theta_0 + L\psi''(0)\cos\theta_0 = 0,$$
$$L\psi''(0) + \theta''(0)\cos\theta_0 = 0.$$
$$(4.29)$$

These are solved to give

$$\theta''(0) = \frac{\sin\theta_0}{\mu l^2 \cos^2\theta_0 + \sin^2\theta_0},$$

and hence the second-order Taylor series of $\theta(\tau)$ is

$$\theta(\tau) = \theta_0 + \frac{\sin\theta_0}{2(\mu l^2 \cos^2\theta_0 + \sin^2\theta_0)}\tau^2 + \cdots.$$
$$(4.30)$$

Since, for small δ, $\cos(\theta_0 + \delta) = \cos\theta_0 - \delta\sin\theta_0 + \cdots$, this also gives

$$\cos\theta = \cos\theta_0 - \frac{\sin^2\theta_0}{2(\mu l^2 \cos^2\theta_0 + \sin^2\theta_0)}\tau^2 + \cdots.$$
$$(4.31)$$

If $\mu = 0$ and $\theta_0 \neq 0$, this is just Equation (4.19), the free-fall approximation, as would be expected from Exercise 4.28. But if $\theta_0 = 0$, this approximation gives $\theta = \theta_0$, which is correct. Notice that the coefficient of τ^2 in Equation (4.30) has the property that the limits $\mu \to 0$ and $\theta_0 \to 0$ give different values according to the order in which they are taken. This strange mathematical property is a reflection of physical reality.

For $\psi(\tau)$ we proceed in a different manner, because we know that $\psi(\tau) = 0$ when $\theta \simeq \pi - \theta_0$ and it is clear that its second-order Taylor series cannot behave like this. For this function we use approximation (4.15) (page 186) to Equation (4.25), which is valid when both $|\psi|$ and $|\psi'|$ are small. With the approximation to $\cos\theta$ derived above, this gives

$$L\psi'' + (\sin\theta)'' + \frac{\mu l^2 \cos^2\theta_0}{\sin^2\theta_0 + \mu l^2 \cos^2\theta_0}\psi = 0. \qquad (4.32)$$

The third term is small because both μ and ψ are small, so a first approximation is $L\psi'' = -(\sin\theta)''$, which gives

$$\psi(\tau) = \frac{1}{L}(\sin\theta_0 - \sin\theta(\tau)), \quad \theta(\tau) = \theta_0 + \frac{\sin\theta_0}{2(\mu l^2 \cos^2\theta_0 + \sin^2\theta_0)}\tau^2. \qquad (4.33)$$

A procedure to compute τ_L

Here we provide a procedure `Tlift(th0,L,l,l4,m)` in which Equation (4.27) is solved for τ_L, using the approximations derived above. This procedure also computes the values of all dependent variables, (θ, ψ, ϕ), and their first derivatives at $\tau = \tau_L$; it works in the following manner.

1. The left-hand side of Equation (4.27) is denoted by `z`, in line #1. We do not use `fsolve` directly on this, but increment τ in steps of `dt` $= 0.1$ to find where the left-hand side first exceeds the right-hand side; this search is performed in the loop beginning at line #3. The reason for this elaboration is simply that we cannot be sure that Equation (4.27) has only one real root, although physical arguments suggest this to be the case; the following method increases the likelihood of finding the first root if more than one exists. It also gives `fsolve` a smaller interval in which to search. In general it is not good practice to assume that 'black-box' procedures will find the desired result without guidance.

2. Line #2: the maximum time `tmax` is defined by the condition that $\phi = \pi/2$; the root must lie in the interval $(0, \tau_{max})$.

3. The output of `Tlift` is a list of four elements. The first is the value of τ_L; the remaining elements are three lists containing the values of $(\theta(\tau_L), \theta'(\tau_L))$, $(\psi(\tau_L), \psi'(\tau_L))$ and $(\phi(\tau_L), \phi'(\tau_L))$.

```
>   Tlift := proc(th0,L,l,l4,m)
>       local z,x,theta,thetap,theta2p,tlift,psi,phi,ic,dt,
        k,zz,phii,tt,tmax,N;
```

Define the approximation to θ, given in Equation (4.30), and its second derivative at $\tau = 0$.

```
>       theta2p := sin(th0)/((m*l^2*cos(th0)^2+sin(th0)^2));
>       theta := th0+theta2p*t^2/2;        # Definition of theta
>       thetap := theta2p*t;               # Definition of theta'
```

Now define ψ and ϕ, using Equations (4.33) and (4.24).

```
>    psi := (sin(th0)-sin(theta))/L;
>    phi := arcsin((cos(th0)-cos(theta))/l4);
>    x := phi-theta;
>    z := theta2p*cos(x)+thetap^2*(sin(x)
             +sin(theta)^2/(l4*cos(phi)^2));
```

Now define the left-hand side of Equation (4.27).

```
>    z := l*z*sin(phi);                              #1
```

Define the value of $\tau_{\max}$ by putting $\phi = \pi/2$ in Equation (4.24) and using Equation (4.31) to approximate $\cos\theta_0 - \cos\theta$.

```
>    tmax := evalf(sqrt(2*l4*(1+m*l^2/tan(th0)^2)));    #2
>    dt := 0.1:  N := trunc(tmax/dt);
>    for k from 1 to N do:                              #3
>      tt := k*dt;
>      zz := evalf(eval(z,t=tt));
>      phii := evalf(eval(phi,t=tt));
>      if zz>cos(phii)^2 then                # Find the root
>        tlift := fsolve(z=cos(phi)^2,t=dt*(k-1)..dt*k);
>        break;
>      fi;
>    od;
```

Finally, define a list of the initial conditions for the start of the phase II motion.

```
>    ic := eval([theta,diff(theta,t)],t=tlift);
>    ic := ic,eval([psi,diff(psi,t)],t=tlift);
>    ic := ic,eval([phi,diff(phi,t)],t=tlift);
>    [tlift,ic];
>  end proc:
```

Exercise 4.38

(a) Use the procedure `Tlift` with $\theta_0 = 0.7$, $l = 7$, $l_4 = 0.7$ and $L = 1$ to show that for $\mu = 0.1$, 0.01, 0.001 and 0.0001, τ_L has the values 2.0, 0.62, 0.41 and 0.39, respectively, and find the values when $l_4 = 0.4$.

(b) By solving Equations (4.25) and (4.26) numerically for $0 \le \tau \le \tau_L$ with the four sets of parameters defined in part (a), show graphically that the approximation to $\theta(\tau)$ defined in Equation (4.30) is superior to the approximation given by the free-fall approximation Equation (4.19) (page 190), especially when $\mu = 0.1$.

Exercise 4.39

In this exercise we derive the lift-off time τ_L and initial conditions for the fixed counterweight trebuchet. These results are needed in Section 4.9.

(a) Show that the second-order Taylor series solution of Equation (4.28) is

$$\theta(\tau) = \theta_0 + \frac{\sin\theta_0}{2(1 + \mu l^2 \cos^2\theta_0)}\tau^2.$$

(b) Use this expression and the equivalent expression for the normal swinging counterweight trebuchet to show that initially the beam of the fixed counterweight trebuchet moves slower.

(c) Write a procedure `Tliftfxd`, equivalent to the procedure `Tlift`, that computes the lift-off time τ_L and the values of $(\theta, \phi, \theta', \phi')$ at this time, for the fixed counterweight trebuchet. Use your procedure to compare lift-off times with those obtained in Exercise 4.38(a).

4.8.3 Phase II motion

The basic geometry of the trebuchet during phase II of the motion and the definitions of all angles are given in Figure 4.27, but now the projectile P is not constrained to the x-axis, so ϕ is not algebraically connected to θ and ψ.

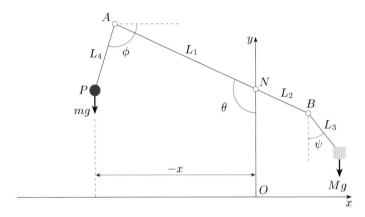

Figure 4.27   Sketch showing the variables needed to describe the phase II motion

Important variables are the coordinates (x_P, y_P) of the projectile P with respect to the Oxy-axes, because from these the final velocity of the projectile is determined. They are

$$x_P = L_4 \cos \phi - L_1 \sin \theta, \quad y_P = H - L_4 \sin \phi - L_1 \cos \theta, \qquad (4.34)$$

where $H = ON$, so the velocity components of the projectile are

$$\dot{x}_P = -L_4 \dot{\phi} \sin \phi - L_1 \dot{\theta} \cos \theta, \quad \dot{y}_P = -L_4 \dot{\phi} \cos \phi + L_1 \dot{\theta} \sin \theta. \qquad (4.35)$$

These, together with the equivalent formulae for the coordinates of the counterweight, are all that is necessary to derive the equations of motion.

Exercise 4.40

Using elementary geometry, derive Equations (4.34) for x_P and y_P. Differentiate these relations to derive Equations (4.35).

As with the phase I motion, the addition of the projectile gives an additional length, AP, denoted by L_4. Using the scaling introduced in Equation (4.24) this gives another parameter $l_4 = L_4/L_1$. Intuitively, we expect the value of l_4 to be important in determining the velocity of the projectile when launched. For completeness we list the four system parameters:

$$L = \frac{L_3}{L_2} \simeq 1, \quad l = \frac{L_1}{L_2} \gg 1, \quad l_4 = \frac{L_4}{L_1} < 1, \quad \mu = \frac{m}{M} \ll 1. \qquad (4.36)$$

In terms of the dimensionless time $\tau = \omega t$, where $\omega^2 = g/L_2$, the equation for the beam angle θ can be shown to be (see the course website)

$$(1 + \mu l^2)\theta'' - (1 - \mu l)\sin\theta + L\left(\psi''\cos(\theta + \psi) - \psi'^2\sin(\theta + \psi)\right)$$
$$- \mu l^2 l_4\left(\phi''\sin(\theta - \phi) - \phi'^2\cos(\theta - \phi)\right) = 0. \qquad (4.37)$$

Note that apart from the last term this is the same as Equation (4.9) (page 182), and also that this last term is small when $\mu l^2 l_4 \ll 1$. The equation for the counterweight angle ψ is

$$L\psi'' + \sin\psi + \theta''\cos(\theta + \psi) - \theta'^2\sin(\theta + \psi) = 0. \qquad (4.38)$$

Notice that the equation for ψ is identical to Equation (4.10) (page 182) for the simple system without a sling. The new equation for the sling angle ϕ is

$$l l_4 \phi'' - \cos\phi - l\left(\theta''\sin(\theta - \phi) + \theta'^2\cos(\theta - \phi)\right) = 0. \qquad (4.39)$$

Note that this equation does not depend directly on either L or μ. Equations (4.37), (4.38) and (4.39) describe the phase II motion of the trebuchet. The initial conditions for these equations are obtained by integrating the phase I equations of motion until $\tau_{\rm L}$, when the projectile lifts off the slide, as described in Subsection 4.8.2.

By putting $L = 0$ in Equation (4.37), we see that the equations of the phase II motion for the fixed counterweight trebuchet are

$$(1 + \mu l^2)\theta'' - (1 - \mu l)\sin\theta$$
$$- \mu l^2 l_4\left(\phi''\sin(\theta - \phi) - \phi'^2\cos(\theta - \phi)\right) = 0, \qquad (4.40)$$
$$l l_4 \phi'' - \cos\phi - l\left(\theta''\sin(\theta - \phi) + \theta'^2\cos(\theta - \phi)\right) = 0. \qquad (4.41)$$

The launch condition

Integration of the phase II equations stops when the angle between the sling and the spigot decreases through the appropriate value, denoted by $\beta_{\rm ss}$; as discussed in the Introduction, $0 \le \beta_{\rm ss} \le \pi/2$. If $\beta_{\rm ss} = 0$, the launch occurs when the sling and spigot are parallel.

Elementary geometry shows that the angle between the sling and the spigot is $\pi/2 + \beta + \theta - \phi$, so the projectile is launched if and when $\phi - \theta$ reaches the value

$$\phi - \theta = \frac{\pi}{2} + \beta - \beta_{\rm ss} = \beta_d. \qquad (4.42)$$

This condition depends upon only the single parameter β_d, and since $0 < \beta \le \pi/2$ and $0 \le \beta_{\rm ss} \le \pi/2$, we have $0 < \beta_d \le \pi$. The angles β and $\beta_{\rm ss}$ have distinct physical meaning and it is often helpful to use their values to compute β_d. Also, if $\beta_{\rm ss} = \pi/2$ – probably a good approximation because there will be little friction between the spigot and sling – then $\beta_d = \beta$. In the animation `rocktec-anim.mws`, $\beta_{\rm ss} = \pi/2$ and $\beta = \beta_d = \pi/2$.

Exercise 4.41

Show that the angle between the sling and the spigot before the launch is $\pi/2 + \beta + \theta - \phi$.

Range scaling

Here we derive a convenient expression for the range of the projectile in terms of the values of $(\theta, \phi, \theta', \psi')$ at the time of launch. The range is given in Equation (4.1) (page 177): dividing this by L_2 and remembering that $g = \omega^2 L_2$ gives

$$\frac{R}{L_2} = \frac{v^2}{\omega^2 L_2^2} \left(\sin\alpha + \sqrt{\gamma + \sin^2\alpha} \right) \cos\alpha, \quad \gamma = \frac{2gh}{v^2},$$

where v, h and α are the launch speed, height and angle, respectively. The launch velocity is given in Equation (4.35), and in scaled variables the components are

$$\frac{x_P'}{L_2} = -l\theta'\cos\theta - ll_4\phi'\sin\phi, \quad \frac{y_P'}{L_2} = l\theta'\sin\theta - ll_4\phi'\cos\phi,$$

so the speed is given by $v^2 = \dot{x}_P^2 + \dot{y}_P^2 = L_2^2\omega^2\bar{v}^2$, where

$$\bar{v}^2 = \left(\frac{x_P'}{L_2}\right)^2 + \left(\frac{y_P'}{L_2}\right)^2 = l^2 \left(\theta'^2 + l_4^2\phi'^2 + 2l_4\theta'\phi'\sin(\phi - \theta) \right). \quad (4.43)$$

Since $h = y_P$, the constant γ can be expressed in the form

$$\gamma = 2gL_2 \left(\frac{h}{L_2}\right) \frac{1}{L_2^2\omega^2\bar{v}^2} = \frac{2l\bar{\gamma}}{\bar{v}^2}, \quad \bar{\gamma} = \frac{y_P}{L_2} = \cos\theta_0 - \cos\theta - l_4\sin\phi,$$

and the angle of projection is defined by the relations

$$\sin\alpha = \frac{\dot{y}_P}{v} = \frac{y_P'/L_2}{\bar{v}} = \frac{lS}{\bar{v}}, \quad S = \theta'\sin\theta - l_4\phi'\cos\phi,$$

$$\cos\alpha = \frac{\dot{x}_P}{L_2} = \frac{x_P'/L_2}{\bar{v}} = \frac{lC}{\bar{v}}, \quad C = -\theta'\cos\theta - l_4\phi'\sin\phi.$$

Thus the range, which may be negative, can be expressed in the form

$$\frac{R}{L_2} = Cl^2 \left(S + \sqrt{S^2 + \frac{2\bar{\gamma}}{l}} \right). \quad (4.44)$$

The right-hand side of Equation (4.44) depends only on scaled variables. This means that if all lengths are increased by a factor of κ, the right-hand side remains constant, and R must also increase by the same factor κ. Thus for a long range, a large trebuchet is needed. The trebuchet toy with dimensions of order $30\,\text{cm}$ throws a light missile $10\,\text{m}$, which suggests that one of size $10\,\text{m}$ could throw a light missile about $300\,\text{m}$, which is consistent with known data.

4.9   Some simulations

In this section we simulate various types of trebuchet; in particular, we examine the difference between the fixed and swinging counterweight trebuchets. There are too many free parameters to allow all to vary without causing confusion, so here we fix the ratio of beam lengths $l = L_1/L_2$, and the ratio $L = L_3/L_2$, where L_3 is the distance between the counterweight and its support.

In practice, both the counterweight mass M and the spigot angle β are fixed, as is β_{ss}, when the trebuchet is constructed. The projectile mass m and the sling length L_4 can vary; indeed, variations in the latter are used to adjust the range. Thus here we set

$$l = \frac{L_1}{L_2} = 7, \quad L = \frac{L_3}{L_2} = 1 \quad \text{and} \quad \theta_0 = 0.8,$$

and allow $l_4 = L_4/L_1$, $\mu = m/M$ and $\beta_d = \beta - \beta_{\text{ss}} + \pi/2$ to vary.

4.9.1   The fixed counterweight trebuchet

The motion of the fixed counterweight trebuchet is described by
Equations (4.40) and (4.41). These equations are solved numerically in the
procedure `Trebfxd`, which computes the range of the projectile. This
procedure calls two other procedures: the first is `Tliftfxd` which
computes the lift-off time τ_L and the initial conditions at this time, using
the approximation described in Subsection 4.8.2: this procedure is given in
the solution to Exercise 4.39. The second procedure, `Range`, computes the
range of the projectile. Using the initial conditions supplied by `Tliftfxd`,
the procedure `Trebfxd` solves the equations for (θ, ϕ), from the time τ_L.
The motion of this type of trebuchet is relatively simple because the
counterweight does not oscillate once the beam passes the vertical. Thus
we stop the integration when $\phi - \theta = \beta_d$ or when $\theta = 2\pi - \theta_0$, whichever
occurs first. If the latter occurs first, we set the range to zero, but this
rarely happens. In practice we expect the projectile to be launched before
the beam is vertical; for a swinging counterweight this is essential. If the
condition $\phi - \theta = \beta_d$ is reached first, the projectile is deemed launched and
the range R defined in Equation (4.44) is computed using the procedure
`Range`; the launch speed $\bar{v}$ defined in Equation (4.43) and the angle of
projection α are also computed. The efficiency of energy transfer is defined
by

$$
\begin{aligned}
\varepsilon_f &= \frac{\text{kinetic energy of projectile}}{\text{change in counterweight potential energy}} \\
&= \frac{\frac{1}{2}mv^2}{MgL_2(\cos\theta_0 - \cos\theta(\tau_L))} = \frac{\mu\bar{v}^2}{2(\cos\theta_0 - \cos\theta(\tau_L))}.
\end{aligned} \tag{4.45}
$$

The procedure `Range` is short, self-explanatory and listed below: the input
variables are $(\theta, \theta', \phi, \phi')$ and the output is a list containing the range,
computed using Equation (4.44) (page 206) and the angle of projection, in
degrees. In addition, here we make θ_0, l and l_4 global variables because in
the present application they are fixed constants and including them in
argument lists is cumbersome. In other applications, where one of these
parameters varies, it may be more convenient to move it to the argument
list.

```
>   Range := proc(th,thv,ph,phv)
>     local C,S,gb;
>     global th0,l,l4;
>     S := thv*sin(th)-l4*phv*cos(ph);
>     C := -thv*cos(th)-l4*phv*sin(ph);
>     gb := cos(th0)-cos(th)-l4*sin(ph);
>     evalf([C*l*l*(S+sqrt(S^2+2*gb/l)),180*arctan(S,C)/Pi]);
>   end proc:
```

The main procedure, `Trebfxd(th0,l,l4,m,betadd)` is listed below. The
input variables are $(\theta_0, l, l_4, \mu, \beta_d)$, where the angle β_d is expressed in
degrees. The output is a list containing the quantities R/L_2, $\bar{v}^2$, α and ε_f.

```
>   Trebfxd := proc(th0,l,l4,m,betadd)
>     local eq1,eq2,par1,par2,par3,betad,d,s,c,ic,stc,p,z,
          th1,thv1,ph1,phv1,ran,v2f,ang,eff,TL;
>     _Env_dsolve_nowarnstop := true;
>     betad := evalf(betadd*Pi/180);        # Convert to radians
```

First compute the initial conditions:

```
>    ic := Tliftfxd(th0,l,l4,m):   TL := ic[1]:
>    th1 := ic[2,1];   thv1 := ic[2,2];
>    ph1 := ic[3,1];   phv1 := ic[3,2];
```

Then the equations of motion are

```
>    d := th(t)-ph(t);   s := sin(d);   c := cos(d);
```

Equation (4.41) for ϕ is

```
>    eq1 := l*l4*diff(ph(t),t,t)-cos(ph(t))
              -l*(s*diff(th(t),t,t)+c*diff(th(t),t)^2)=0;
```

Equation (4.40) for θ is given by

```
>    par1 := 1+m*l^2;   par2 := 1-m*l;   par3 := m*l^2*l4;
>    eq2 := par1*diff(th(t),t,t)-par2*sin(th(t))
              -par3*(s*diff(ph(t),t,t)-c*diff(ph(t),t)^2)=0;
>    ic := th(TL)=th1, D(th)(TL)=thv1, ph(TL)=ph1,
              D(ph)(TL)=phv1;
```

There are two stop conditions, as described in the text.

```
>    stc := stop_cond=[ph(t)-th(t)-betad,th(t)-2.0*Pi+th0];
>    p := dsolve({eq1,eq2,ic},{th(t),ph(t)},numeric,stc);
```

Integrate up to a stop condition and then check whether $\theta \geq 2\pi - \theta_0$; if so, then end the computation.

```
>    z := p(10);
>    th1 := eval(th(t),z);
>    if th1>=evalf(2*Pi-th0) then
>       return [0,0,evalf(2*Pi-th0),0];
>    fi;
```

Now find the values of $(\theta, \theta', \phi, \phi')$, and compute the initial projectile speed and range.

```
>    ph1 := eval(ph(t),z):
>    thv1 := eval(diff(th(t),t),z):
>    phv1 := eval(diff(ph(t),t),z):
>    v2f := l^2*(thv1^2+(l4*phv1)^2
              +2*l4*thv1*phv1*sin(ph1-th1));
>    z := Range(th1,thv1,ph1,phv1);
>    ran := z[1];   ang := z[2];
>    eff := 0.5*v2f*m/(2*(1+cos(th0)));
>    evalf[6]([ran,v2f,ang,eff]);
>  end proc:
```

Thus for $\mu = 0.001$, $\beta = 30°$ and $\beta_{ss} = 0$, that is, $\beta_d = 120°$, the following set of commands prints the values of these parameters as a table, with l_4 increasing from 0.3 to 1.2 in steps of 0.05; some of the results of this calculation are presented on the left-hand side of Table 4.5. Also, the values are collected as lists grR, grv and grang which can be used to plot appropriate graphs; three graphs of the range are shown in Figure 4.28.

```
>  th0 := 0.8:  l := 7.0:  m := 0.001:
>  betadd := 120:
>  printf(" l4    range     alpha     speed^2   efficiency"):
>  grR := NULL:  grv := NULL:  grang := NULL:
>  for l4 from 0.3 to 1.2 by 0.05 do:
>      g := Trebfxd(th0,l,l4,m,betadd);
>      grR := grR,[l4,g[1]]:  grv := grv,[l4,g[2]]:
>      grang := grang,[l4,g[3]]:
>      printf("%4.3f    %8.3f    %7.3f    %8.3f    %6.5f\n",
>             l4,g[1],g[3],g[2],g[4]);
>  od:
>  grR := [grR]:  grv := [grv]:  grang := [grang]:
```

In Table 4.5 we give some of the results from this calculation for $\beta_d = 120°$ and $30°$.

Table 4.5   Various data, including the range, for the case $\theta_0 = 0.8$, $\mu = 0.001$, $l = 7$

l_4	$\beta = 30°, \beta_{ss} = 0, \beta_d = 120°$				$\beta = 30°, \beta_{ss} = 90°, \beta_d = 30°$			
	range	α	$\bar{v}^2$	efficiency	range	α	$\bar{v}^2$	efficiency
0.300	−0.65	−98.2	196.0	0.029	−128.67	120.3	145.8	0.021
0.400	49.28	−11.7	315.8	0.047	−148.78	108.9	240.6	0.035
0.500	52.34	−13.2	528.0	0.078	−87.85	97.0	362.1	0.053
0.600	31.83	−24.3	734.5	0.108	95.54	84.6	508.6	0.075
0.700	19.91	−36.4	950.7	0.140	402.19	71.9	675.3	0.100
0.800	12.42	−48.5	1164.7	0.172	764.41	58.8	853.1	0.126
0.900	7.16	−60.7	1358.6	0.200	1042.81	45.1	1028.2	0.152
1.000	3.31	−73.0	1509.8	0.222	1066.74	30.8	1181.2	0.174

The results quoted in Table 4.5 show that when $\beta_d = \beta - \beta_{ss} + \pi/2$ is large (small β_{ss}), the range is usually smaller than when β_d is small. We can see why this is, for if $\beta_{ss} = 0$ then the sling needs to rotate through a larger angle for the projectile to launch than if $\beta_{ss} = \pi/2$; we shall see later that sometimes the trebuchet beam rotates too fast for ϕ to catch up and make $\phi - \theta$ sufficiently large before θ exceeds π. If $\beta_d = 120°$ only for $0.41 < l_4 < 0.53$ is the final value of $\theta < \pi$; but if $\beta_{ss} = \pi/2$ this is true if $0 < l_4 < 0.91$. This property is examined in more detail in Exercise 4.43.

The data in Table 4.5 are easier to understand when plotted as a graph, as shown in Figure 4.28, which shows the range for three values of β_d; in all cases the grid in l_4 is 0.02. These graphs show that as β_d decreases, the maximum range increases.

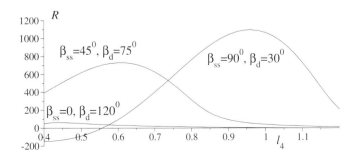

Figure 4.28   Graph showing the dependence of the range R on l_4, for $\theta_0 = 0.8$, $l = 7$, $\mu = 0.001$ and $\beta = 30°$, and various β_{ss} and hence β_d

Exercise 4.42

(a) Repeat the above calculation to reproduce the data quoted in Table 4.5, but in the loop round l_4 add some code that computes the maximum range over the values computed. Also, modify the variable stc in the procedure Trebfxd so that θ is not allowed to exceed π and to output the list [0,0,0,0] if θ reaches π before the projectile is launched. Note that this condition is different from that used for Table 4.5.

(b) Write another procedure Rangemx(th0,l,m,betadd) that contains the loop round l_4 in the interval $(0.2, 1.2)$, in steps of 0.02, and outputs a list containing:

   (i)   the list [Rmax,l4max,effmax] of the maximum range and the values of l_4, and the efficiency at this range;

   (ii) the plot structure containing the graph of $R(l_4)$.

   Use this procedure to find the maximum range for $\theta_0 = 0.8$, $l = 7$, $\beta_d = 75°$ and $\mu = 0.01$, 0.001 and 0.0001 for each β_d. Explain why the range increases but the efficiency decreases as μ decreases.

(c) Find the maximum range for the 12 sets of data $\theta_0 = 0.8$, $l = 7$ and $\beta_d = 30°$, $60°$, $90°$ and $120°$, and $\mu = 0.01$, 0.001 and 0.0001.

> Because Trebfxd is now called within a procedure, it is advisable to change all the global variables to local ones.

Exercise 4.43

Modify the Maple code used to create Table 4.5 to also print out the values of θ, ϕ and τ at the launch time. Find the values of these variables for the parameter values considered in Table 4.5.

The results obtained in Exercise 4.43 show that if β_{ss} is small, so the sling and spigot need to be nearly parallel, the projectile is launched when θ is near or beyond π, because ϕ does not increase fast enough for $\phi - \theta$ to reach the required value until θ is also quite large.

This becomes important when the fixed counterweight is replaced by a swinging counterweight. Then θ increases faster and the launch must occur before $\theta = \pi$ because of the oscillations of the counterweight. As we shall see in the next subsection, if μ is small, the consequence is that if β_{ss} is small the projectile cannot be launched.

We complete this subsection by introducing a Maple procedure for the creation of 3d-plots from numerical data. This allows the visualisation of the behaviour of R with two variables, rather than just one as in Figure 4.28.

We illustrate this by plotting the range $R(l_4, \beta_d)$. This graph can be constructed using the Maple procedure surfdata which converts appropriate lists of data into 3d-plots. The Maple Help files explain how to use this procedure, and here we use the implementation that assumes the data is on equally-spaced grids; with this use, only the values of R need be passed to surfdata.

The following commands define the relevant parameters, including the grid-spacing along each axis and the number of grid points. First define the system parameters, $\theta_0 = 0.8$, $l = 7$, $\mu = 0.001$.

```
>  th0 := 0.8:   l := 7.0:   m := 0.001:
```

Now define the maximum and minimum values of l_4 and β_d

```
>  l4mx := 1.2:   l4mn := 0.4:
>  betadmx := 120:   betadmn := 30:
```

and the number of points to be used in each direction; note that the interval lengths in each direction need not be identical.

```
>  N14 := 40:   Nbetad := 40:
```

In the following set of commands, `fdat` will eventually contain the required data and `temp` is a sequence containing the data as β_d varies and l_4 is fixed.

```
>  fdat := NULL:
>  for il4 from 0 to N14 do:                # Loop round l4
>    l4 := evalf(l4mn+il4*(l4mx-l4mn)/N14);
>    temp := NULL:
>    for ibetad from 0 to Nbetad do:        # Loop round betad
>       betadd :=
       evalf(betadmn+ibetad*(betadmx-betadmn)/Nbetad):
>       ran := Trebfxd(th0,l,l4,m,betadd)[1];
>       if ran<0 then ran:=0;  fi:          # Set R=0 if R<0
>       temp := temp,ran:
>    od:                          # End of loop round betas
>    fdat := fdat,[temp];         # Create a sequence of lists
>  od:                                 # End of loop round l4
>  fdat := [fdat]:        # Convert fdat to a list of lists
```

First define a sequence of options to be used in `surfdata`. The values of the contours shown are defined by the statement

```
>  cont := contours=[seq(100*k,k=1..11)]:
```

and we avoid the zero contour because the range is zero in a 2d region of the plane, not just along a line. The orientation is first determined on the screen by moving the figure using the cursor to obtain a suitable view.

```
>  conds := axes=boxed,labels=["l4","betad","R"],
         orientation=[130,50],style=patchcontour:
```

The plot, shown on the left-hand side of Figure 4.29, is created with the command

```
>  surfdata(fdat,l4mn..l4mx,betadmn..betadmx,conds,cont);
```

You will need to load the `plots` package before calling `surfdata`.

A black and white contour plot of this figure can be created simply by using the `orientation` option to view the figure from above (by setting $\phi = 0$) or below ($\phi = 180$), defining a suitable value of θ (here -90), changing the colour to black and the `style` to `contour`. The following commands define these parameters and create the contour plot, which is given on the right-hand side of Figure 4.29.

Do not confuse the ϕ and θ used to define the orientation with the variables used to describe the trebuchet. Note also that it is more common for the symbol θ to label the latitude and ϕ the longitude, rather than the reverse as in Maple.

```
>  conds2 := axes=boxed,orientation=[-90,180],style=contour,
         colour=black:
>  surfdata(fdat,l4mn..l4mx,betadmn..betadmx,conds2,cont);
```

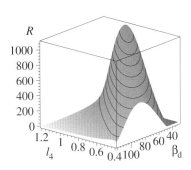 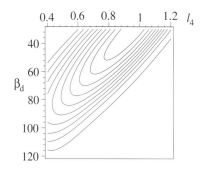

Figure 4.29   A Graph and a contour plot of $R(l_4, \beta_d)$ for $\theta_0 = 0.8$, $l = 7$, $\mu = 0.001$. Using the Maple worksheet we can see that the maximum value of R is about 1100, and this occurs at $\beta_d \simeq 30°$ and $l_4 \simeq 0.96$.

These graphs show that the maximum of $R(l_4, \beta_d)$ is at $\beta_d \simeq 30°$ and $l_4 \simeq 0.96$ and is about 1100. The decline from its maximum is smooth, and is slowest along a line along which l_4 decreases and β_d increases. Plots of the same function for the swinging counterweight trebuchet are quite different; see Exercise 4.46.

Exercise 4.44

For values of β_d corresponding to $\beta_{ss} = \pi/2$ and $10° \leq \beta \leq 90°$, plot the graph of $R(l_4, \beta_d)$ for $0.4 \leq l_4 \leq 1.2$, with $\theta_0 = 0.8$, $l = 7$ and $\mu = 0.001$.

All other parameters remaining the same, plot the graph of $R(l_4, \beta_d)$ for $\mu = 0.01$ and 0.0001.

4.9.2   The swinging counterweight trebuchet

This subsection completes our study with a brief comparison of the swinging and fixed counterweight dynamics. First we consider a necessary condition for the projectile to be launched, which, of course, does not guarantee that it flies in the correct direction.

The projectile launches when $\phi - \theta = \beta_d = \beta + (\pi/2 - \beta_{ss}) > 0$; initially, $\phi - \theta \simeq -0.8$, so it is necessary that $\phi(\tau)$ increases faster than $\theta(\tau)$ while $\theta < \pi$. For a fixed counterweight trebuchet we saw, in Exercise 4.43, that there are some parameter values for which $\phi - \theta$ is never large enough before θ reaches π; for a swinging counterweight, since $\theta(\tau)$ increases faster, we expect this problem to be exacerbated.

For given values of the parameters $(\theta_0, L, l, l_4, \mu)$, we can determine whether the system will launch the projectile, for any β_d, simply by plotting the graph of $\phi(\tau) - \theta(\tau)$, up to the time when $\theta = \pi$. Such graphs for both types of trebuchet are shown in Figure 4.30, for four values of μ.

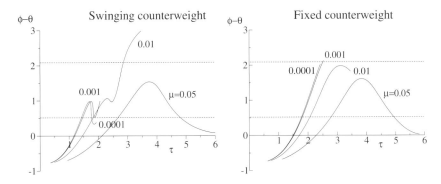

Figure 4.30 Graphs of $\phi(\tau) - \theta(\tau)$ up to the time when $\theta = \pi$, for the parameters $\theta_0 = 0.8$, $L = 0.5$, $l = 7$, $l_4 = 0.5$ and for various values of μ. The red dashed horizontal lines correspond to $\beta_d = 30°$ and $120°$.

In both cases the red dashed horizontal lines represent the values of $\beta_d = 30°$ and $120°$. For the swinging counterweight we see that except when $\mu = 0.01$ the function $\phi - \theta$ has a maximum with a value between the given limits, so the projectile cannot launch for all allowed values of β_d. For instance, if $\mu = 0.001$ the maximum is about 1.0, so the projectile can launch only if $\beta_d < 60°$. The fixed counterweight trebuchet behaves differently and will launch for a wider range of β_d.

In general, for most parameter values, such graphs show that the swinging counterweight trebuchet will normally launch the projectile only if β_d is small. The reason for this is simply that if β_d is large, the beam rotates too fast for $\phi - \theta$ to reach the necessary value while θ is in an acceptable range. In practice, this means that β_{ss} needs to be large, that is, the sling must slide easily on the spigot.

In Figure 4.31 we compare $R(l_4, \beta_d)$ for both types of trebuchet, in the case $\theta_0 = 0.8$, $l = 7.0$, $L = 1$ and $\mu = 0.001$. These graphs are created in the Maple worksheets `range-3d-swg.mws` and `range-3d-fxd.mws`, both given on the course CD and website; you may use these worksheets to examine these figures from different viewpoints and to produce similar figures for other parameter values.

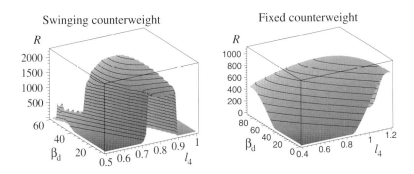

Figure 4.31 Graphs of $R(l_4, \beta_d)$ with parameters $\theta_0 = 0.8$, $L = 1$, $l = 7$, $\mu = 0.001$. The contours are equally spaced, with interval 100 and starting at 100; for the swinging counterweight the largest is 2200, and for the fixed counterweight it is 1100. Note that the ranges of l_4 and β_d are different for each case.

From these graphs, and the contour plots shown in Figure 4.32, we see that the maximum range of the swinging counterweight trebuchet occurs when $\beta_d \simeq 37°$, $l_4 \simeq 0.76$, and is about 2250, which is far larger than the maximum range of the fixed counterweight system of about 1100, occurring at $\beta_d \simeq 29°$, $l_4 \simeq 0.96$. Also, we see that as l_4 increases, for fixed β_d, R increases to a maximum then falls to zero; for the swinging counterweight this decrease is quite dramatic, as shown by the contour plots of Figure 4.32, or by using Maple and viewing the plots in Figure 4.31 from a different angle.

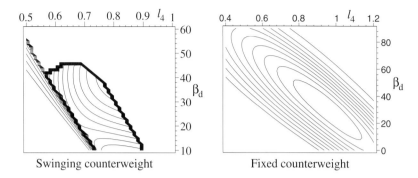

Swinging counterweight   Fixed counterweight

Figure 4.32   Contour plots of $R(l_4, \beta_d)$ for the parameters used in Figure 4.31; the contours are also the same as drawn in that figure. Note that for the swinging counterweight trebuchet these contours suggest that, in practice, it would be very difficult to consistently achieve the maximum possible range.

The contours show that for the swinging counterweight the function $R(l_4, \beta_d)$ falls to zero very sharply in some regions; the fixed counterweight trebuchet behaves quite differently. In general, the region of (l_4, β_d) for which the projectile is launched is smaller for the swinging counterweight, and for this trebuchet there are regions where $R(l_4, \beta_d)$ is very sensitive to both l_4 and β_d.

The Rocktec trebuchet

In Figure 4.33 we show similar graphs for the parameters describing the Rocktec trebuchet, $\theta_0 = 0.8$, $L = 0.5$, $l = 3.2$ and $\mu = 0.05$ (see Table 4.2, page 181). In this example the maximum range of the fixed counterweight trebuchet is slightly larger.

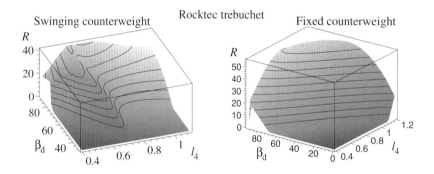

Figure 4.33   Graphs of $R(l_4, \beta_d)$ for the Rocktec trebuchet with parameters $\theta_0 = 0.8$, $L = 0.5$, $l = 3.2$, $\mu = 0.05$. The contours are equally spaced, with interval 5 and starting at 5.

From the data used to plot these figures we can extract the positions and value of the maximum range; these are given in Table 4.6.

Table 4.6   The positions and values of the maximum range for the Rocktec and Warwick trebuchets as approximated with the parameters used in Figures 4.33 and 4.35. In these calculations 41 points were used in each direction.

	Rocktec			Warwick		
Counterweight	l_4	β_d	$\max(R)$	l_4	β_d	$\max(R)$
Swinging	0.58	90°	40.8	0.67	50°	618
Fixed	1.04	65°	54.9	1.00	36°	523

The plots in Figure 4.33 and the contours in Figure 4.34 show that the swinging counterweight trebuchet is more sensitive to l_4, and β_d and has its maximum range at different values.

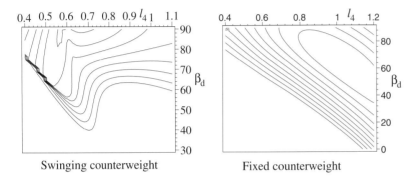

Swinging counterweight   Fixed counterweight

Figure 4.34   Contour plots of $R(l_4, \beta_d)$ for the parameters used in Figure 4.33; the contours are also the same as in that figure

Increasing L to 1 removes the shoulder at $l_4 \simeq 0.7$ and increases the maximum range slightly, as seen in Exercise 4.45. In all cases the rise to the maximum in any direction is steep, suggesting that the range is sensitive to both β_d and l_4.

Exercise 4.45

Use the worksheet `range-3d-swg.mws` to plot $R(l_4, \beta_d)$ for the same parameters as used to plot Figure 4.33, but with $L = 0.25$, 1.0 and 1.5, $0.4 \leq l_4 \leq 1.1$ and $40° \leq \beta_d \leq 120°$. For these values of L you should find that, using 21 points in each direction, the position and value of the maximum range are as given below.

L	l_4	β_d	$\max(R)$
0.25	1.04	68°	33.6
0.5	0.68	100°	42.9
1.0	0.76	88°	50.6
1.5	0.80	88°	52.1

From these graphs you should observe that $R(l_4, \beta_d)$ is a smoother function for the larger values of L.

Note that some of the numerical values quoted here differ slightly from those in Table 4.6 because the number of points used is different.

The Warwick trebuchet

Finally, in Figures 4.35 and 4.36 we show the equivalent plots for the parameters approximating the Warwick trebuchet, $\theta_0 = 0.8$, $L = 1.5$, $l = 6$ and $\mu = 0.005$ (to partly compensate for the mass of the beam). For this trebuchet, from the photograph in Figure 4.14 (page 175), we estimate that β is in the range $(25°, 40°)$ and $l_4 \simeq 0.7$; we assume that $\beta_{ss} = \pi/2$, so that $\beta_d = \beta$.

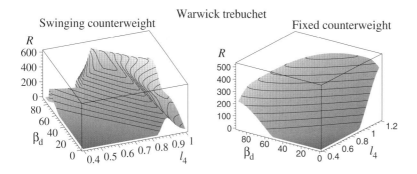

Figure 4.35   Graphs of $R(l_4, \beta_d)$ for the Warwick trebuchet with parameters $\theta_0 = 0.8$, $L = 1.5$, $l = 6$, $\mu = 0.005$. The contours are equally spaced, with interval 50 and starting at 50.

These graphs and the associated contour plots in Figure 4.36 should be compared with Figures 4.33 and 4.34, respectively. Clearly the range of the Warwick trebuchet is significantly larger, which is mainly because the ratio of the counterweight to projectile mass, μ, is much smaller. Also, the function $R(l_4, \beta_d)$ of the Warwick trebuchet is flatter in the vicinity of its maximum, suggesting that this machine is more reliable.

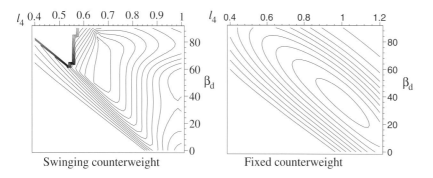

Figure 4.36   Contour plots of $R(l_4, \beta_d)$ for the parameters used in Figure 4.35; the contours are also the same as in that figure

Exercise 4.46

Use the worksheet `range-3d-swg.mws` to plot the graphs of $R(l_4, \beta_d)$ for the Warwick trebuchet, but with $L = 0.5$, 1.0, 2.0 and 3.0, rather than $L = 1.5$, for $0.4 \leq l_4 \leq 1$ and $10° \leq \beta_d \leq 90°$. In each case find the position and value of the maximum range.

Exercise 4.47

Modify the worksheet `range-3d-swg.mws` to plot the graph of $R(l_4, \log m)$ for $0.4 \le l_4 \le 1$, $-4 \le \log m \le -1$, where $\log m$ is the logarithm to the base 10 of m, for given values of l, L and β_d, and to estimate the maximum value of R in the region.

For $\theta_0 = 0.8$, $l = 6$, $L = 1$, plot these graphs for $\beta_d = 20°$, $40°$, $45°$, $50°$, $60°$, $80°$ and $90°$. Using data collected during these calculations, also plot the graphs of the maximum range against β_d, and the value of l_4 at which R has its maximum against β_d.

What conclusions do you draw from these graphs?

4.10   End of part exercises

These exercises cover Sections 4.5–4.9.

Exercise 4.48

The equations of motion of a projectile of mass m moving in the Oxy-plane under the influence of gravity, acting along the negative y-axis, and in a medium exerting a resistance proportional to the velocity, are

$$m\ddot{x} = -k\dot{x}, \quad x(0) = 0, \quad \dot{x}(0) = v\cos\alpha,$$
$$m\ddot{y} = -mg - k\dot{y}, \quad y(0) = 0, \quad \dot{y}(0) = v\sin\alpha,$$

where k is a constant and g is the gravitational acceleration, with v and α the initial speed and direction of motion.

(a) Define new variables $X = x/L$, $Y = y/L$ and $\tau = \omega t$, and choose the constants L and ω so that these equations may be cast in the following simpler forms, containing no constants:

$$X'' = -X', \quad X(0) = 0, \quad X'(0) = V\cos\alpha, \quad V = \frac{vk}{mg},$$
$$Y'' = -1 - Y', \quad Y(0) = 0, \quad Y'(0) = V\sin\alpha.$$

(b) Without using Maple, find the solution of these equations.

(c) For the cases $V = 10$, $\alpha = 0.1$, 0.5, 1.0 and 1.4, plot the trajectory in the OXY-plane for $0 \le \tau \le \tau_{\max}$, where $\tau_{\max} > 0$ and $Y(\tau_{\max}) = 0$. Consider also the cases where $V = 1$ and the same values of α.

Explain why the shapes of the graphs for $V = 1$ and $V = 10$ differ.

Exercise 4.49

In this exercise we assume throughout that $\mu l < 1$.

The equilibrium position of the simplified trebuchet depicted in Figure 4.16 (page 180) is clearly $\theta = \pi$, $\psi = 0$, $\dot{\theta} = \dot{\psi} = 0$. The small-amplitude motion about this point is obtained by putting $\theta = \pi - \phi$ in Equations (4.9) and (4.10) (page 182) and assuming that all angles and their rates of change are small.

(a) If $\theta = \pi - \phi$, show that to first order in $(\phi, \psi, \phi', \psi')$, Equations (4.9) and (4.10) can be written in the matrix form

$$\begin{pmatrix} 1 + \mu l^2 & L \\ 1 & L \end{pmatrix} \mathbf{x}'' + \begin{pmatrix} 1 - \mu l & 0 \\ 0 & 1 \end{pmatrix} \mathbf{x} = \mathbf{0}, \quad \mathbf{x} = \begin{pmatrix} \phi \\ \psi \end{pmatrix}.$$

(b) We expect the solution of these equations to be oscillatory, so set $\mathbf{x} = \mathbf{a}\exp(i\omega t)$, where $\mathbf{a}$ and ω are constants, to show that if this is a solution, then ω^2 is an eigenvalue of

$$\mathbf{A} = \begin{pmatrix} 1 + \mu l^2 & L \\ 1 & L \end{pmatrix}^{-1} \begin{pmatrix} 1 - \mu l & 0 \\ 0 & 1 \end{pmatrix} = \frac{1}{\mu l^2 L} \begin{pmatrix} L(1 - \mu l) & -L \\ -(1 - \mu l) & 1 + \mu l^2 \end{pmatrix}$$

and $\mathbf{a}$ is the associated eigenvector.

(c) Consider the associated matrix

$$\mathbf{B} = \begin{pmatrix} L(1 - \mu l) & -L \\ -(1 - \mu l) & 1 + \mu l^2 \end{pmatrix} \quad (\text{so } \mathbf{B} = \mu l^2 L \mathbf{A}),$$

and show that, to $O(\mu)$, the eigenvalues of $\mathbf{B}$ satisfy the equation

$$\lambda^2 - (L + 1)\lambda = \mu l \left(\lambda(l - L) - lL \right) + \mu^2 l^3 L.$$

Hence show that if $\mu = 0$, the eigenvalues are 0 and $1 + L$.

(d) If μ is small, show that the eigenvalues are

$$\lambda \simeq \frac{Ll^2}{1 + L}\mu \quad \text{and} \quad \lambda \simeq 1 + L - \frac{\mu l}{L + 1}(L^2 + L - l).$$

Deduce that

$$\omega \simeq \frac{1}{\sqrt{L + 1}} \quad \text{and} \quad \omega \simeq \sqrt{\frac{L + 1}{\mu l^2 L}},$$

and that for small μ and most initial conditions the speed of the motion is $O(\mu^{-1/2})$.

Exercise 4.50   The mangonel

A stone-throwing engine, the mangonel, was mentioned in the Introduction to this part. This machine uses a torsion spring to rotate a beam in a vertical plane. One end of the beam is attached to the horizontal spring, which is perpendicular to the beam; at the other end is a cup to hold the missile. A cross-section of this machine is shown in Figure 4.37, and here the beam rotates in the clockwise direction. The beam is stopped suddenly when it is nearly vertical, by the construction of the frame. The torsional spring, in this and similar machines, used twisted tendons, horse hair or, in extreme circumstances, human hair; see page 279 of Rihll's book (referenced on page 170).

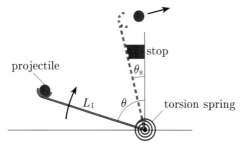

Figure 4.37 Sketch of a mangonel, with the axis of the beam perpendicular to the page. The arm angle θ decreases during the launch, starting at θ_0 and ending at $\theta_s < \theta_0$; both these parameters and the arm length are fixed by the construction of the machine.

The mangonel is a mechanical device with one moving part that inefficiently converts some of the potential energy of a twisted fibre to projectile kinetic energy. Because of this, the dynamics of this system is simple and its analysis is helpful when dealing with the onager treated in the next exercise.

The potential energy of the twisted fibre is a function $V(\theta)$ that increases as θ increases: here we assume that this energy far exceeds the gravitational energy, which we ignore. The beam is assumed to be uniform, with mass m_B, and it can be shown that its kinetic energy is $T_B = m_B(L_1\dot\theta)^2/6$. The kinetic energy of the projectile, with mass m_P, is $T_P = m_P(L_1\dot\theta)^2/2$. If the beam is forced to stop at $\theta = \theta_s$, the projectile is launched perpendicular to the beam and at this instant it has speed $L_1\dot\theta_s$; the kinetic energy of the beam is lost.

Conservation of energy ensures that up to the time when $\theta = \theta_s$, the total energy E is constant, that is,

$$\tfrac{1}{2}\left(m_P + \tfrac{1}{3}m_B\right)L_1^2\dot\theta^2 + V(\theta) = E.$$

(a) Show that the angle of projection of the projectile is θ_s, and that the range R, ignoring the projectile height at the launch time, is given by

$$R = \frac{2}{gm_B}\frac{V(\theta_0) - V(\theta_s)}{1/3 + \mu}\sin 2\theta_s, \quad \mu = \frac{m_P}{m_B}.$$

(b) It is reasonable to assume that the torque from twisted fibre is proportional to $(\theta + \alpha)$, where α is a positive constant such that the torque is zero when $\theta = -\alpha$. With this assumption the potential energy is $V(\theta) = k(\theta + \alpha)^2/2$, where k is some positive constant.

Using this potential energy, show that if θ_s can be varied, then the maximum range of the mangonel occurs at $\theta_s = \gamma$ and is given by

$$R_{max} = \max(R) = \frac{3k}{gm_B(1+3\mu)}f(\theta_0, \alpha), \qquad (4.46)$$

where $f(\theta_0, \alpha) = \left[(\theta_0 + \alpha)^2 - (\gamma + \alpha)^2\right]\sin 2\gamma$ and $\gamma(\theta_0, \alpha)$ is the only real root of

$$\tan 2\gamma = \frac{(\theta_0 + \alpha)^2 - (\gamma + \alpha)^2}{\gamma + \alpha} \quad \text{in the interval } (0, \pi/4).$$

(c) Show that if α is large, the equation for γ is given approximately by $\tan 2\gamma = 2(\theta_0 - \gamma)$, and deduce that for large α, γ is almost independent of α.

Using the first two terms of the Taylor series of $\tan 2\gamma$, show that this equation may be written in the form

$$\gamma = \frac{\theta_0}{2 + \tfrac{4}{3}\gamma^2}.$$

From this equation, form an iterative sequence for γ, starting at $\gamma = \theta_0/2$, to show that an approximate solution of the original equation is

$$\gamma = \frac{\theta_0}{2 + \theta_0^2/3}.$$

Write a Maple procedure `gam(th0,alpha)` to solve the original equation for γ for given θ_0 and α, and for $\alpha = \pi$ and 4π plot the graphs of the exact values of γ and the approximate values for $\pi/4 \le \theta_0 \le \pi/2$.

The monagkon or onager appears to be the first beam-slinging machine and first appeared in Macedonia about 350 BC; the name mangonel is also used.

This machine is a more efficient version of the machine described in the previous exercise. Instead of the missile being held by a cup, there is a sling, as shown in Figure 4.38; this hangs on a spigot and is launched exactly as that of the trebuchet. The beam is stopped suddenly by the construction of the frame when it is approximately vertical, which is why the whole structure kicks. Reputedly, a large version of this machine weighed 2 tons and was able to throw an 8 lb stone 500 yards; a lighter version weighed 1000 lb and threw a 3–4 lb stone 100 yards.

We assume that initially the sling hangs vertically, with the projectile resting on the frame. If the arm and sling have lengths L_1 and L_4, respectively, it follows that $L_4 = L_1 \cos\theta_0$, where θ is the angle between the beam and the vertical, and θ_0 is its initial value.

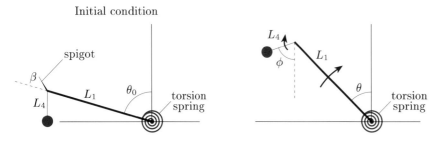

Figure 4.38   Sketch of an onager: the initial condition is shown on the left. The angles θ and ϕ are defined on the right: note that both are different from the equivalent angles used for the trebuchet in the main text.

The equation of motion of the arm is similar to that of the mangonel described in the previous exercise, but is modified by the sling. Assuming, as in Exercise 4.50, that during the launch the torsional force far exceeds the gravitational force on the beam, the equations of motion can be shown to be

$$L_1^2\left(m_P + \tfrac{1}{3}m_B\right)\ddot{\theta} + k(\theta + \alpha)$$
$$+ m_P L_1 L_4\left(\ddot{\phi}\cos(\theta + \phi) - \dot{\phi}^2\sin(\theta + \phi)\right) = 0,$$
$$L_4\ddot{\phi} + g\sin\phi + L_1\left(\ddot{\theta}\cos(\theta + \phi) - \dot{\theta}^2\sin(\theta + \phi)\right) = 0,$$

with the initial conditions $\cos\theta_0 = L_4/L_1$, $\phi(0) = \dot{\phi}(0) = \dot{\theta}(0) = 0$.

(a) Show that if $L_4 = 0$, the first equation reduces to the energy equation of the mangonel given in Exercise 4.50, with $V(\theta) = (\theta + \alpha)^2/2$.

(b) By introducing the dimensionless variables

$$l_4 = \frac{L_4}{L_1}, \quad \tau = \omega t, \quad \omega^2 = \frac{g}{L_1}, \quad \mu = \frac{m_P}{m_B}, \quad \overline{k} = \frac{k}{\omega^2 m_B L_1^2},$$

show that these equations of motion can be written in the form

$$\theta'' + \frac{3\bar{k}}{1+3\mu}(\theta + \alpha)$$

$$+ \frac{3\mu l_4}{1+3\mu}\left(\phi'' \cos(\theta + \phi) - \phi'^2 \sin(\theta + \phi)\right) = 0, \qquad (4.47)$$

$$l_4\phi'' + \sin\phi + \theta'' \cos(\theta + \phi) - \theta'^2 \sin(\theta + \phi) = 0, \qquad (4.48)$$

with the initial conditions $\theta(0) = \theta_0 = \cos^{-1} l_4$, $\theta'(0) = 0$ and $\phi(0) = \phi'(0) = 0$. Note that these equations contain the three independent constants

$$\frac{3\bar{k}}{1+3\mu}, \quad \frac{3\mu l_4}{1+3\mu} \quad \text{and} \quad l_4.$$

In this system $\theta_0 \leq \theta(\tau) \leq \pi/2$, because the beam motion is constrained.

(c) Using the same assumptions as in the main text (Subsection 4.8.3), show that the projectile launches when

$$\theta + \phi = \beta_d = \pi + \beta - \beta_{ss}, \quad \frac{\pi}{2} < \beta_d \leq \frac{3\pi}{2},$$

Note that β_d for the onager differs from that for the trebuchet in Equation (4.42).

provided that $0 \leq \theta \leq \theta_0$.

If $\theta(\tau)$ decreases to 0 before $\theta + \phi$ reaches β_d, you should assume that no launch occurs.

If the projectile launch is satisfactory, it can be shown that the initial projectile velocity is

$$\mathbf{v} = \omega L_1 \left(-\theta' \cos\theta - l_4\phi' \cos\phi, -\theta' \sin\theta + l_4\phi' \sin\phi\right).$$

Hence, on ignoring the launch height, show that the range of the projectile can be written in the form

$$\frac{R}{L_1} = 2(\theta' \cos\theta + l_4\phi' \cos\phi)(\theta' \sin\theta - l_4\phi' \sin\phi).$$

(d) Using the scaled variables introduced above, show that the expression for $R_{\max}$, Equation (4.46) of the previous exercise, can be written in the form

$$\frac{R_{\max}}{L_1} = \frac{3\bar{k}}{1+3\mu}f(\theta_0, \alpha).$$

Hence deduce that the constant $3\bar{k}/(1+3\mu)$ occurring in Equation (4.47) for θ can be replaced by $R_{\max}/(L_1 f(\theta_0, \alpha))$, thus replacing the unknown quantity k by the observable range $R_{\max}$ of the mangonel.

(e) Write a procedure to numerically solve Equations (4.47) and (4.48) for given values of l_4, α and $R_{\max}/L_1$, and to compute the range R/L_1. You should set $R = 0$ if θ reaches 0 before the projectile is launched.

(i) For $\alpha = \pi$, $\mu = 0.1$ and $R_{\max}/L_1 = 10$, 50 and 100, $\beta_d = 100°$, use your procedure to compute the ratio $R/R_{\max}$ for $0.1 \leq l_4 \leq 0.5$.

(ii) Repeat the above for $\alpha = 4\pi$.

(iii) For $\mu = 0.1$, $\alpha = 2\pi$, $R_{\max}/L_1 = 10$ and $0.1 \leq l_4 \leq 0.5$, plot the 3d-graphs of $R(l_4, \beta_d)/R_{\max}$, $90° \leq \beta_d \leq 200°$.

Discuss the results of these calculations.

A simpler fixed counterweight trebuchet

In the following set of exercises we introduce another approximation that eliminates the phase I motion, so making the calculation far simpler yet yielding similar results. The importance of this approximation is that it allows quick and simple preliminary calculations on other varieties of trebuchet; it will be used in some of the following exercises for this purpose.

Consider the trebuchet for which the projectile is initially resting on the edge of a ledge, as shown in Figure 4.39.

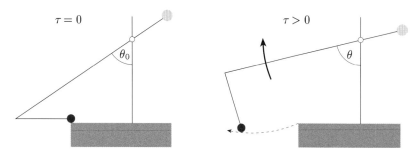

Figure 4.39

When released, the projectile falls slightly, but is eventually lifted above the beam and launched, as normal. In this case the complete motion is described by Equations (4.40) and (4.41), with the initial conditions

$$\theta(0) = \theta_0, \quad \dot\theta(0) = \phi(0) = \dot\phi(0) = 0.$$

Exercise 4.52

Modify the procedure `Trebfxd` to solve this problem and show that for the parameters given in Table 4.5 (page 209) the modified trebuchet behaves similarly.

Also, compare the results given by this approximation with those obtained in Exercise 4.42(c) (page 210).

Exercise 4.53

The results from Exercise 4.52 show that the dynamics of the simple fixed counterweight system, defined in Figure 4.39, and the system with two phases of motion are similar. We can partly understand this by examining the initial variation of $\theta(\tau)$ in each case.

Using the `series` option of `dsolve`, show that for the normal fixed counterweight trebuchet with $0 \le \tau \ll \tau_{\mathrm{L}}$, that is, during the phase I motion,

$$\theta(\tau) = \theta_0 + \frac{\sin\theta_0}{2(1 + \mu l^2 \cos^2\theta_0)}\tau^2 + A\tau^4$$

for some constant A, which you should use Maple to determine.

For the simplified trebuchet of Figure 4.39, show that

$$\theta(\tau) = \theta_0 + \frac{\sin\theta_0}{2(1 + \mu l^2 \cos^2\theta_0)}\tau^2 + B\tau^4,$$

where B is another constant, which you should also use Maple to determine.

Further, use Maple to show that

$$A - B = \frac{\mu \cos \theta_0}{24 l_4} \frac{3 + 7l \sin^2 \theta_0 + 3\mu l^2 \cos^2 \theta_0}{(1 + \mu l^2 \cos^2 \theta_0)^2},$$

and deduce that the beam of the conventional fixed counterweight trebuchet initially rotates a little faster than that of the simplified system.

Exercise 4.54 *A vertically falling counterweight*

A version of the trebuchet that allows the counterweight to fall vertically is shown in Figure 4.40.

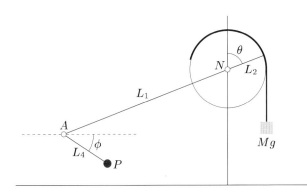

Figure 4.40

Here the beam AN is fixed to a drum of radius L_2, around which a rope holding the counterweight is rolled. The falling counterweight rotates the drum and hence lifts the beam.

In this exercise we consider the same arrangement as in Exercise 4.52 where the projectile is initially perched on a ledge with the sling horizontal. The equations for θ and ϕ are

$$(1 + \mu l^2)\theta'' + \mu l \sin \theta - 1 - \mu l^2 l_4 \left(\phi'' \sin(\theta - \phi) - \phi'^2 \cos(\theta - \phi) \right) = 0,$$
$$ll_4 \phi'' - \cos \phi - l \left(\theta'' \sin(\theta - \phi) + \theta'^2 \cos(\theta - \phi) \right) = 0.$$

(a) Write a procedure that solves these equations with the initial conditions

$$\theta(0) = \theta_0, \quad \dot\theta(0) = \phi(0) = \dot\phi(0) = 0,$$

stops the integration at the first occurrence of either $\theta = \pi$ or $\phi - \theta = \beta_d = \beta + \pi/2 - \beta_{ss}$, and in the latter case computes the range of the projectile, its initial speed and its angle of projection.

(b) For the same parameters as used in Exercise 4.52 (and Exercise 4.42(c)), show that for a given value of β_d, as l_4 varies, the maximum range of this contraption is larger. Provide a possible explanation for this.

Exercise 4.55 *Trebuchet on wheels*

It was demonstrated in Section 4.6 that the fixed counterweight trebuchet is less efficient than the swinging counterweight system, because the counterweight does not fall vertically. One suggested remedy to this problem is to put the trebuchet on wheels, so as the counterweight falls and moves horizontally, the whole structure will tend to move in the opposite direction: this should partly straighten the curved trajectory of the counterweight. In this exercise we test this idea.

The mass of the trebuchet structure, not including the counterweight and projectile, is M_T, and we define $\mu_T = M_T/M$; the x-coordinate of its centre of mass is defined to be X.

It can be shown that the two equations of motion for θ and ϕ are

$$\left(ML_2^2 + mL_1^2\right)\ddot\theta - \left(ML_2 - mL_1\right)g\sin\theta$$
$$- mL_1L_4\left(\ddot\phi\sin(\theta-\phi) - \dot\phi^2\cos(\theta-\phi)\right) + \left(ML_2 - mL_1\right)\ddot X\cos\theta = 0,$$

$$L_4\ddot\phi - g\cos\phi - L_1\left(\ddot\theta\sin(\theta-\phi) + \dot\theta^2\cos(\theta-\phi)\right) - \ddot X\sin\phi = 0,$$

and the equation for X, which represents conservation of horizontal momentum, is

$$(M + M_T + m)\dot X + (ML_2 - mL_1)\dot\theta\cos\theta - mL_4\dot\phi\sin\phi = 0.$$

Also, the velocity of the projectile is

$$\mathbf{v}_P = \left(\dot X - L_4\dot\phi\sin\phi - L_1\dot\theta\cos\theta,\; L_1\dot\theta\sin\theta - L_4\dot\phi\cos\phi\right).$$

(a) Use the scaled variables defined in the text, together with $\mu_T = M_T/M$ and $x = X/L_2$, to show that these equations can be cast in the form

$$(1 + \mu l^2)\theta'' - (1 - \mu l)\sin\theta - \mu l^2 l_4\left(\phi''\sin(\theta-\phi) - \phi'^2\cos(\theta-\phi)\right)$$
$$+ (1 - \mu l)x''\cos\theta = 0, \tag{4.49}$$

$$ll_4\phi'' - \cos\phi - l\left(\theta''\sin(\theta-\phi) + \theta'^2\cos(\theta-\phi)\right)$$
$$- x''\sin\phi = 0, \tag{4.50}$$

and that conservation of horizontal momentum becomes

$$(1 + \mu + \mu_T)x = \text{constant} - (1 - \mu l)\sin\theta - \mu l l_4\cos\phi.$$

Apart from the last terms in Equations (4.49) and (4.50), these are identical to Equations (4.40) and (4.41) (page 205); the extra terms are due to the trebuchet motion.

(b) Put $l_4 = 0$ to derive the equation of motion for the equivalent system as dealt with in Sections 4.6 and 4.7. In particular, show that the equation for θ can be written in the form

$$(1 + \mu l^2)\theta'' - (1 - \mu l)\sin\theta - \frac{(1-\mu l)^2}{1 + \mu + \mu_T}(\sin\theta)''\cos\theta = 0.$$

Show that this equation can be integrated once to give

$$\tfrac{1}{2}\theta'^2\left(1 + \mu l^2 - \frac{(1-\mu l)^2}{1 + \mu + \mu_T}\cos^2\theta\right) = (1 - \mu l)(\cos\theta_0 - \cos\theta).$$

By comparing this with Equation (4.16) (page 186), deduce that for the present system, θ increases from θ_0 to $\pi - \theta_0$ faster than the system described in Equation (4.16).

Numerically integrate the equation for θ for the parameters considered in Table 4.4 (page 189) and with $\mu_T = 10^{-p}$, $p = -1, 0, \ldots, 2$, to show that if μ_T is sufficiently small, the time taken for θ to increase from θ_0 to $\pi - \theta_0$, with $\theta_0 = 0.6$, is similar to the swinging counterweight system (τ_{swg} in Table 4.4) and less than that for the fixed counterweight system (τ_{fxd}).

(c) Write a procedure to integrate Equations (4.49) and (4.50) from $\theta = \theta_0$ to $\theta = \pi$ and to plot the graphs of $x(\tau)$, the x-coordinate of the counterweight in the stationary reference frame OXY, $x + \sin\theta$ and the x-coordinate in the moving reference frame Oxy, that is, $\sin\theta$.

Consider the case $l = 6$ and $\theta_0 = 0.6$ and a variety of values of μ and μ_T. In particular, show that if μ_T is sufficiently small, the counterweight falls almost vertically.

(d) For the simple case described before Exercise 4.52, where there is no phase I motion and the initial conditions are $\theta(0) = \theta_0$, $\theta'(0) = \phi(0) = \phi'(0) = 0$, write a procedure that numerically solves Equations (4.49) and (4.50), and computes the range of the projectile, if satisfactorily launched. For suitable values of μ_T, compare your results with those obtained in Exercise 4.52. Remember that the velocity of the projectile has an additional factor, so the quantity C in Equation (4.44) needs modification.

Exercise 4.56 *Inclusion of the beam mass*

The trebuchet beam can be heavy, and for light projectiles this can have a significant effect on the dynamics, because a heavy beam rotates more slowly. In general, for a swinging counterweight this will decrease the range, but it also makes it less sensitive to the various parameters.

The addition of the beam mass directly changes only the equation for θ, that is, Equation (4.26) (page 200) for the phase I motion and Equation (4.37) (page 205) for the phase II motion, by changing the coefficients of θ'' and $\sin\theta$. If the beam is uniform, there is only one additional parameter, the beam mass m_B; otherwise, two are required. Hence for simplicity we assume the beam to be uniform. For the phase I motion the equation for θ is

$$\left(ML_2^2 + mL_1^2 f(\theta)^2 + \tfrac{1}{12}m_B(L_1^2 - L_1L_2 + L_2^2)\right)\ddot{\theta}$$
$$+ mL_1^2 f(\theta)f'(\theta)\dot{\theta}^2 + ML_2L_3\left(\ddot{\psi}\cos(\theta+\psi) - \dot{\psi}^2\sin(\theta+\psi)\right)$$
$$- \left(ML_2 - \tfrac{1}{2}m_B(L_1 - L_2)\right)g\sin\theta = 0,$$

and for the phase II motion it is

$$\left(ML_2^2 + mL_1^2 + \tfrac{1}{12}m_B(L_1^2 - L_1L_2 + L_2^2)\right)\ddot{\theta}$$
$$+ ML_2L_3\left(\ddot{\psi}\cos(\theta+\psi) - \dot{\psi}^2\sin(\theta+\psi)\right)$$
$$- mL_1L_4\left(\ddot{\phi}\sin(\theta-\phi) - \dot{\phi}^2\cos(\theta-\phi)\right)$$
$$- \left(ML_2 - mL_1 - \tfrac{1}{2}m_B(L_1 - L_2)\right)g\sin\theta = 0.$$

(a) Show that the scaled equation for the phase I motion is

$$\left(1 + \mu l^2 f(\theta)^2 + \tfrac{1}{12}\mu_B(l^2 - l + 1)\right)\theta'' + \mu l^2 f(\theta)f'(\theta)\theta'^2$$
$$+ L\left(\psi''\cos(\theta+\psi) - \psi'^2\sin(\theta+\psi)\right) - \left(1 - \tfrac{1}{2}\mu_B(l - 1)\right)\sin\theta = 0,$$

where $\mu_B = m/m_B$. Hence show that the Taylor series approximation to $\theta(\tau)$, equivalent to Equation (4.30) (page 201), is

$$\theta(\tau) = \theta_0 + \frac{(1 - \mu_B(l - 1)/2)\sin\theta_0}{2(\sin^2\theta_0 + \mu l^2 \cos^2\theta_0 + \mu_B(l^2 - l + 1)/12)}\tau^2 + \cdots.$$

(b) Show that the scaled equation for the phase II motion is

$$\left(1 + \mu l^2 + \tfrac{1}{12}\mu_B(l^2 - l + 1)\right)\theta'' + L\left(\psi''\cos(\theta+\psi) - \psi'^2\sin(\theta+\psi)\right)$$
$$- \mu l^2 l_4\left(\phi''\sin(\theta-\phi) - \phi'^2\cos(\theta-\phi)\right)$$
$$- \left(1 - \mu l - \tfrac{1}{2}\mu_B(l - 1)\right)\sin\theta = 0.$$

(c) Using the results found in parts (a) and (b), modify the procedure `range-3d-swg.mws` to deal with this more general case, and to plot graphs like those shown in Figure 4.30 (page 213).

For the same parameters as used in Figure 4.30, create four plots corresponding to $\mu = 0.0001$, 0.001, 0.01 and 0.05, and in each plot draw the graph of $\phi - \theta$ for $\mu_B = 0$, 0.1, 0.2 and 0.3.

Exercise 4.57 *The propped counterweight*

A suggestion for increasing the range of a trebuchet is to start the system
with the counterweight at an angle, rather than hanging vertically
downwards; in our notation this means that $\psi(0) = \psi_0 \neq 0$, with no
phase I motion. In this exercise this idea is tested using the simplified
system where the projectile is initially resting on a ledge, so there is no
phase I motion.

Suitably modify the worksheet **range-3d-swg.mws** to work for the initial
conditions $\phi(0) = 0$ and $\psi(0) = \psi_0$, a variable parameter. For the
parameters associated with the Warwick trebuchet ($l = 6$, $L = 1.5$,
$\mu = 0.005$, $\theta_0 = 0.8$) and the Rocktec trebuchet ($l = 3.2$, $L = 0.5$, $\mu = 0.05$,
$\theta_0 = 0.8$), estimate the maximum range for $0.4 \leq l_4 \leq 1$, $30° \leq \beta_d \leq 120°$,
and for $\psi_0 = 0$, ± 0.1, ± 0.2, ± 0.3, 1 and $\pi/2$.

Solutions to Exercises

Part I

Solution 4.1

(a) The following Maple code produces the desired outcome.

```
> N := 5:  L := 20:
> pos := [seq((n-1)*L/N,n=1..N)];
> speed := [1$N];
```
$$pos := [0, 4, 8, 12, 16]$$
$$speed := [1, 1, 1, 1, 1]$$

(b) The list of distances is obtained using the `seq` command, and the mean distance can be calculated by converting the list into a sum using `convert`. (Alternatively, you can add the elements of the list by using `sum` or `add`.)

```
> dist := [seq(pos[n+1]-pos[n],
          n=1..nops(pos)-1)];
```
$$dist := [4, 4, 4, 4]$$
```
> meandist := convert(dist,'+')/nops(dist);
```
$$meandist := 4$$

Alternatively, use the `Mean` function from the `Statistics` package:

```
> meandist := Statistics[Mean](dist);
```
$$meandist := 4.$$

Solution 4.2

(a) Maple input and output:

```
> 3 mod 5; 7 mod 5; 10 mod 5; -2 mod 5;
                3
                2
                0
                3
```

Note that the output is always an integer between 0 and 4, even if the argument is negative.

(b) This part of the exercise explores the precedence of addition and the `mod` function in Maple.

```
> 4 + 7 mod 5;   4 + (7 mod 5);
                1
                6
```

In the first case, 4 and 7 are added to give 11, which modulo 5 equals 1. In the second case, Maple first evaluates 7 mod 5 = 2, then adds 4.

(c) Using the `seq` command with a `mod` function to distinguish even and odd elements is one possible solution.

```
> [seq(i/(2-(i mod 2)), i=1..20)];
```
$$[1, 1, 3, 2, 5, 3, 7, 4, 9, 5, 11,$$
$$6, 13, 7, 15, 8, 17, 9, 19, 10]$$

Alternatively, you could use `piecewise`

```
> [seq(piecewise(i mod 2=0,i/2, i),
       i=1..20)];
```

or a quoted `if` statement

```
> [seq('if'(i mod 2=0, i/2, i), i=1..20)];
```

which both yield the same result.

Solution 4.3

(a) We now calculate the distances modulo L, including the distance between the last and first cars.

```
> N := 5:  L := 20:
> pos := [seq((n-1)*L/N,n=1..N)]:
> speed := [1$N]:
> circdist := [seq((pos[n+1]-pos[n]) mod L,
       n=1..nops(pos)-1),(pos[1]-pos[-1]) mod L];
```
$$circdist := [4, 4, 4, 4, 4]$$

Note that `pos[-1]` gives the last element in the list `pos`, so it is equivalent to `pos[nops(pos)]`. The mean distance can be obtained as

```
> meancircdist
    := convert(circdist,'+')/nops(circdist);
```
$$meancircdist := 4$$

Alternatively, use

```
> Statistics[Mean](circdist);
```

(b) The mean distance $\overline{d}$ between N cars on a circular road of length L is

$$\overline{d} = \frac{1}{N}\left((p_1 - p_N) \bmod L \right.$$
$$\left. + \sum_{n=1}^{N-1} (p_{n+1} - p_n) \bmod L \right).$$

However, adding up all these distances between cars, including the distance between the last and first cars, just gives the total length L of the road, so $\overline{d} = L/N$ is just the inverse of the density of cars. To demonstrate this explicitly, assume that $0 \le p_1 \le p_2 \le \cdots \le p_N \le L - 1$, so that the mean becomes

$$\overline{d} = \frac{1}{N}\left((p_1 - p_N + L) + \sum_{n=1}^{N-1} (p_{n+1} - p_n) \right)$$
$$= \frac{1}{N}\left((p_1 - p_N + L) + (p_N - p_1) \right)$$
$$= \frac{L}{N}.$$

The mean distance is constant; it does not depend on the actual configuration of the cars on the road, and thus is not a useful quantity for analysing the traffic situation.

Solution 4.4

The car in cell $p = 7$ with speed $v = 3$ moves to cell $p' = p + v = 7 + 3 = 10$. The car in cell $p = 19$ on a circular road consisting of $L = 20$ cells moves to cell

$$p' = (p + v) \bmod L = (19 + 3) \bmod 20 = 2.$$

Solution 4.5

Here we use a loop to apply the function `drive` ten times.

```
>  N := 5:  L := 20:
>  pos := [seq((n-1)*L/N,n=1..N)]:
>  speed := [1$N]:
>  for i to 10 do
>    pos := drive(pos,speed,L);
>  end do;
```

$$pos := [1, 5, 9, 13, 17]$$
$$pos := [2, 6, 10, 14, 18]$$
$$pos := [3, 7, 11, 15, 19]$$
$$pos := [4, 8, 12, 16, 0]$$
$$pos := [5, 9, 13, 17, 1]$$
$$pos := [6, 10, 14, 18, 2]$$
$$pos := [7, 11, 15, 19, 3]$$
$$pos := [8, 12, 16, 0, 4]$$
$$pos := [9, 13, 17, 1, 5]$$
$$pos := [10, 14, 18, 2, 6]$$

The change in positions is as expected – the cars in cells $0 \le p \le 18$ move forward one cell at a time, while cars at position $p = 19$ move into the first cell, $p = 0$.

Solution 4.6

The procedure `accelerate` uses as input the current list of speeds and the maximum speed, and returns the updated speeds according to the specified rule.

```
>  accelerate := proc(sl,vmax)
>    local n;
>    [seq(min(sl[n]+1,vmax),n=1..nops(sl))];
>  end proc:
```

Solution 4.7

Starting from the configuration of Figure 4.3, two steps are performed using the `drive` function and `brake` procedure.

```
>  L := 10:  pos := [0,2,6]:
>  speed := [0,2,1]:
>  for i to 2 do
>    pos := drive(pos,speed,L);
>    speed := brake(pos,speed,L);
>  end do;
```

$$pos := [0, 4, 7]$$
$$speed := [0, 2, 1]$$
$$pos := [0, 6, 8]$$
$$speed := [0, 1, 1]$$

The positions and speeds of the cars agree with those depicted in Figure 4.3.

Solution 4.8

Performing four steps on the initial configuration of Figure 4.4 confirms that the function `drive` and procedure `adjust` work as expected.

```
>  L := 10:  pos := [0,2,6]:
>  speed := [0,2,1]:
>  for i to 4 do
>    pos := drive(pos,speed,L);
>    speed := adjust(pos,speed,L,3);
>  end do;
```

$$pos := [0, 4, 7]$$
$$speed := [1, 2, 2]$$
$$pos := [1, 6, 9]$$
$$speed := [2, 2, 1]$$
$$pos := [3, 8, 0]$$
$$speed := [3, 1, 2]$$
$$pos := [6, 9, 2]$$
$$speed := [2, 2, 3]$$

Solution 4.9

Changing the parameters as required produces the following code and plot.

```
>  L := 150:  N := 5:
>  vmax := 5:  nstep := 100:
>  pos := [[0,10,20,30,40]]:
>  speed := [0$N]:
>  for i to nstep do
>    speed
       := adjust(pos[-1],speed,L,vmax);
>    pos := [op(pos),drive(pos[-1],speed,L)];
>  end do:
>  with(plots):
>  display(seq(carplot(n),n=1..N),
     carline(1));
```

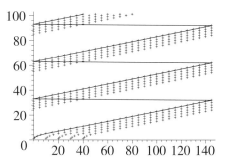

You can clearly identify the five cars as they initially accelerate and then move around the circular road at maximal speed several times.

Solution 4.10

The following Maple code draws five samples of ten random numbers, and calculates the number of 1s by summing the ten numbers.

```
> for i to 5 do
>    srv := Sample(Bernoulli(0.3),10);
>    convert(srv,'+');
> end do;
```

$$srv := [0., 0., 1., 0., 0., 1., 1., 0., 0., 0.]$$
$$3.$$
$$srv := [1., 0., 0., 0., 0., 1., 0., 0., 0., 0.]$$
$$2.$$
$$srv := [0., 1., 0., 0., 0., 0., 0., 0., 0., 1.]$$
$$2.$$
$$srv := [0., 1., 1., 1., 1., 0., 0., 0., 0., 1.]$$
$$5.$$
$$srv := [0., 0., 0., 0., 1., 0., 0., 0., 0., 0.]$$
$$1.$$

Note that we assumed that the `Statistics` package was loaded. The random numbers returned are floating point numbers, so if you wish to work with integers 0 and 1 you should use `round` to convert the numbers to integers.

The examples show that the number of 1s in the samples fluctuates around the expected value, which is 3. As with all examples involving random numbers, the actual values you observe will vary and can be different from those shown here.

Solution 4.11

This can be done most conveniently using a loop.

```
> speed := [3$10];
> for i to 10 do
>    speed := dawdle(speed,
        Sample(Bernoulli(0.3),10));
> end do;
```

$$speed := [3, 3, 3, 3, 3, 3, 3, 3, 3, 3]$$
$$speed := [2, 3, 3, 2, 2, 3, 3, 3, 3, 2]$$
$$speed := [2, 2, 3, 2, 2, 3, 3, 2, 2, 1]$$
$$speed := [2, 1, 3, 1, 2, 3, 2, 1, 2, 1]$$
$$speed := [2, 1, 3, 1, 2, 2, 2, 1, 2, 1]$$
$$speed := [1, 0, 3, 1, 2, 1, 2, 1, 1, 1]$$
$$speed := [0, 0, 3, 1, 1, 1, 1, 1, 1, 1]$$
$$speed := [0, 0, 2, 1, 0, 1, 1, 1, 0, 1]$$
$$speed := [0, 0, 1, 1, 0, 1, 0, 1, 0, 1]$$
$$speed := [0, 0, 0, 0, 0, 0, 0, 1, 0, 0]$$
$$speed := [0, 0, 0, 0, 0, 0, 0, 0, 0, 0]$$

Solution 4.12

(a) The random numbers are drawn and stored in a vector `rsl` and then used sequentially as follows (modified lines are indicated).

```
> circtraffic2 :=
            proc(len,cars,vmax,dawprob,nstep)
>    local pl,sl,i,j,n,rsl,rs;      # Altered
>    uses Statistics;
>    if cars>len then
>       return("error-too many cars");
>    end if;
>    pl := [[seq(trunc(n*len/cars),
            n=0..cars-1)]];
>    sl := [0$cars];
>    rsl := Sample(Bernoulli(dawprob),
            nstep*cars);              # New
>    for i to nstep do
>       rs := [seq(rsl[j],
            j=(i-1)*cars+1..i*cars)];  # New
>       sl := dawdle(adjust(pl[-1],sl,
            len,vmax),rs);
>       pl := [op(pl),drive(pl[-1],sl,len)];
>    end do;
>    pl;
> end proc:
```

(b) Timing the procedure `circtraffic1` gives

```
> timing := time():
> pos := circtraffic1(500,100,5,0.1,200):
> timing := time()-timing;
> display(seq(carplot(n),n=1..100));
```

$$timing := 0.229$$

```
> timing := time():
> pos := circtraffic2(500,100,5,0.1,200):
> timing := time()-timing;
> display(seq(carplot(n),n=1..100));
```

$$timing := 0.091$$

Of course, the actual times will vary according to your computer specification. Here, the procedure `circtraffic2` was clearly faster than `circtraffic1`.

Solution 4.13

The plot is obtained with the following Maple code.

```
>  pos := circtraffic2(500,100,5,0.01,200):
>  display(seq(carplot(n),n=1..100));
```

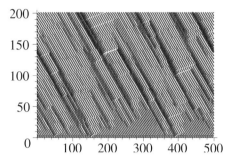

Compared to the results of the previous exercise, this graph shows much less pronounced density variations in traffic. The reason is that with decreasing probability that cars slow down, fewer traffic jams emerge, and for small probability we recover a regular traffic flow observed for the model without the stochastic element.

Solution 4.14

(a) One way to do this is to use code for the speed list `sl` which is similar to that for the position list `pl` in `circtraffic2`. The modified procedure is as follows.

```
>  circtraffic3
     := proc(len,cars,vmax,dawprob,nstep)
>    local pl,sl,i,j,n,rsl,rs;
>    uses Statistics;
>    if cars>len then
>      return("error-too many cars");
>    end if;
>    pl := [[seq(trunc(n*len/cars),
             n=0..cars-1)]];
>    sl := [[0$cars]];
>    rsl := Sample(Bernoulli(dawprob),
             nstep*cars);
>    for i to nstep do
>      rs := [seq(rsl[j],
             j=(i-1)*cars+1..i*cars)];
>      sl := [op(sl),dawdle(adjust
             (pl[-1],sl[-1],len,vmax),rs)];
>      pl := [op(pl),
             drive(pl[-1],sl[-1],len)];
>    end do;
>    pl,sl;
>  end proc:
```

Alternatively, we could use `circtraffic2` to obtain the positions p_n at all time steps, then deduce the speeds using the fact that at any time step T:

$$v_n(T) = (p_n(T+1) - p_n(T)) \bmod L.$$

To check this we use small parameter values:

```
>  pos,speed := circtraffic3(10,3,5,0.1,5):
>  pos;
```

$$[[0, 3, 6], [1, 3, 7], [2, 4, 9],$$
$$[3, 6, 1], [5, 9, 2], [8, 1, 3]]$$

```
>  speed;
```

$$[[0, 0, 0], [1, 0, 1], [1, 1, 2],$$
$$[1, 2, 2], [2, 3, 1], [3, 2, 1]]$$

(b) Following the hint in the text, we redefine `carplot` and `carline` with `symbolsize=3` and `thickness=3`:

```
>  carplot := n -> plot(
     [seq([pos[t,n],t],t=1..nops(pos))],
     style=point,symbolsize=3):
>  carline := n -> plot(
     [seq([pos[t,n],t],t=1..nops(pos))],
     style=line,colour=black,thickness=3):
```

Now the simulation and plot are obtained by

```
>  pos,speed
     := circtraffic3(500,150,5,0.1,250):
>  with(plots):
>  display(seq(carplot(i),i=1..150),
     carline(1));
```

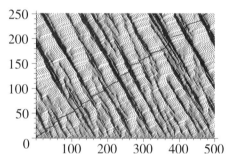

(c) The functions `posline` and `speedline` are defined by analogy with `carline` in Example 4.5, while noting that we now plot time horizontally.

```
>  posline := n ->
     plot([seq([t,pos[t,n]],t=1..nops(pos))]):
>  speedline := n ->
     plot([seq([t,speed[t,n]],t=1..nops(speed))]):
```

The plots are then obtained by

```
>  posline(1);   speedline(1);
```

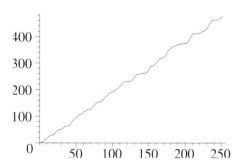

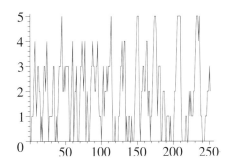

Both plots show that the speed varies strongly during
the motion of the car, including periods where the car
is at rest (corresponding to horizontal parts of the
curve of position versus time). There are also periods
where the car moves at maximum speed.

(d) Adding up the speed values for the first car, and
dividing by the number of data points, gives an
average of

```
>   evalf(add(speed[t,1],t=1..nops(speed))/
        nops(speed));
```
$$1.872509960$$

You can use the **add** command to calculate the total
average as well; here we use **convert** twice, which
adds up the double list:

```
>   evalf(convert(convert(speed,'+'),'+')/
        (150*nops(speed)));
```
$$1.907782205$$

Your values may differ slightly according to the
random numbers used in the simulation; however, you
should observe that the two averages roughly agree
with each other, and are close to the values shown
here. Clearly, with an average speed of less than 2, the
cars travel on average much slower than the maximum
speed $v_{max} = 5$, and also considerably slower than the
maximum achievable speed. The maximum achievable
average speed is based on the average distance
between cars, which for 150 cars on a road of
length 500 is $500/150 \simeq 3.33$. So according to the rules
of the model, the maximum achievable speed is given
by the average number of empty cells in front of a car,
which is $(500 - 150)/150 \simeq 2.33$.

Solution 4.15

(a) To speed up the procedure, unnecessary
operations in `circtraffic2` are removed; in
particular, it is not necessary to store the positions for
all time steps. In the following procedure there are
now two main loops, one for the initial **ninit** steps,
and another for the **nstep** steps which are used to
calculate the mean speed. This is computed by adding
up all the speeds over **nstep** steps, and dividing by the
number of data points (**nstep*cars**) at the end.

```
>   circtraffic4
    := proc(len,cars,vmax,dawprob,ninit,nstep)
>     local pl,sl,i,j,n,rsl,rs,meanspeed;
>     uses Statistics;
>     if cars>len then
>       return("error - too many cars");
>     end if;
```

```
>     pl := [seq(trunc(n*len/cars),
              n=0..cars-1)];
>     sl := [0$cars];
>     rsl := Sample(Bernoulli(dawprob),
               ninit*cars);
>     for i to ninit do
>       rs := [seq(rsl[j],
              j=(i-1)*cars+1..i*cars)];
>       sl := dawdle(adjust(
              pl,sl,len,vmax),rs);
>       pl := drive(pl,sl,len);
>     end do;
>     rsl := Sample(Bernoulli(dawprob),
               nstep*cars);
>     meanspeed := 0;
>     for i to nstep do
>       rs := [seq(rsl[j],
              j=(i-1)*cars+1..i*cars)];
>       sl := dawdle(adjust(
              pl,sl,len,vmax),rs);
>       pl := drive(pl,sl,len);
>       meanspeed := meanspeed
                +convert(sl,'+');
>     end do;
>     evalf(meanspeed/(nstep*cars));
>   end proc:
```

(b) The data are collected by performing simulations
within a **seq** command, for the three specified values
of the slowing down probability.

```
>   mspdata0 := [seq([10*nc/500,
    circtraffic4(500,10*nc,5,0.,100,500)],
    nc=1..50)]:
>   mspdata1 := [seq([10*nc/500,
    circtraffic4(500,10*nc,5,0.1,100,500)],
    nc=1..50)]:
>   mspdata2 := [seq([10*nc/500,
    circtraffic4(500,10*nc,5,0.2,100,500)],
    nc=1..50)]:
```

Note that this calculation may take quite a while.

(c) The results of part (b) are plotted with

```
>   plot([mspdata0,mspdata1,mspdata2],
        colour=[red,black,grey]);
```

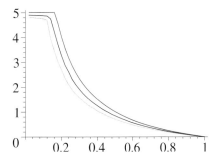

The upper red curve corresponds to the case where
cars do not slow down randomly. In this case, the
average speed equals the maximum speed $v_{max} = 5$ so

long as the density is low enough to allow this. This occurs so long as there are, on average, 5 free cells in front of each car, i.e. when $(L - N)/N \geq 5$, or $N/L \leq 1/6$. For $N/L > 1/6$ the mean speed rapidly decreases, and it reaches zero for $N/L = 1$ where all cells are occupied by cars, so no motion is possible.

Adding randomness reduces the mean speed for low density slightly, but there is still a low-density region with roughly constant mean speed. The rapid decline of the mean speed starts at a lower density, and it appears that the sharp edge near $N/L = 1/6$ becomes smoother in the stochastic model. Nevertheless, the pronounced drop persists, and the mean speed rapidly decreases if the density is larger than the width of the low-density plateau.

(d) For the model without randomness, the average speed is

$$\bar{v} = \min(v_{\max}, (L - N)/N) = \min(5, (1 - d)/d),$$

where $d = N/L$ is the traffic density. Plotting this function together with `mspdata0` demonstrates their equivalence (see the Maple worksheet).

As a function of the inverse density $s = 1/d = L/N$, the average speed therefore has the form $\bar{v} = \min(5, s - 1)$ $(s \geq 1)$, that is, a linear graph which saturates at $v_{\max} = 5$. The result for the stochastic cases is similar, but with a slightly smaller slope and lower saturation value. We produce the plots by using the `map` command to apply an appropriate function `inv` to each element of the list obtained above.

```
>  inv := i -> [1/i[1],i[2]]:
>  plot([map(inv,mspdata0),
        map(inv,mspdata1),map(inv,mspdata2)],
        colour=[red,black,grey]);
```

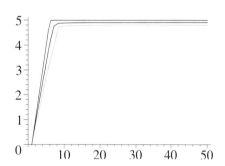

Part II

For the Maple solutions to these exercises, see the accompanying Maple worksheet.

Solution 4.16

(a) If $h = 0$, then

$$R = \frac{v^2}{g} \left(\tfrac{1}{2} \sin 2\alpha + \sin \alpha \cos \alpha \right) = \frac{v^2}{g} \sin 2\alpha.$$

Since $0 < \alpha < \pi/2$, the maximum value of $\sin 2\alpha$ is at $2\alpha = \pi/2$, giving $R_{max} = v^2/g$.

(b) We need the maximum value of the function

$$f(\alpha) = \tfrac{1}{2} \sin 2\alpha + \cos \alpha \sqrt{\gamma + \sin^2 \alpha},$$

which occurs at the solutions of

$$0 = f'(\alpha) = \cos 2\alpha - \sin \alpha \sqrt{\gamma + \sin^2 \alpha} + \frac{\sin \alpha \cos^2 \alpha}{\sqrt{\gamma + \sin^2 \alpha}}.$$

This equation can be rearranged to give

$$\cos 2\alpha + \frac{\sin \alpha \cos^2 \alpha}{\sqrt{\gamma + \sin^2 \alpha}} = \sin \alpha \sqrt{\gamma + \sin^2 \alpha}.$$

Now multiply by $\sqrt{\gamma + \sin^2 \alpha}$, rearrange, and use the identity $\cos 2\alpha = \cos^2 \alpha - \sin^2 \alpha$ to obtain

$$\cos 2\alpha \sqrt{\gamma + \sin^2 \alpha} = \sin \alpha \left(\gamma - \cos 2\alpha \right).$$

Square this and rearrange to obtain

$$\gamma \cos^2 2\alpha = \gamma \sin^2 \alpha \left(\gamma - 2 \cos 2\alpha \right).$$

Finally, put $\sin^2 \alpha = (1 - \cos 2\alpha)/2$ to give

$$\cos 2\alpha = \frac{\gamma}{2 + \gamma}.$$

If $\gamma = 0$, this gives $\cos 2\alpha = 0$, so $\alpha = \pi/4$, as hoped for. If $\gamma = 0$ this is at a maximum value of $f(\alpha)$: by continuity it must also be a maximum when $\gamma \neq 0$. Note that if the stationary point changes from a maximum to a minimum at some value of γ, then here $f''(\alpha) = 0$ and two roots of $f'(\alpha) = 0$ must coincide: there is only one root, so this cannot happen.

Since

$$\sin^2 \alpha = \tfrac{1}{2}(1 - \cos 2\alpha) = \frac{1}{2 + \gamma}$$

and

$$\cos^2 \alpha = \tfrac{1}{2}(1 + \cos 2\alpha) = \frac{1 + \gamma}{2 + \gamma},$$

the maximum range is given by

$$R_{\max} = \frac{v^2}{g} \left(\frac{\sqrt{1 + \gamma}}{2 + \gamma} + \sqrt{\frac{1 + \gamma}{2 + \gamma}} \sqrt{\gamma + \frac{1}{2 + \gamma}} \right)$$

$$= \frac{v^2}{g} \sqrt{1 + \gamma}.$$

Solution 4.17

If we assume that the counterweight and projectile energy satisfy $E_C \propto M$ and $E_P \propto mv^2$, and $R \propto v^2$, then $E_P \propto mR$. If $E_C \simeq E_P$, then $M \propto mR$ and hence mR/M is a constant. The data given produce the following values.

M /kg	m /kg	R /m	mR/M
30×10^3	100	400	1.33
30×10^3	250	160	1.33
15×10^3	100	217	1.45
15×10^3	60	365	1.46

Solution 4.18

A simple way of deriving this result is to consider the beam as a balance. Elementary consideration then show that it rotates clockwise only if $ML_2 > mL_1$. The mathematics is harder.

Put $\phi = \dot{\theta}$, to cast Equation (4.6) in the form

$$\dot{\theta} = \phi, \quad \dot{\phi} = k \sin \theta, \quad k = \frac{(ML_2 - mL_1)g}{ML_2^2 + mL_1^2}.$$

The fixed points are at $\phi = 0$ and $\theta = 0$ and π. In each case the beam is vertical, and if $\theta = 0$ the counterweight is above the pivot, if $\theta = \pi$ it is below the pivot.

Near $\theta = 0$, $\sin \theta \simeq \theta$, so the linearised equations are $\dot{\theta} = \phi$, $\dot{\phi} = k\theta$, which is a saddle (unstable) if $k > 0$ or a centre (stable) if $k < 0$.

Near $\theta = \pi$, put $\theta = \pi + \psi$, so $\sin \theta \simeq -\psi$ if $|\psi|$ is small, and the linearised equations are $\dot{\psi} = \phi$, $\dot{\phi} = -k\psi$, which is a centre if $k > 0$ and a saddle if $k < 0$.

If $k < 0$, that is, $ML_2 < mL_1$, then the fixed point with the counterweight above the pivot is stable and the trebuchet cannot launch the projectile, because it would initially rotate anticlockwise.

Solution 4.19

Divide Equation (4.3) by ML_2^2 to give

$$\left(1 + \frac{mL_1^2}{ML_2^2}\right)\ddot{\theta} - \frac{g}{L_2}\left(1 - \frac{mL_1}{ML_2}\right)\sin\theta$$
$$+ \frac{L_3}{L_2}\left(\ddot{\psi}\cos(\theta+\psi) - \dot{\psi}^2\sin(\theta+\psi)\right) = 0,$$

which is the required result since $\mu = m/M$, $l = L_1/L_2$ and $L = L_3/L_2$.

Similarly, dividing Equation (4.4) by L_2 gives

$$L\ddot{\psi} + \frac{g}{L_2}\sin\psi + \ddot{\theta}\cos(\theta+\psi) - \dot{\theta}^2\sin(\theta+\psi) = 0.$$

Solution 4.20

From Table 4.1 we see that $L_2 = 2.9\,\text{m}$, and using $g = 9.81\,\text{m}\,\text{s}^{-2}$, we see that $\omega^2 \simeq 3.38$ and hence $\omega = 1.84\,\text{s}^{-1}$.

Solution 4.21

Using the trigonometric addition formulae we find that

$$\psi''\cos(\theta+\psi) - \psi'^2\sin(\theta+\psi)$$
$$= \left(\psi''\cos\psi - \psi'^2\sin\psi\right)\cos\theta$$
$$\quad - \left(\psi''\sin\psi + \psi'^2\cos\psi\right)\sin\theta$$

and

$$\theta''\cos(\theta+\psi) - \theta'^2\sin(\theta+\psi)$$
$$= \left(\theta''\cos\theta - \theta'^2\sin\theta\right)\cos\psi$$
$$\quad - \left(\theta''\sin\theta + \theta'^2\cos\theta\right)\sin\psi.$$

But

$$(\cos z)' = -z'\sin z \quad \text{and} \quad (\sin z)' = z'\cos z,$$

so

$$(\cos z)'' = -z''\sin z - z'^2\cos z$$

and

$$(\sin z)'' = \quad z''\cos z - z'^2\sin z.$$

Hence

$$\psi''\cos(\theta+\psi) - \psi'^2\sin(\theta+\psi)$$
$$= \cos\theta(\sin\psi)'' + \sin\theta(\cos\psi)'',$$
$$\theta''\cos(\theta+\psi) - \theta'^2\sin(\theta+\psi)$$
$$= \cos\psi(\sin\theta)'' + \sin\psi(\cos\theta)''$$

Thus we obtain Equations (4.11) and (4.12).

Solution 4.22

If $\mu = 0$ and $\theta + \psi = 0$, Equations (4.9) and (4.10) become, respectively,

$$\theta'' - \sin\theta + L\psi'' = 0,$$
$$L\psi'' + \sin\psi + \theta'' = 0.$$

But $\sin\psi = -\sin\theta$, so these are identical. If $\theta + \psi = \pi$, the equations become

$$\theta'' - \sin\theta - L\psi'' = 0,$$
$$L\psi'' + \sin\psi - \theta'' = 0,$$

and $\sin\psi = \sin(\pi - \theta) = \sin\theta$, so again these are identical.

Solution 4.23

(a) Using a Taylor expansion and assuming $|\psi|$ to be small gives

$$\cos(\theta+\psi) = \cos\theta - \psi\sin\theta - \tfrac{1}{2}\psi^2\cos\theta + \cdots,$$
$$\sin(\theta+\psi) = \sin\theta + \psi\cos\theta - \tfrac{1}{2}\psi^2\sin\theta + \cdots,$$

and to first order in ψ, $\sin\psi = \psi$, so

$$\frac{x_C}{L_2} = \sin\theta + L\psi.$$

(b) If $|\psi|$ and $|\psi'|$ are small, Equation (4.9) becomes, on ignoring the product $(\psi')^2$,

$$(1 + \mu l^2)\theta'' - (1 - \mu l)\sin\theta + L\psi''\cos\theta = 0,$$

and Equation (4.12) becomes

$$L\psi'' + \psi + (\sin\theta)'' + (\cos\theta)''\psi = 0.$$

(c) Differentiating the expression for x_C gives $(x_C/L_2)'' = (\sin\theta)'' + L\psi''$, and this expression occurs in the left-hand side of the above equation, hence $(x_C/L_2)'' = -(1 + (\cos\theta)'')\psi.$

Solution 4.24

See the Maple worksheet.

Solution 4.25

Since

$$\frac{1}{2}\frac{d}{d\tau}(\theta'^2) = \theta'\theta'' \quad \text{and} \quad \frac{d}{d\tau}(\cos\theta) = -\theta'\sin\theta,$$

multiplying Equation (4.16) by θ' and integrating gives

$$\tfrac{1}{2}(1 + \mu l^2)\theta'^2 + (1 - \mu l)\cos\theta = \text{constant}.$$

Initially, $\theta = \theta_0$ and $\theta' = 0$, so this becomes

$$\theta'^2 = \frac{2(1 - \mu l)}{1 + \mu l^2}(\cos\theta_0 - \cos\theta).$$

Integrating again, assuming that $\theta' > 0$, gives

$$\int_{\theta_0}^{\theta} d\theta\, \frac{1}{\sqrt{\cos\theta_0 - \cos\theta}} = \tau\sqrt{\frac{2(1 - \mu l)}{1 + \mu l^2}}.$$

Thus the time for θ to increase from θ_0 to $\pi - \theta_0$ is

$$\tau_{\text{fxd}} = \sqrt{\frac{1 + \mu l^2}{2(1 - \mu l)}} \int_{\theta_0}^{\pi - \theta_0} d\theta \, \frac{1}{\sqrt{\cos \theta_0 - \cos \theta}}.$$

Solution 4.26 – 4.27

See the Maple worksheet.

Solution 4.28

Putting $\mu l = \mu l^2 = 0$ into Equations (4.11) and (4.12) gives the quoted results. The relations derived in Exercise 4.21 are

$$(\cos \theta)'' = -\theta'' \sin \theta - \theta'^2 \cos \theta,$$
$$(\sin \theta)'' = \theta'' \cos \theta - \theta'^2 \sin \theta,$$

and on multiplying the second equation by $\cos \theta$ and the first by $\sin \theta$ and subtracting, we obtain

$$\cos \theta (\sin \theta)'' - \sin \theta (\cos \theta)'' = \theta''.$$

Differentiating x and y, and substituting in the first equation for $L(\sin \psi)''$ and $L(\cos \psi)''$, gives

$$\theta'' - \sin \theta + (x'' - (\sin \theta)'') \cos \theta$$
$$+ ((\cos \theta)'' - y'') \sin \theta = 0$$

and hence

$$x'' \cos \theta - y'' \sin \theta - \sin \theta = 0.$$

Substituting for $(\sin \theta)''$ and $(\cos \theta)''$ in the second equation similarly gives

$$L\psi'' + \sin \psi + (x'' - L(\sin \psi)'') \cos \psi$$
$$+ (y'' + L(\cos \psi)'') \sin \psi = 0$$

and hence

$$x'' \cos \psi + y'' \sin \psi + \sin \psi = 0.$$

Finding x'' and y'' from these two equations gives

$$x'' \sin(\theta + \psi) = 0 \quad \text{and} \quad (1 + y'') \sin(\theta + \psi) = 0.$$

For the times when $\sin(\theta + \psi) \neq 0$ we must have $x'' = 0$ and $y'' = -1$. But $x'(0) = y'(0) = 0$, so these equations integrate to $x(\tau) = x(0)$ and $y(\tau) = y(0) - \tau^2/2$, hence the quoted results.

Solution 4.29

(a) Differentiating Equation (4.19) gives $\theta' \sin \theta = \tau$. But according to the free-fall approximation, $\theta = \pi - \theta_0$ when $\tau = 2\sqrt{\cos \theta_0}$, and hence at this time $\theta' = 2\sqrt{\cos \theta_0}/ \sin \theta_0$.

Differentiating Equation (4.20) gives $L\psi' = -\theta' \cos \theta$. Putting $\theta = \pi - \theta_0$ and using the first result gives $L\psi' = 2(\cos \theta_0)^{3/2}/ \sin \theta_0$.

(b) See the Maple worksheet.

Solution 4.30 – 4.34

See the Maple worksheet.

Solution 4.35

Initially $h_1 = 0$, so $\cos \theta_0 = H/L_1$. Hence, using Equation (4.22) (page 200) for H,
$$\cos \theta_0 - \cos \theta = (L_4/L_1) \sin \phi.$$

Solution 4.36

First use the identities given in Exercise 4.21 to rewrite Equation (4.27) in the form

$$l \sin \phi \left(\cos \phi (\sin \theta)'' - \sin \phi (\cos \theta)'' + \frac{(\theta' \sin \theta)^2}{l_4 \cos^2 \phi} \right)$$
$$= \cos^2 \phi.$$

Using the relation $\sin \phi = (\cos \theta_0 - \cos \theta)/l_4$ gives $l_4 (\sin \phi)' = -(\cos \theta)'$, and since $\theta' \sin \theta = -(\cos \theta)'$, this relation becomes

$$l \sin \phi \left(\cos \phi (\sin \theta)'' + l_4 \sin \phi (\sin \phi)'' + \frac{l_4 (\sin \phi)'^2}{\cos^2 \phi} \right)$$
$$= \cos^2 \phi.$$

But

$$\sin \phi (\sin \phi)'' + \frac{(\sin \phi)'^2}{\cos^2 \phi}$$
$$= \phi'' \sin \phi \cos \phi - \phi'^2 \sin^2 \phi + \phi'^2$$
$$= \cos \phi \left(\phi'' \sin \phi + \phi'^2 \cos \phi \right)$$
$$= - \cos \phi (\cos \phi)'',$$

hence the lift-off condition becomes

$$l \sin \phi \left((\sin \theta)'' - l_4 (\cos \phi)'' \right) = \cos \phi.$$

Solution 4.37

Observing that

$$\frac{1}{2} \frac{d}{d\tau} \left(f(\theta)^2 \theta'^2 \right) = \theta' \left(f(\theta)^2 \theta'' + f(\theta) f'(\theta) \theta'^2 \right),$$

we can write Equation (4.28) in the form

$$\theta' \theta'' + \mu l^2 \theta' \left(f(\theta)^2 \theta'' + f(\theta) f'(\theta) \theta'^2 \right) - \theta' \sin \theta = 0.$$

Now integrate to give

$$\tfrac{1}{2} \theta'^2 + \tfrac{1}{2} \mu l^2 f(\theta)^2 \theta'^2 - \cos \theta = \text{constant}.$$

But $\theta(0) = \theta_0$, $\theta'(0) = 0$, hence the quoted result.

Solution 4.38

See the Maple worksheet.

Solution 4.39

(a) At $\tau = 0$, $f = -\cos \theta_0$, and since $\dot{\theta} = \dot{\phi} = 0$, Equation (4.28) becomes

$$(1 + \mu l^2 \cos^2 \theta_0)\theta''(0) = \sin \theta_0,$$

which gives the required result.

(b) For the normal swinging counterweight trebuchet,

$$\theta''(0) = \frac{\sin \theta_0}{\mu l^2 \cos^2 \theta_0 + \sin^2 \theta_0} > \frac{\sin \theta_0}{1 + \mu l^2 \cos^2 \theta_0},$$

since $\sin^2 \theta_0 < 1$.

(c) See the Maple worksheet.

Solution 4.40

The value of x_P is the sum of the projections of AN and AP on the x-axis, with care taken of the signs. These projections are, respectively $-L_1 \cos(\theta - \pi/2)$ and $-L_4 \sin(\phi - \pi/2)$, which give

$$x_P = -L_1 \cos(\theta - \pi/2) - L_4 \sin(\phi - \pi/2)$$
$$= -L_1 \sin\theta + L_4 \cos\phi.$$

Similarly, the value of y_P is the sum of H and the projections of AN and AP on the y-axis. These are, respectively, $L_1 \sin(\theta - \pi/2)$ and $-L_4 \cos(\phi - \pi/2)$, and hence

$$y_P = H + L_1 \cos(\pi - \theta) - L_4 \cos(\phi - \pi/2)$$
$$= H - L_1 \cos\theta - L_4 \sin\phi.$$

Differentiating these expressions gives Equations (4.35).

Solution 4.41

The angle $A'AP$, where AP is the sling, is (from Figure 4.41) $\pi/2 + \theta - \phi$, so the angle between the sling and the spigot is $\beta + \pi/2 + \theta - \phi$.

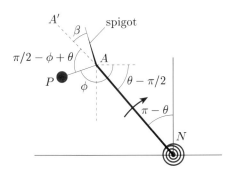

Figure 4.41 Diagram of the angle between the spigot and the sling

Solution 4.42 – 4.47

See the Maple worksheet.

Solution 4.48

(a) In terms of X, Y and τ, the equations are

$$mL\omega^2 X'' = -kL\omega X',$$
$$X(0) = 0, \quad X'(0) = \frac{v}{\omega L} \cos\alpha,$$
$$mL\omega^2 Y'' = -mg - kL\omega Y',$$
$$Y(0) = 0, \quad Y'(0) = \frac{v}{\omega L} \sin\alpha.$$

Divide these equations by $mL\omega^2$ and choose $\omega = k/m$ and $L = g/\omega^2 = gm^2/k^2$. With these values for ω and L, the scaled equations become $X'' = -X'$ and $Y'' = -1 - Y'$.

(b) You can use the methods for solving inhomogeneous second-order linear differential equations introduced in MST209. Alternatively, notice that the equation for Y can be written in the form

$$\frac{d}{d\tau}\left(e^\tau \frac{dY}{d\tau}\right) = -e^\tau,$$

and integration gives

$$Y' = -Ce^{-\tau} - 1.$$

A further integration gives

$$Y = D - \tau + C\exp(-\tau).$$

Similar, but simpler, algebra gives

$$X = A + B\exp(-\tau).$$

The initial conditions give, for $X(\tau)$,

$$0 = A + B \quad \text{and} \quad -B = V\cos\alpha,$$

hence

$$X(\tau) = \left(1 - e^{-\tau}\right) V \cos\alpha, \quad \text{where } V = \frac{vk}{mg}.$$

For $Y(\tau)$,

$$0 = C + D \quad \text{and} \quad -1 - C = V\sin\alpha,$$

and hence

$$Y(\tau) = \left(1 - e^{-\tau}\right)(1 + V\sin\alpha) - \tau.$$

(c) See the Maple worksheet for the graphs. Since $V = vk/(mg)$, for fixed v an increase in V signifies a relatively stronger resistive force. If k is small, the resistive force is weak and the trajectories will approximate the parabolic shape of the unresisted motion. For large k, the motion is slowed more effectively, resulting in the projectile falling nearly vertically.

Solution 4.49

(a) If $|\psi|$ and $|\phi|$ are small, we have, to first order, $\sin\theta = \sin\phi \simeq \phi$, $\sin\psi \simeq \psi$, $\cos(\theta + \psi) = -\cos(\psi - \phi) \simeq -1$ and $\sin(\theta + \psi) = -\sin(\psi - \phi) \simeq \phi - \psi$. Substituting these approximations into Equation (4.9), and ignoring the term proportional to ψ'^2, gives

$$(1 + \mu l^2)\phi'' + (1 - \mu l)\phi + L\psi'' = 0.$$

Similarly for Equation (4.10), since $\theta'^2 \sin(\theta + \psi) \simeq -\phi'^2(\phi - \psi)$ can be neglected, we have

$$L\psi'' + \psi + \phi'' = 0.$$

These two equations can be expressed as a single linear matrix equation

$$\mathbf{A}_1 \mathbf{x}'' + \mathbf{A}_2 \mathbf{x} = \mathbf{0}, \quad \text{for } \mathbf{x} = \begin{pmatrix} \phi \\ \psi \end{pmatrix},$$

where

$$\mathbf{A}_1 = \begin{pmatrix} 1 + \mu l^2 & L \\ 1 & L \end{pmatrix}, \quad \mathbf{A}_2 = \begin{pmatrix} 1 - \mu l & 0 \\ 0 & 1 \end{pmatrix}.$$

(b) If $0 < \mu l < 1$, both $\mathbf{A}_1$ and $\mathbf{A}_2$ are nonsingular, so multiply this equation by $\mathbf{A}_1^{-1}$ to give

$$\mathbf{x}'' + \mathbf{A}\mathbf{x} = \mathbf{0}, \tag{4.51}$$

where

$$\mathbf{A} = \mathbf{A}_1^{-1}\mathbf{A}_2 = \frac{1}{\mu l^2 L}\begin{pmatrix} L(1 - \mu l) & -L \\ -(1 - \mu l) & 1 + \mu l^2 \end{pmatrix}.$$

(c) If $\mathbf{x} = \mathbf{a}\exp(i\omega t)$, $\mathbf{x}'' = -\omega^2 \mathbf{a}\exp(i\omega t)$, Equation (4.51) becomes $\mathbf{A}\mathbf{a} = \omega^2\mathbf{a}$, that is, ω^2 is an eigenvalue of $\mathbf{A}$. Since $\mathbf{B} = \mu l^2 L\mathbf{A}$, if λ is an eigenvalue of $\mathbf{B}$, an eigenvalue of $\mathbf{A}$ is $\lambda/(\mu l^2 L)$. The trace and determinant of $\mathbf{B}$ are, respectively,

$$1 + \mu l^2 + L(1 - \mu l) \quad \text{and} \quad \mu l^2 L(1 - \mu l),$$

so the equation for the eigenvalues of $\mathbf{B}$ is

$$\lambda^2 - \left(1 + \mu l^2 + L(1 - \mu l)\right)\lambda + \mu l^2 L(1 - \mu l) = 0.$$

There are two ways of dealing with this type of problem when $0 < \mu \ll 1$. The first is to treat the equation as any other quadratic: use the formula to find the two roots (which are always real) and expand these as a series in μ to the required order.

A simpler method is to write the equation in the form

$$\lambda^2 - (L+1)\lambda = \mu l\left(\lambda(l-L) - lL\right) + \mu^2 l^3 L \qquad (4.52)$$

because the right-hand side is $O(\mu)$ and this makes the subsequent analysis easier. In particular, if $\mu = 0$, the two solutions are $\lambda = 0$ and $L + 1$.

(d) You can use Maple to solve for λ and then find its Taylor series in μ. Alternatively, proceed as follows.

If $0 < \mu \ll 1$, we expect the solutions for λ to differ from those in part (c) by $O(\mu)$. For the smaller root, set $\lambda = \beta\mu$, for some $\beta = O(1)$; then to $O(\mu)$, Equation (4.52) becomes $-(L+1)\mu\beta = -\mu l^2 L$. For the other eigenvalue, put $\lambda = L + 1 + \mu\gamma$, with $\gamma = O(1)$, into Equation (4.52) to obtain

$$\gamma(L+1)\mu = \mu l\left((l-L)(L+1) - lL\right),$$

that is,

$$\gamma = -\frac{L^2 + L - l}{L+1}l.$$

Hence the approximate eigenvalues of $\mathbf{B}$ are

$$\lambda_1 \simeq \frac{\mu l^2 L}{L+1} \quad \text{and} \quad \lambda_2 \simeq L + 1 - \mu l\frac{L^2 + L - l}{L+1},$$

and the frequencies $\omega^2 = \lambda/(\mu l^2 L)$ are

$$\omega_1 \simeq \frac{1}{\sqrt{L+1}} \quad \text{and} \quad \omega_2 \simeq \sqrt{\frac{L+1}{\mu l^2 L}}.$$

The general solution of the linear equations is a linear combination of these two solutions (and their complex conjugates), that is,

$$\mathbf{x} = \mathbf{a}_+ \exp(i\omega_1\tau) + \mathbf{a}_- \exp(-i\omega_1\tau)$$
$$+ \mathbf{b}_+ \exp(i\omega_2\tau) + \mathbf{b}_- \exp(-i\omega_2\tau).$$

Except for the very special cases where $\mathbf{b}_\pm = 0$, the solution contains the high-frequency term $\exp(\pm i\omega_2\tau)$, and hence the speed of motion is $O(\mu^{-1/2})$.

Solution 4.50

(a) The initial velocity $\mathbf{v}$ of the projectile is perpendicular to the beam; see Figure 4.42.

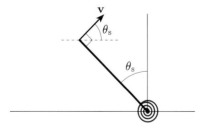

Figure 4.42

Elementary geometry shows that the angle between $\mathbf{v}$ and the horizontal is θ_s.

The range is given by Equation (4.1) (page 177), with

$h = 0$ and $\alpha = \theta_s$. Initially $\theta = \theta_0$ and $\dot{\theta} = 0$, so $E = V(\theta_0)$ and the speed is given by the relation

$$v^2 = \frac{2}{m_P + \frac{1}{3}m_B}\left(V(\theta_0) - V(\theta_s)\right),$$

hence

$$R = \frac{v^2}{g}\sin 2\theta_s = \frac{2}{gm_B}\frac{V(\theta_0) - V(\theta_s)}{1/3 + \mu}\sin 2\theta_s,$$

where $\mu = \dfrac{m_P}{m_B}$.

(b) If $V = k(\theta + \alpha)^2/2$, the range becomes

$$R(\theta_s) = \frac{3k}{gm_B(1 + 3\mu)}\left((\theta_0 + \alpha)^2 - (\theta_s + \alpha)^2\right)\sin 2\theta_s,$$

and

$$\frac{dR}{d\theta_s} = \frac{6k}{gm_B(1 + 3\mu)}\left\{\left[(\theta_0 + \alpha)^2 - (\theta_s + \alpha)^2\right]\cos 2\theta_s \right.$$
$$\left. - (\theta_s + \alpha)\sin 2\theta_s\right\}.$$

Thus $R(\theta_s)$ is stationary when $\theta_s = \gamma$, where

$$\tan 2\gamma = \frac{(\theta_0 + \alpha)^2 - (\gamma + \alpha)^2}{\gamma + \alpha}.$$

Since $\tan 2\gamma$ increases monotonically from zero at $\gamma = 0$ to infinity at $\gamma = \pi/4$, and the right-hand side of the equation decreases monotonically as γ increases from zero to θ_0, where it is zero, this equation has one and only one real root in $(0, \pi/4)$.

Further, $R(0) > 0$ and $R(\theta_0) = 0$, so this stationary point is a maximum of $R(\theta_s)$.

(c) The right-hand side of the equation for $\tan 2\gamma$ can be written as

$$\frac{2(\theta_0 - \gamma) + (\theta_0^2 - \gamma^2)/\alpha}{1 + \gamma/\alpha} \simeq 2(\theta_0 - \gamma)$$

provided that α is sufficiently large. This approximation then gives $\tan 2\gamma = 2(\theta_0 - \gamma)$, which is independent of α.

Since $\tan x \simeq x + x^3/3$, this equation becomes

$$2\gamma + \tfrac{8}{3}\gamma^3 = 2(\theta_0 - \gamma),$$

that is,

$$\gamma\left(1 + \tfrac{2}{3}\gamma^2\right) = \tfrac{1}{2}\theta_0,$$

which can be written in the form quoted.

Let γ_n, $n = 0, 1, \ldots$, be a sequence of numbers satisfying

$$\gamma_{n+1} = g(\gamma_n) = \frac{\theta_0}{2 + 4\gamma_n^2/3}, \qquad \gamma_0 = \tfrac{1}{2}\theta_0.$$

The fixed point of this sequence is the required root, and the sequence converges to this root if $|g'(\gamma)| < 1$, which is always true provided that $\theta_0 < 8\sqrt{2}/3 \simeq 3.77$.

See the Maple worksheet for the last part of this solution.

Solution 4.51

(a) If $L_4 = 0$, the first equation is

$$\left(m_P + \tfrac{1}{3}m_B\right)L_1^2\ddot{\theta} + k(\theta + \alpha) = 0.$$

Multiplying by $\dot{\theta}$ and integrating gives the energy equation

$$\tfrac{1}{2}\left(m_P + \tfrac{1}{3}m_B\right)L_1^2\dot{\theta}^2 + \tfrac{1}{2}k(\theta + \alpha)^2 = \text{constant}.$$

Using the initial conditions $\theta(0) = \theta_0$ and $\dot{\theta}(0) = 0$ gives the required result.

(b) Dividing the equation for ϕ by L_1, setting $g = \omega^2 L_1$ and using the scaled variables, gives

$$l_4\phi'' + \sin\phi + \theta''\cos(\theta + \phi) - \theta'^2\sin(\theta + \phi) = 0.$$

Dividing the equation for θ by ML_1^2 gives

$$\theta'' + \frac{3\bar{k}}{1 + 3\mu}(\theta + \alpha)$$
$$+ \frac{3\mu l_4}{1 + 3\mu}\left(\phi''\cos(\theta + \phi) - \phi'^2\sin(\theta + \phi)\right) = 0.$$

(c) The angle between the sling and the spigot, shown in Figure 4.43, is $\pi + \beta - \phi - \theta$.

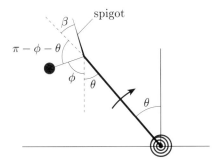

Figure 4.43

Hence the projectile is launched when

$$\phi + \theta = \pi + \beta - \beta_{\text{ss}} = \beta_d.$$

Equation (4.1) (page 177) for the range, with $h = 0$, can be written in the form

$$\frac{R}{L_1} = \frac{2v^2}{gL_1}\sin\alpha\cos\alpha$$
$$= 2\frac{v_x v_y}{\omega^2 L_1^2}$$
$$= 2\left(\theta'\cos\theta + l_4\phi'\cos\phi\right)\left(\theta'\sin\theta - l_4\phi'\sin\phi\right).$$

(d) On replacing $3\bar{k}/(1 + 3\mu)$ as suggested, the equation for θ becomes

$$\theta'' + \frac{R_{\max}}{L_1 f(\theta_0, \alpha)}(\theta + \alpha)$$
$$+ \frac{3\mu l_4}{1 + 3\mu}\left(\phi''\cos(\theta + \phi) - \phi'^2\sin(\theta + \phi)\right) = 0.$$

(e) See the Maple worksheet.

Solution 4.52 – 4.53

See the Maple worksheet.

Solution 4.54

(a) See the Maple worksheet.

(b) Some typical values of the maximum range in $0.2 \le l_4 \le 1.2$ for $\theta_0 = 0.8$, $l = 7$ and $\mu = 0.01$ and 0.001, for various values of β_d, are given in the following table taken from the Maple worksheet. It shows that in most cases the vertically falling system has a larger range.

β_d	$\mu = 0.01$		$\mu = 0.001$	
	R_{fxd}	R_{falling}	R_{fxd}	R_{falling}
30	251	395	1158	1285
60	315	405	994	1039
90	264	288	502	551
120	115	69	48.7	0
150	23.4	0	7.0	0
180	4.9	0	3.8	0

Solution 4.55

(a) Using the scaled variables and dividing the equation for ϕ by $\omega^2 L_2$ gives

$$ll_4\phi'' - \cos\phi - l\left(\theta''\sin(\theta - \phi) + \theta'^2\cos(\theta - \phi)\right)$$
$$- x''\sin\phi = 0.$$

Similarly, dividing the equation for θ by $ML_2\omega^2$ gives

$$(1 + \mu l^2)\theta'' - (1 - \mu l)\sin\theta$$
$$- \mu l^2 l_4\left(\phi''\sin(\theta - \phi) - \phi'^2\cos(\theta - \phi)\right)$$
$$+ (1 - \mu l)x''\cos\theta = 0.$$

The equation for the conservation of momentum becomes

$$(1 + \mu + \mu_{\text{T}})x' + (1 - \mu l)(\sin\theta)' + \mu ll_4(\cos\phi)' = 0,$$

which can be integrated directly to give

$$(1 + \mu + \mu_{\text{T}})x = \text{constant} - (1 - \mu l)\sin\theta - \mu ll_4\cos\phi.$$

(b) If the sling length is zero, so $l_4 = 0$, the equation for θ becomes, on using the relation for x,

$$(1 + \mu l^2)\theta'' - (1 - \mu l)\sin\theta$$
$$- \frac{(1 - \mu l)^2}{1 + \mu + \mu_{\text{T}}}(\sin\theta)''\cos\theta = 0.$$

But

$$\tfrac{1}{2}\left(\theta'^2\right)' = \theta'\theta'', \quad (\cos\theta)' = -\theta'\sin\theta,$$
$$(\sin\theta)' = \theta'\cos\theta,$$

so

$$\theta'\cos\theta(\sin\theta)' = (\sin\theta)'(\sin\theta)'' = \frac{1}{2}\frac{d}{d\tau}\left(\theta'^2\cos^2\theta\right),$$

the last result following because $gg' = \frac{1}{2}(g^2)'$, with $g = (\sin\theta)'$. Hence, after multiplying the equation for θ by θ', we find that it may be written in the form

$$\tfrac{1}{2}(1 + \mu l^2)\left(\theta'^2\right)' - \frac{1}{2}\frac{(1 - \mu l)^2}{1 + \mu + \mu_{\text{T}}}\frac{d}{d\tau}\left(\theta'^2\cos^2\theta\right)$$
$$= -(1 - \mu l)(\cos\theta)'.$$

$\theta' = 0$ and $\theta = \theta_0$ at $\tau = 0$, so integration gives

$$\tfrac{1}{2}\theta'^2\left(1 + \mu l^2 - \frac{(1 - \mu l)^2}{1 + \mu + \mu_{\text{T}}}\cos^2\theta\right)$$
$$= (1 - \mu l)(\cos\theta_0 - \cos\theta).$$

Since

$$1 + \mu l^2 - \frac{(1 - \mu l)^2}{1 + \mu + \mu_{\text{T}}}\cos^2\theta \le 1 + \mu l^2,$$

if $\tfrac{1}{2}(1 + \mu l^2)z'^2 = (1 - \mu l)(\cos\theta_0 - \cos z)$, with θ and z having the same initial conditions, then $\theta' < z'$, so the counterweight falls faster when the system moves freely on wheels. Calculations that illustrate this are described in the associated Maple worksheet, and there we see that values of β_d can be chosen so that the range of the moving trebuchet is, for small μ, far larger than that of the stationary system.

In practice, such a moving system will not work, because battlefields are generally rough and not flat, so there will be a great deal of resistance to the motion. Moving toy systems on smooth, flat surfaces can, however, show a significant improvement.

(c) See the Maple worksheet.

(d) See the Maple worksheet.

Solution 4.56

(a) Divide the equation for the phase I motion by $ML_2\omega^2$, where $g = \omega^2 L_2$, and use the scaled time $\tau = \omega t$ to obtain the required equation for θ. The equation for ψ remains unchanged, so is given by Equation (4.25) (page 200). At $\tau = 0$, where $\theta' = \psi' = \psi = 0$ and $f = -\cos\theta_0$, these two equations become

$$\left(1 + \mu l^2 \cos^2\theta_0 + \tfrac{1}{12}\mu_{\mathrm{B}}(l^2 - l + 1)\right)\theta''(0)$$
$$+ L\psi''(0)\cos\theta_0 - \left(1 - \tfrac{1}{2}\mu_{\mathrm{B}}(l - 1)\right)\sin\theta_0 = 0,$$

$$L\psi''(0) + \theta''(0)\cos\theta_0 = 0.$$

Hence

$$\theta''(0) = \frac{\left(1 - \tfrac{1}{2}\mu_{\mathrm{B}}(l - 1)\right)\sin\theta_0}{\sin^2\theta_0 + \mu l^2\cos^2\theta_0 + \tfrac{1}{12}\mu_{\mathrm{B}}(l^2 - l + 1)},$$

which gives the required result.

(b) Divide the equation for the phase II motion by $ML_2\omega^2$, where $g = \omega^2 L_2$, and use the scaled time $\tau = \omega t$ to obtain the required equation.

(c) See the Maple worksheet.

Solution 4.57

Some results of the calculation described in the Maple part of this solution are given in the following table. Here we have used a grid of 31 points for both l_4 and β_d; for the larger values of $\psi(0)$ we consider only positive values because large negative values cause practical difficulties.

	Warwick			Rocktec		
	$l = 6,\ L = 1.5,$ $\mu = 0.005$			$l = 3.2,\ L = 0.5,$ $\mu = 0.05$		
ψ_0	$\max(R)$	l_4	β_d	$\max(R)$	l_4	β_d
0	612.2	0.70	48	39.9	0.80	102
0.1	592.1	0.68	52	41.7	0.82	102
−0.1	628.5	0.74	42	38.2	0.80	105
0.2	572.1	0.64	57	43.4	0.82	99
−0.2	644.6	0.76	39	36.5	0.80	108
0.3	549.6	0.62	60	45.0	0.84	96
−0.3	662.8	0.78	33	35.1	0.78	108
1.0	401.7	0.52	87	56.2	0.92	93
1.57	443.9	0.50	90	67.5	0.96	94

These sample results show that starting the system with $\psi(0) \neq 0$, can slightly increase the range, but it can also decrease it. For small values of $|\psi(0)|$, the change is not substantial, as would be expected because the increase in the potential energy is not large. For larger values of $\psi(0)$, the changes are significant, but not always advantageous.

Index